SOLARO

STUDY GUIDE

Functions Mathematics 11 University Preparation (MCR3U)

SOLARO Study Guide is designed to help students achieve success in school. The content in each study guide is 100% curriculum aligned and serves as an excellent source of material for review and practice. To create this book, teachers, curriculum specialists, and assessment experts have worked closely to develop the instructional pieces that explain each of the key concepts for the course. The practice questions and sample tests have detailed solutions that show problem-solving methods, highlight concepts that are likely to be tested, and point out potential sources of errors. ***SOLARO Study Guide*** is a complete guide to be used by students throughout the school year for reviewing and understanding course content, and to prepare for assessments.

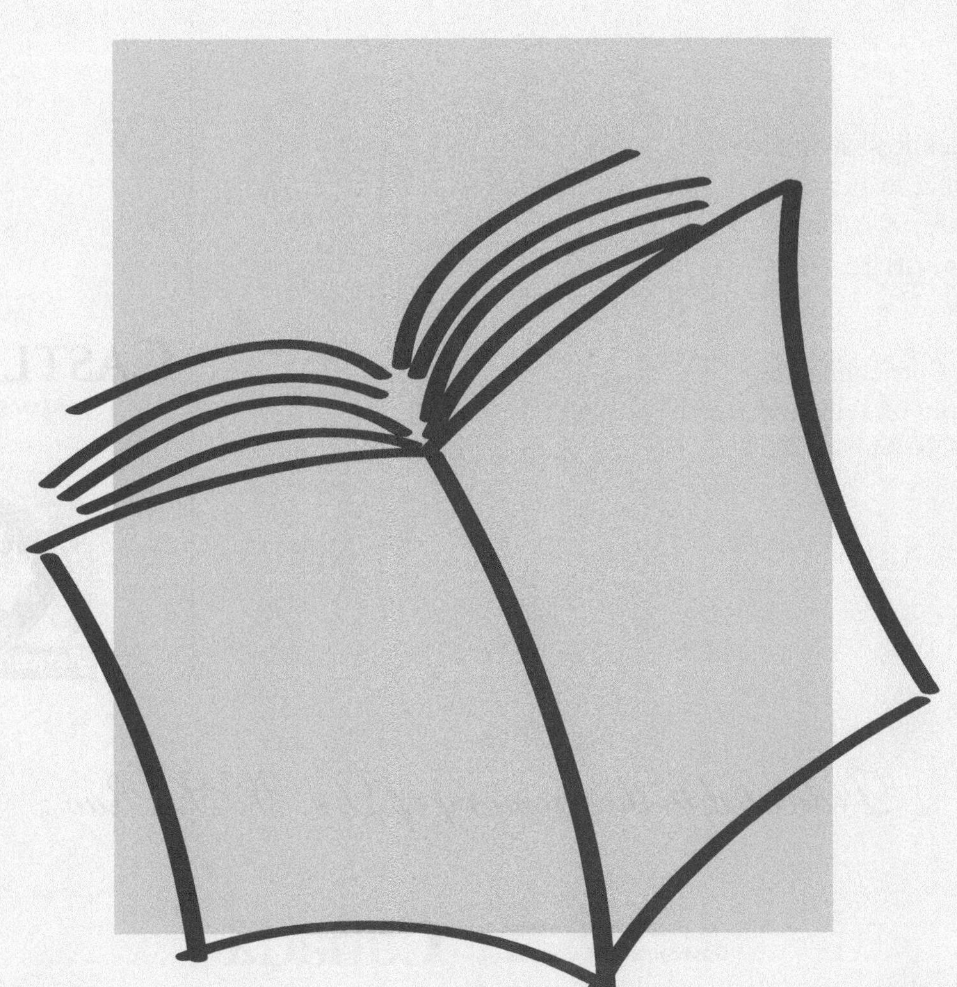

Publisher
Gautam Rao

Contributors
Jasmin Benavides
Monica Dhamrait
Katie Pallos-Haden
Jane Gannon
Renee Nutt

Rao, Gautam, 1961 –
SOLARO Study Guide: Mathematics Grade 11: Functions and Applications University/College Prep (MCR3U) Ontario
ISBN: 978-1-4876-0480-6

1. Mathematics – Juvenile Literature. I. Title

Castle Rock Research Corp.
2000 First & Jasper
10065 Jasper Avenue
Edmonton, AB T5J 3B1

Canadian Curriculum Press
is an imprint of Telegraph Road,
Toronto, ON M4B 3G8.

Dedicated to the memory of Dr. V.S. Rao

With the participation of the Government of Canada | Canada

SOLARO STUDY GUIDE

Each ***SOLARO STUDY GUIDE*** consists of the following sections:

Key Tips for Being Successful at School gives examples of study and review strategies. It includes information about learning styles, study schedules, and note taking for test preparation.

Class Focus includes a unit on each area of the curriculum. Units are divided into sections, each focusing on one of the specific expectations, or main ideas, that students must learn about in that unit. Examples, definitions, and visuals help to explain each main idea. Practice questions on the main ideas are also included. At the end of each unit is a test on the important ideas covered. The practice questions and unit tests help students identify areas they know and those they need to study more. They can also be used as preparation for tests and quizzes. Most questions are of average difficulty, though some are easy and some are hard—the harder questions are called *Challenger Questions*. Each unit is prefaced by a ***Table of Correlations***, which correlates questions in the unit (and in the practice tests at the end of the book) to the specific curriculum expectations. Answers and solutions are found at the end of each unit.

Key Strategies for Success on Tests helps students get ready for tests. It shows students different types of questions they might see, word clues to look for when reading them, and hints for answering them.

Practice Tests includes one to three tests based on the entire course. They are very similar to the format and level of difficulty that students may encounter on final tests. In some regions, these tests may be reprinted versions of official tests, or reflect the same difficulty levels and formats as official versions. This gives students the chance to practice using real-world examples. Answers and complete solutions are provided at the end of the section.

For the complete curriculum document (including specific expectations along with examples and sample problems), visit http://www.edu.gov.on.ca/eng/curriculum/

SOLARO STUDY GUIDE *Study Guides* are available for many courses. Check www.castlerockresearch.com for a complete listing of books available for your area.

For information about any of our resources or services, please call Castle Rock Research at 1.800.840.6224 or visit our website at http://www.castlerockresearch.com.

At Castle Rock Research, we strive to produce an error-free resource. If you should find an error, please contact us so that future editions can be corrected.

CONTENTS

KEY Tips for being Successful at School

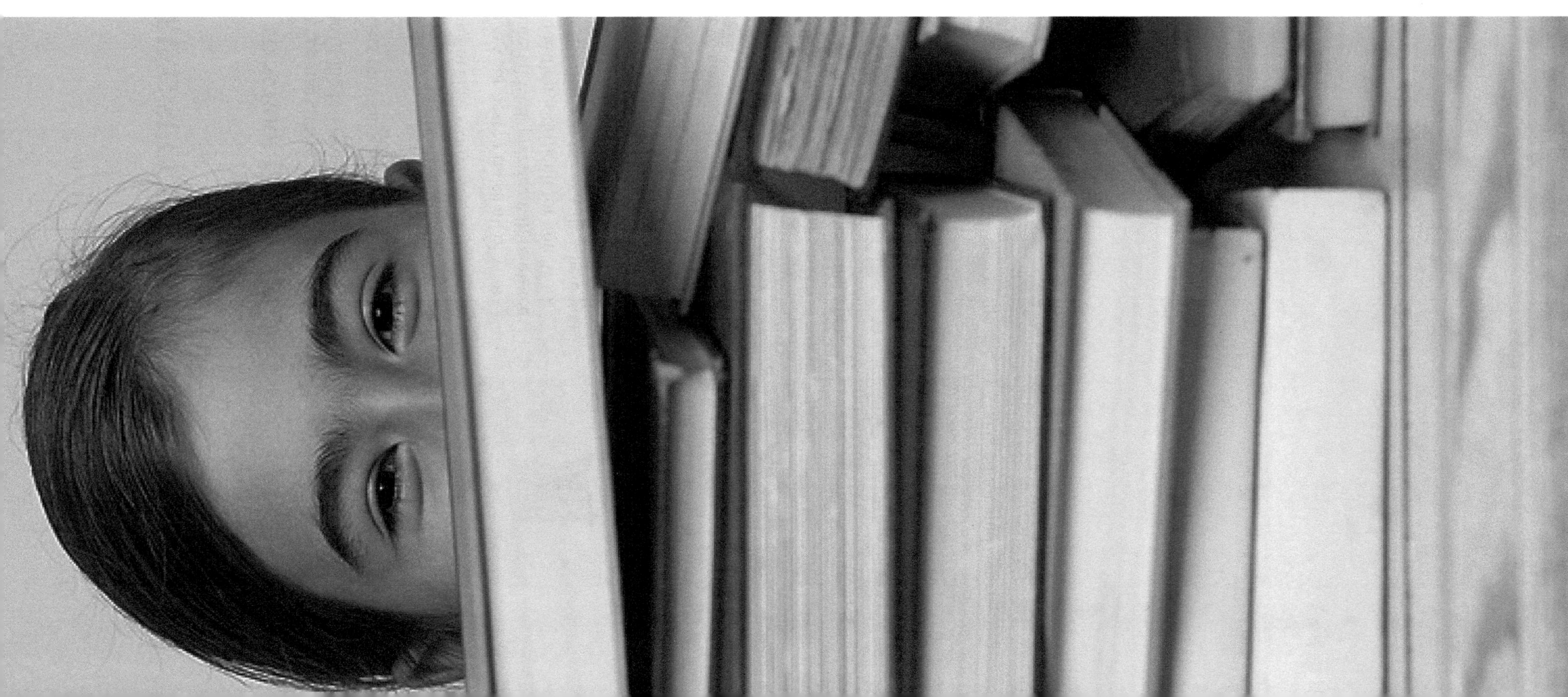

KEY TIPS FOR BEING SUCCESSFUL AT SCHOOL

Key Factors Contributing to School Success

In addition to learning the content of your courses, there are some other things that you can do to help you do your best at school. You can try some of the following strategies:

- **Keep a positive attitude:** Always reflect on what you can already do and what you already know.
- **Be prepared to learn:** Have the necessary pencils, pens, notebooks, and other required materials for participating in class ready.
- **Complete all of your assignments:** Do your best to finish all of your assignments. Even if you know the material well, practice will reinforce your knowledge. If an assignment or question is difficult for you, work through it as far as you can so that your teacher can see exactly where you are having difficulty.
- **Set small goals for yourself when you are learning new material:** For example, when learning the parts of speech, do not try to learn everything in one night. Work on only one part or section each study session. When you have memorized one particular part of speech and understand it, move on to another one. Continue this process until you have memorized and learned all the parts of speech.
- **Review your classroom work regularly at home:** Review to make sure you understand the material you learned in class.
- **Ask your teacher for help:** Your teacher will help you if you do not understand something or if you are having a difficult time completing your assignments.

- **Get plenty of rest and exercise:** Concentrating in class is hard work. It is important to be well-rested and have time to relax and socialize with your friends. This helps you keep a positive attitude about your schoolwork.
- **Eat healthy meals:** A balanced diet keeps you healthy and gives you the energy you need for studying at school and at home.

How to Find Your Learning Style

Every student learns differently. The manner in which you learn best is called your learning style. By knowing your learning style, you can increase your success at school. Most students use a combination of learning styles. Do you know what type of learner you are? Read the following descriptions. Which of these common learning styles do you use most often?

- **Linguistic Learner:** You may learn best by saying, hearing, and seeing words. You are probably really good at memorizing things such as dates, places, names, and facts. You may need to write down the steps in a process, a formula, or the actions that lead up to a significant event, and then say them out loud.
- **Spatial Learner:** You may learn best by looking at and working with pictures. You are probably really good at puzzles, imagining things, and reading maps and charts. You may need to use strategies like mind mapping and webbing to organize your information and study notes.
- **Kinesthetic Learner:** You may learn best by touching, moving, and figuring things out using manipulatives. You are probably really good at physical activities and learning through movement. You may need to draw your finger over a diagram to remember it, tap out the steps needed to solve a problem, or feel yourself writing or typing a formula.

SCHEDULING STUDY TIME

You should review your class notes regularly to ensure that you have a clear understanding of all the new material you learned. Reviewing your lessons on a regular basis helps you to learn and remember ideas and concepts. It also reduces the quantity of material that you need to study prior to a test. Establishing a study schedule will help you to make the best use of your time.

Regardless of the type of study schedule you use, you may want to consider the following suggestions to maximize your study time and effort:

- Organize your work so that you begin with the most challenging material first.
- Divide the subject's content into small, manageable chunks.
- Alternate regularly between your different subjects and types of study activities in order to maintain your interest and motivation.
- Make a daily list with headings like "Must Do," "Should Do," and "Could Do."
- Begin each study session by quickly reviewing what you studied the day before.
- Maintain your usual routine of eating, sleeping, and exercising to help you concentrate better for extended periods of time.

CREATING STUDY NOTES

MIND-MAPPING OR WEBBING

Use the key words, ideas, or concepts from your reading or class notes to create a mind map or web (a diagram or visual representation of the given information). A mind map or web is sometimes referred to as a knowledge map. Use the following steps to create a mind map or web:

1. Write the key word, concept, theory, or formula in the centre of your page.

2. Write down related facts, ideas, events, and information, and link them to the central concept with lines.

3. Use coloured markers, underlining, or symbols to emphasize things such as relationships, timelines, and important information.

The following examples of a Frayer Model illustrate how this technique can be used to study vocabulary.

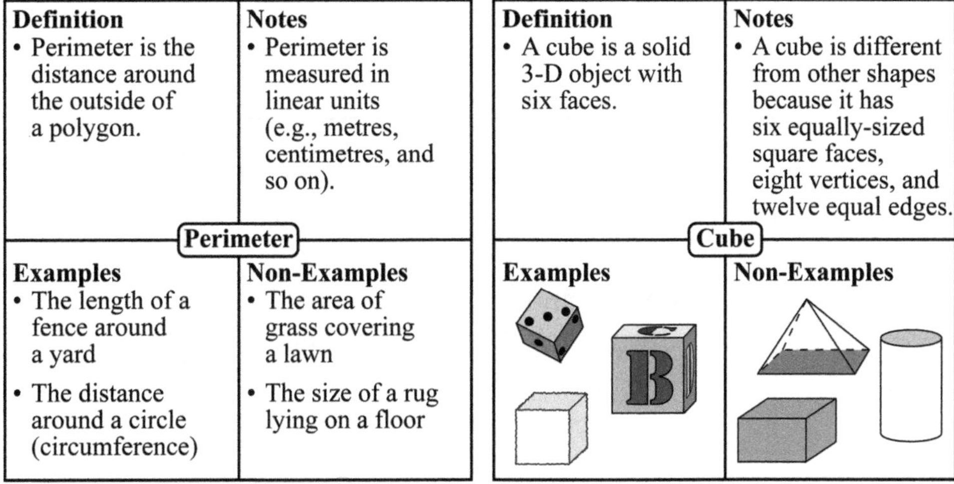

Definition
• Perimeter is the distance around the outside of a polygon.
Notes
• Perimeter is measured in linear units (e.g., metres, centimetres, and so on).
Perimeter
Examples
• The length of a fence around a yard
• The distance around a circle (circumference)
Non-Examples
• The area of grass covering a lawn
• The size of a rug lying on a floor
Definition
• A cube is a solid 3-D object with six faces.
Notes
• A cube is different from other shapes because it has six equally-sized square faces, eight vertices, and twelve equal edges.
Cube
Examples
B
Non-Examples

INDEX CARDS

To use index cards while studying, follow these steps:

1. Write a key word or question on one side of an index card.
2. On the reverse side, write the definition of the word, answer to the question, or any other important information that you want to remember.

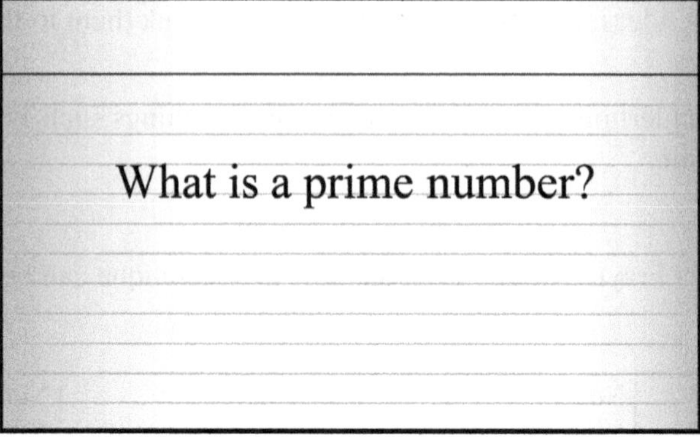

What is a prime number?

A prime number is any number that has exactly 2 factors.
A prime number can be divided evenly only by itself and one.
For example, 2, 3, 5, 7, 19.
The number 1 is not a prime number.

SYMBOLS AND STICKY NOTES—IDENTIFYING IMPORTANT INFORMATION

Use symbols to mark your class notes. The following are some examples:

- An exclamation mark (!) might be used to point out something that must be learned well because it is a very important idea.
- A question mark (?) may highlight something you are not certain about
- A diamond (◊) or asterisk (*) could highlight interesting information that you want to remember.

Sticky notes are useful in the following situations:

- Use sticky notes when you are not allowed to put marks in books.
- Use sticky notes to mark a page in a book that contains an important diagram, formula, explanation, or other information.
- Use sticky notes to mark important facts in research books.

Memorization Techniques

- **Association** relates new learning to something you already know. For example, to remember the spelling difference between dessert and desert, recall that the word *sand* has only one *s*. So, because there is sand in a desert, the word *desert* has only one *s*.
- **Mnemonic** devices are sentences that you create to remember a list or group of items. For example, the first letter of each word in the phrase "Every Good Boy Deserves Fudge" helps you to remember the names of the lines on the treble-clef staff (E, G, B, D, and F) in music.

- **Acronyms** are words that are formed from the first letters or parts of the words in a group. For example, RADAR is actually an acronym for Radio Detecting and Ranging, and MASH is an acronym for Mobile Army Surgical Hospital. HOMES helps you to remember the names of the five Great Lakes (Huron, Ontario, Michigan, Erie, and Superior).
- **Visualizing** requires you to use your mind's eye to "see" a chart, list, map, diagram, or sentence as it is in your textbook or notes, on the chalkboard or computer screen, or in a display.
- **Initialisms** are abbreviations that are formed from the first letters or parts of the words in a group. Unlike acronyms, an initialism cannot be pronounced as a word itself. For example, GCF is an initialism for **G**reatest **C**ommon **F**actor.

Key Strategies for Reviewing

Reviewing textbook material, class notes, and handouts should be an ongoing activity. Spending time reviewing becomes more critical when you are preparing for a test. You may find some of the following review strategies useful when studying during your scheduled study time:

- Before reading a selection, preview it by noting the headings, charts, graphs, and chapter questions.
- Before reviewing a unit, note the headings, charts, graphs, and chapter questions.
- Highlight key concepts, vocabulary, definitions, and formulas.
- Skim the paragraph, and note the key words, phrases, and information.
- Carefully read over each step in a procedure.
- Draw a picture or diagram to help make the concept clearer.

KEY STRATEGIES FOR SUCCESS: A CHECKLIST

Reviewing is a huge part of doing well at school and preparing for tests. Here is a checklist for you to keep track of how many suggested strategies for success you are using. Read each question, and put a check mark (✓) in the correct column. Look at the questions where you have checked the "No" column. Think about how you might try using some of these strategies to help you do your best at school.

Key Strategies for Success	Yes	No
Do you attend school regularly?	✓	
Do you know your personal learning style—how you learn best?		✓
Do you spend 15 to 30 minutes a day reviewing your notes?		✓
Do you study in a quiet place at home?	✓	
Do you clearly mark the most important ideas in your study notes?	✓	
Do you use sticky notes to mark texts and research books?	✓	
Do you practise answering multiple-choice and written-response questions?	✓	
Do you ask your teacher for help when you need it?	✓	✓
Are you maintaining a healthy diet and sleep routine?		✓
Are you participating in regular physical activity?	✓	

Characteristics of Functions

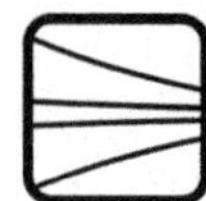

CHARACTERISTICS OF FUNCTIONS

Table of Correlations

	Specific Expectation	Practice Questions	Unit Test Questions	Practice Test 1	Practice Test 2
CF1.0	Representing Functions				
CF1.1	*explain the meaning of the term function, and distinguish a function from a relation that is not a function, through investigation of linear and quadratic relations using a variety of representations (i.e., tables of values, mapping diagrams, graphs, function machines, equations) and strategies*	1, 2	1	1	
CF1.2	*represent linear and quadratic functions using function notation, given their equations, tables of values, or graphs, and substitute into and evaluate functions*	3, 4	2	2	
CF1.3	*explain the meanings of the terms domain and range, through investigation using numeric, graphical, and algebraic representations of the functions $f(x) = x$, $f(x) = x^2$, $f(x) = \sqrt{x}$, and $f(x) = 1/x$; describe the domain and range of a function appropriately; and explain any restrictions on the domain and range in contexts arising from real-world applications*	5, 6	3	3	
CF1.4	*relate the process of determining the inverse of a function to their understanding of reverse processes*	7, 8	4		
CF1.5	*determine the numeric or graphical representation of the inverse of a linear or quadratic function, given the numeric, graphical, or algebraic representation of the function, and make connections, through investigation using a variety of tools between the graph of a function and the graph of its inverse*	9	5		
CF1.6	*determine, through investigation, the relationship between the domain and range of a function and the domain and range of the inverse relation, and determine whether or not the inverse relation is a function*	10, 11	6a, 6b	4	
CF1.7	*determine, using function notation when appropriate, the algebraic representation of the inverse of a linear or quadratic function, given the algebraic representation of the function and make connections, through investigation using a variety of tools between the algebraic representations of a function and its inverse*	12, 13	7	5	
CF1.8	*determine, through investigation using technology, the roles of the parameters a, k, d, and c in functions of the form $y = af(k(x - d)) + c$, and describe these roles in terms of transformations on the graphs of $f(x) = x$, $f(x) = x(^2)$, $f(x) = \sqrt{x}$, and $f(x) = 1/x$ (i.e., translations; reflections in the axes; vertical and horizontal stretches and compressions to and from the x- and y-axes)*	14, 15	8	6	
CF1.9	*sketch graphs of $y = af(k(x - d)) + c$ by applying one or more transformations to the graphs of $f(x) = x$, $f(x) = x(^2)$, $f(x) = \sqrt{x}$, and $f(x) = 1/x$, and state the domain and range of the transformed functions*	16, 17	9, 10	7	
CF2.0	Solving Problems Involving Quadratic Functions				
CF2.1	*determine the number of zeros (i.e., x-intercepts) of a quadratic function, using a variety of strategies*	18, 19	11		1
CF2.2	*determine the maximum or minimum value of a quadratic function whose equation is given in the form $f(x) = ax(^2) + bx + c$, using an algebraic method*	20, 21	12	8	2

CF2.3	*solve problems involving quadratic functions arising from real-world applications and represented using function notation*	22, 23	13a, 13b, 13c, 13d	9	3
CF2.4	*determine, through investigation, the transformational relationship among the family of quadratic functions that have the same zeros, and determine the algebraic representation of a quadratic function, given the real roots of the corresponding quadratic equation and a point on the function*	24, 25	14	10	
CF2.5	*solve problems involving the intersection of a linear function and a quadratic function graphically and algebraically*	26, 27	15	11	
CF3.0	Determining Equivalent Algebraic Expressions*				
CF3.1	*simplify polynomial expressions by adding, subtracting, and multiplying*	28, 29	16, 17	12	4
CF3.2	*verify, through investigation with and without technology, that* $\sqrt{ab} = \sqrt{a} \times \sqrt{b}$, $a \geq 0$, $b \geq 0$, *and use this relationship to simplify radicals and radical expressions obtained by adding, subtracting, and multiplying*	30, 31	18		
CF3.3	*simplify rational expressions by adding, subtracting, multiplying, and dividing, and state the restrictions on the variable values*	32, 33a, 33b, 33c, 33d	19	13	5
CF3.4	*determine if two given algebraic expressions are equivalent (i.e., by simplifying; by substituting values)*	34, 35	20		6

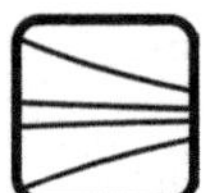

CF1.1 explain the meaning of the term function, and distinguish a function from a relation that is not a function, through investigation of linear and quadratic relations using a variety of representations (i.e., tables of values, mapping diagrams, graphs, function machines, equations) and strategies

Defining and Representing Functions

A **relation** is any set of ordered pairs. A **function** is a relation in which no two ordered pairs have the same x-coordinate or first coordinate.

The set $A = \{(1, 2), (2, 4), (3, 5), (3, 6), (4, 7)\}$ is a relation, but because there are two ordered pairs with x-coordinates of 3, it is not a function.

Points with the same x-coordinate are located vertically above or below each other and are part of the same vertical line. If a vertical line intersects the graph of a relation in two or more points anywhere, then the relation is not a function. This is referred to as the **vertical line test.**

Example

Determine if the relation $x = y^2$ is a function.

Solution

Step 1

Solve the relation for y.

To solve for y, take the square root of each side.

$$x = y^2$$
$$\pm\sqrt{x} = y$$

Step 2

Select any value greater than 0 (the square root of a negative number is undefined) for x to determine an ordered pair of the relation.

For example, choosing a value of 4 for x gives the following results:

$$\begin{aligned} y &= \pm\sqrt{4} \\ &= \pm 2 \end{aligned}$$

This gives the two ordered pairs (4, –2) and (4, 2) with the same x-coordinate.

This relation is not a function. From the graph of $x = y^2$, it can be seen that a vertical line will intersect the graph at two points whenever $x > 0$.

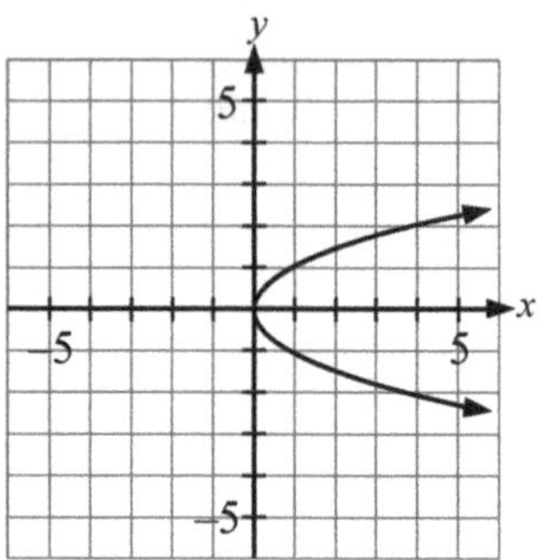

---

1. Which of the following graphs is **not** the graph of a function?

A.

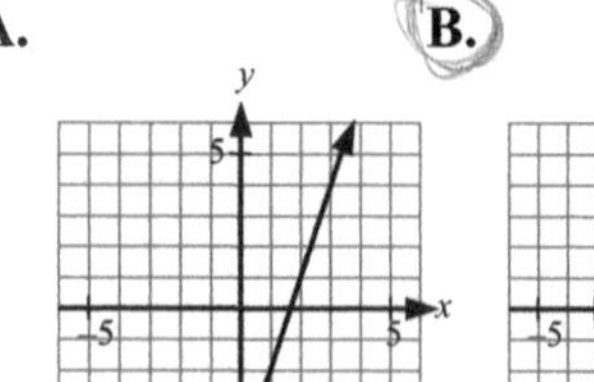

B.

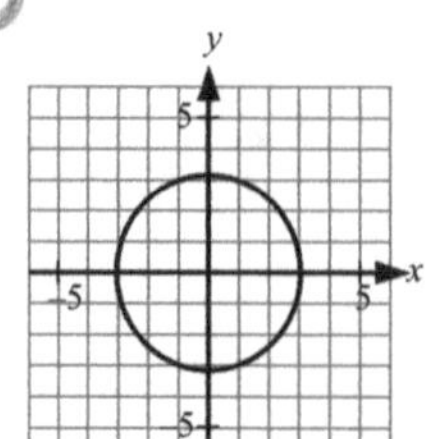

C.

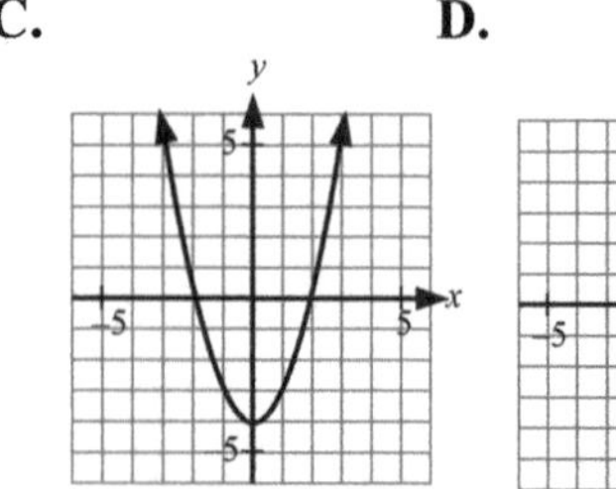

D.

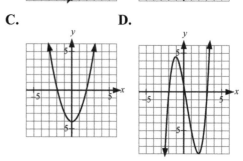

Open Response

2. Determine whether the relation $x + y^2 = 4$ is a function.

CF1.2 represent linear and quadratic functions using function notation, given their equations, tables of values, or graphs, and substitute into and evaluate functions

Representing Functions

The ordered pairs (x, y) that satisfy the equations $y = 2x + 3$ and $y = 2x^2 - 3x + 1$ form two functions. An equation that is a function can be represented using function notation.

- x-y notation
  $y = 2x + 3$
  $y = 2x^2 - 3x + 1$
- Function notation
  $f(x) = 2x + 3$
  $f(x) = 2x^2 - 3x + 1$

The symbol $f(x)$ is read as "the value of f at x" or "f of x." Function notation describes the output $f(x)$ as a result of an input of x into a function machine, f.

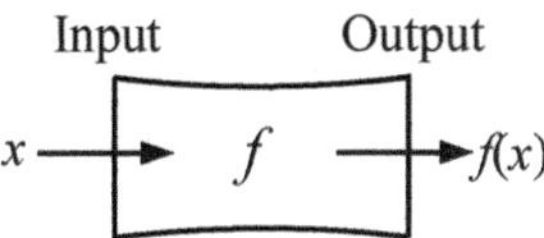

For example, $f(5)$ means to substitute the input value of 5 into the function machine defined by f to produce the resulting output value $f(5)$.

Input (5)	Function (f)	Output [$f(5)$]
5	$2x + 3 = 2(5) + 3$	13
5	$2x^2 - 3x + 1$ $= 2(5)^2 - 3(5) + 1$	36

Example

The function $f(x)$ can be defined by the values in the given table.

x	$f(x)$
1	1
2	4
4	10

With this information, what is the value of $f(3)$?

Solution

Step 1

Determine the function.

When $x = 1$, $f(x) = 1$.

$f(x) = 3 \times x - 2$
$1 = 3 \times 1 - 2$
$1 = 1$

When $x = 2$, $f(x) = 4$.

$f(x) = 3 \times x - 2$
$4 = 3 \times 2 - 2$
$4 = 4$

When $x = 4$, $f(x) = 10$.

$f(x) = 3 \times x - 2$
$10 = 3 \times 4 - 2$
$10 = 10$

Therefore, the function can be written as $f(x) = 3x - 2$.

Step 2

Calculate the value of $f(3)$.

Substitute 3 for x and $f(3)$ for $f(x)$ into the equation $f(x) = 3x - 2$.

$f(x) = 3x - 2$
$f(3) = 3(3) - 2$
$f(3) = 9 - 2$
$f(3) = 7$

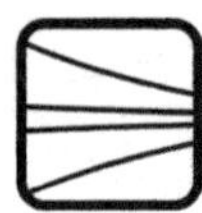

Use the following information to answer the next question.

The graph of a linear function $f(x)$ is shown.

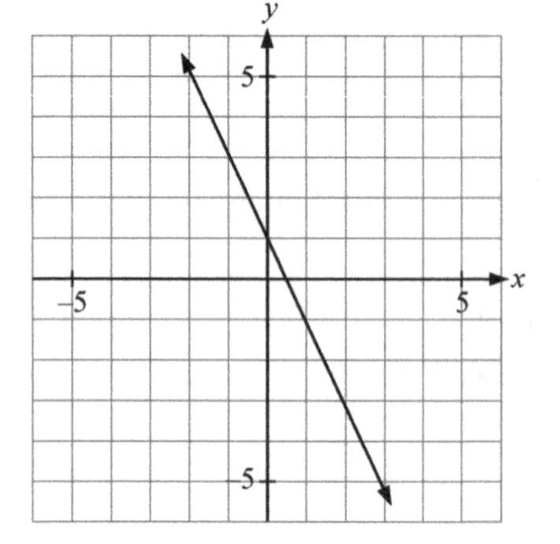

3. The equation of the function is

A. $f(x) = 2x - 1$

B. $f(x) = -2x - 1$

C. $f(x) = 2x + 1$

D. $f(x) = -2x + 1$

Numerical Response

4. For the function $g(x) = -2x^2 - 3x + 15$, the value of $g(-2)$ is _________.

CF1.3 explain the meanings of the terms domain and range, through investigation using numeric, graphical, and algebraic representations of the functions $f(x) = x$, $f(x) = x^2$, $f(x) = \sqrt{x}$, and $f(x) = 1/x$; describe the domain and range of a function appropriately; and explain any restrictions on the domain and range in contexts arising from real-world applications

Domain and Range of a Function

The **domain** of a function (or relation) is the set of x-coordinates for the function. It is the set of permissible replacements for x in the function (or relation) that gives real number values for y.

Example

Identify the domains of $f(x) = x^2$, $g(x) = \sqrt{x}$, and $h(x) = \frac{1}{x}$.

Solution

For $f(x) = x^2$, the domain is $x \in R$ because every real number can be squared to produce another real number.

For $g(x) = \sqrt{x}$, no negative numbers can replace x because the square root of a negative number is not real. The domain is 0 and all positive real numbers, or $x \geq 0$.

For $h(x) = \frac{1}{x}$, zero cannot be used as a replacement for x because division by zero is undefined. All other real numbers will give a real number value for y, so the domain is every real number except zero, or $x \neq 0$.

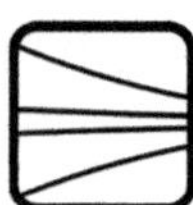

The **range** of a function (or relation) is the set of second or y-coordinates of the function.

Example

Identify the ranges of $f(x) = x^2$ where $x \in R$, $g(x) = \sqrt{x}$ where $x \geq 0$, and $h(x) = \frac{1}{x}$ where $x < 0$.

Solution

For $f(x) = x^2$, the y-coordinates will be greater than or equal to zero, because the square of every real number is either zero or positive. The range is $y \geq 0$.

For $g(x) = \sqrt{x}$, only the positive square root of x is taken, so y cannot be negative.
The smallest value of y is 0, when $x = 0$.
The range is 0 and all positive real numbers, or $y \geq 0$.

If $h(x) = \frac{1}{x}$ is rewritten as $x = \frac{1}{h(x)}$, it is possible to see that $h(x) \neq 0$, or $y \neq 0$. Also, since $x < 0$ then $y < 0$. Therefore the range is $y < 0$.

These domains and ranges can be verified by observing the graphs of these functions.

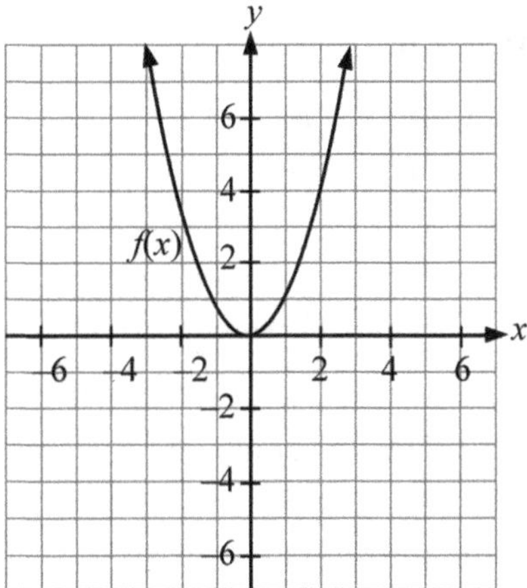

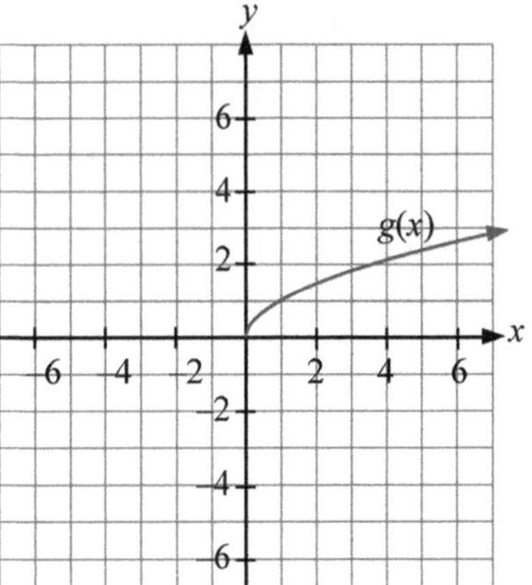

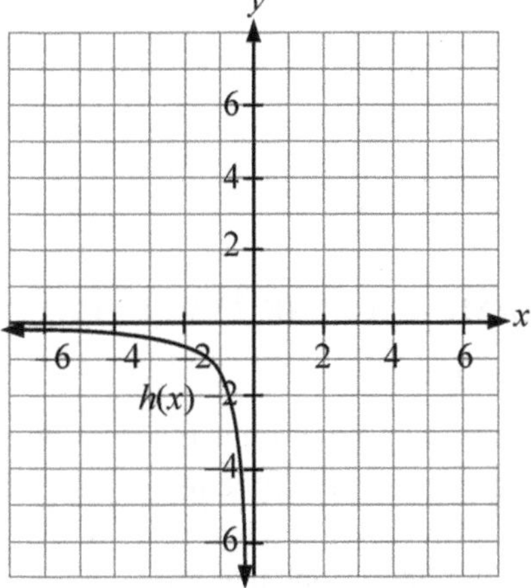

5. What is the domain and the range of the function $f(x) = \sqrt{9 - x}$?

A. $x \geq 9, y \geq 0$

B. $x \leq 9, y \geq 0$

C. $x \geq 9, y \in R$

D. $x \leq 9, y \in R$

Use the following information to answer the next question.

The kinetic energy, E_k, measured in joules of a 1 200 kg car moving at a speed of v measured in kilometres per hour is given by the equation $E_k = 46.3v^2$.

Open Response

6. Describe the physical factors that restrict the domain and range of the given equation, and give reasonable values that would apply to a 1 200 kg car driving on a highway.

CF1.4 relate the process of determining the inverse of a function to their understanding of reverse processes

Determining the Inverse of a Function

The **inverse** of a function is the relation that exists when the values in the function or the ordered pairs of the function are interchanged. When solving for y, all the operations that are applied to the new y-variable (original x-variable) have to be undone or reversed.

Use the following steps to determine the inverse of a function:

1. Interchange x and y.
2. Solve for y.

Example

Write the inverse of the function $y = 3x - 4$.

Solution

Step 1

Interchange x and y.

$y = 3x - 4$
$x = 3y - 4$

Step 2

Solve for y.

To solve for y, undo the two operations, multiplying by 3 and subtracting 4, by adding 4 and then dividing by 3.

$$\begin{aligned} x &= 3y - 4 \\ 3y - 4 &= x \\ 3y &= x + 4 \\ y &= \frac{x + 4}{3} \end{aligned}$$

---

7. Which of the following phrases describes the correct order of the operations involved in performing the inverse of a function in which y is determined by multiplying x by 3 and then adding 5?

A. Multiplying by 3 and adding 5

B. Adding 5 and multiplying by 3

C. Subtracting 5 and dividing by 3

D. Multiplying by 3 and subtracting 5

Use the following information to answer the next question.

A function is defined as follows: y is determined by adding 4 to x and then multiplying by 6.

8. Which of the following statements describes the operations required to determine the inverse of the given function?

A. Divide by 6, and then add 4.

B. Divide by 6, and then subtract 4.

C. Subtract 4, and then divide by 6.

D. Subtract 4, and then multiply by 6.

CF1.5 determine the numeric or graphical representation of the inverse of a linear or quadratic function, given the numeric, graphical, or algebraic representation of the function, and make connections, through investigation using a variety of tools between the graph of a function and the graph of its inverse

GRAPHING THE INVERSE OF A FUNCTION

The inverse of a function can be determined by interchanging the x- and y-values for the numeric or algebraic representations of the function.

For graphical representations, the graph of a function and its inverse are reflections of each other over the diagonal line $y = x$. Every ordered pair, (x, y), on the graph of the original function becomes (y, x) on the graph of the inverse function.

For example, $y = x^2$ and its inverse, $x = y^2$, are graphed on the same plane along with the function $y = x$. The graph of $x = y^2$ is the graph of $y = x^2$ reflected in the line $y = x$.

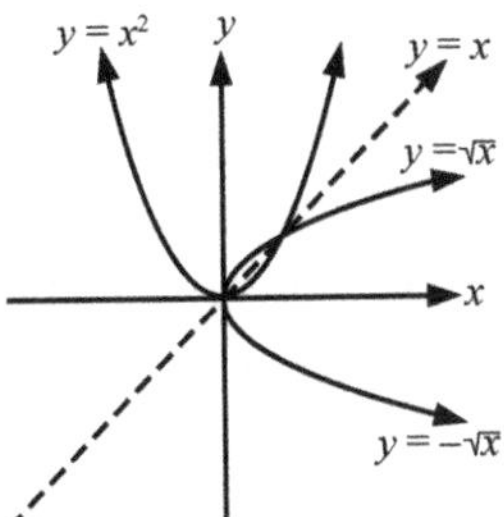

Example

The graph of a function is given.

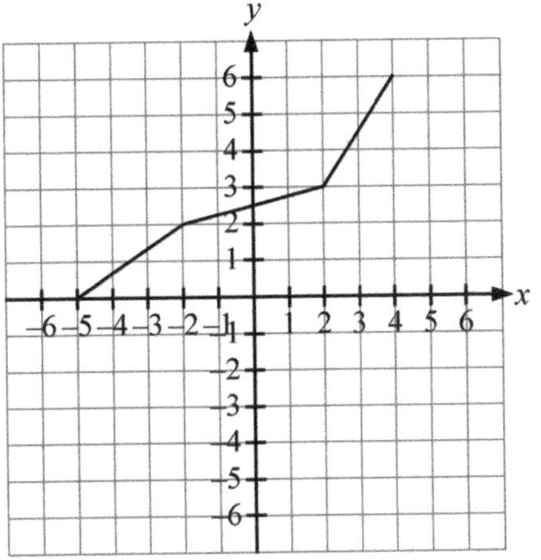

Sketch the graph of the inverse.

Solution

Step 1

Determine the ordered pairs of the inverse.

Some ordered pairs of points that are on the graph of the given function are $(-5, 0)$, $(-2, 2)$, $(2, 3)$, and $(4, 6)$.

Since the inverse of this function has the domain and range values interchanged, some ordered pairs of points on the inverse are $(0, -5)$, $(2, -2)$, $(3, 2)$, and $(6, 4)$.

Step 2

Plot and connect these points to get the graph of the inverse.

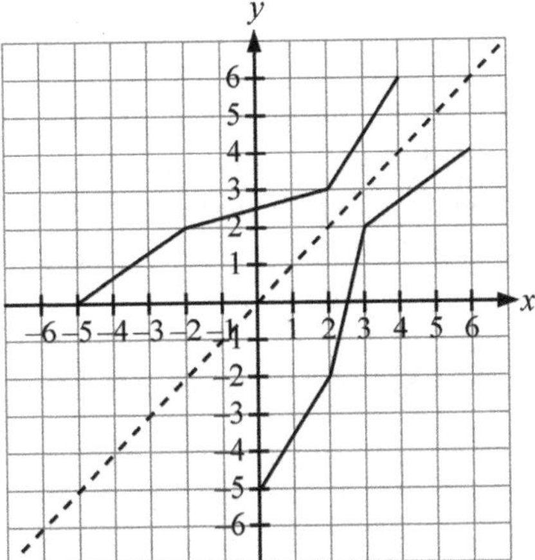

Notice that the inverse is a reflection of the original function in the line $y = x$ (drawn with the dotted line).

Use the following information to answer the next question.

The points (–3, 1), (0, –2), (2, 6), and (4, 22) are part of a quadratic function.

9. The corresponding points on the inverse of this quadratic function are

A. (1, –3), (–2, 0), (6, 2), and (22, 4)

B. (–3, 1), $\left(0, -\frac{1}{2}\right)$, $\left(2, \frac{1}{6}\right)$, and $\left(4, \frac{1}{22}\right)$

C. (–3, 1), (0, 2), (2, –6), and (4, –22)

D. (3, –1), (0, 2), (–2, –6), and (–4, –22)

CF1.6 determine, through investigation, the relationship between the domain and range of a function and the domain and range of the inverse relation, and determine whether or not the inverse relation is a function

Domain and Range of an Inverse Function

Since the inverse of a function or relation is formed by interchanging the x- and y-coordinates, the behaviours of each variable are also interchanged. In the inverse of a function, the values originally found in the domain become the values of the range, and the values originally found in the range become the values of the domain.

Example

The domain and range of a quadratic function are $x \in \mathbb{R}$ and $y \geq 3$. What are the domain and range of the inverse?

Solution

Step 1

Determine the range of the inverse.

Since the variables are interchanged, the domain, $x \in \mathbb{R}$, becomes the range of the inverse, $y \in \mathbb{R}$.

Step 2

Determine the domain of the inverse.

Since the variables are interchanged, the range, $y \geq 3$, becomes the domain of the inverse, $x \geq 3$.

Use the following information to answer the next question.

A graph of a quadratic function is shown.

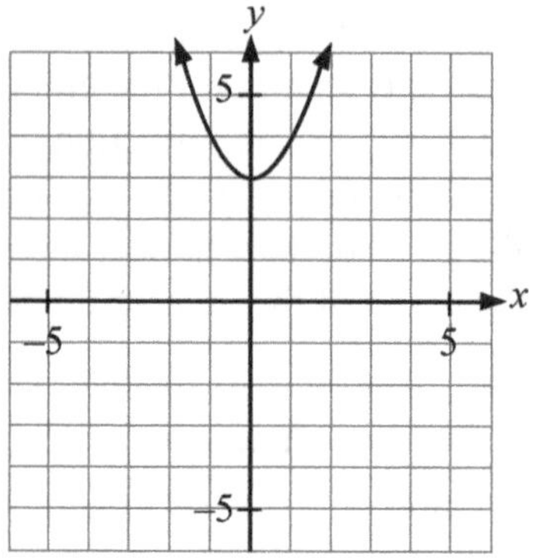

Open Response

10. Determine if the inverse of the given quadratic function is a function. State the domain and range of the inverse.

11. What are the domain and range of the inverse of the quadratic function $f(x) = (x - 3)^2 - 5$?

A. $x \geq 5$ and $y \geq 3$

B. $x \geq 5$ and $y \in R$

C. $x \geq -5$ and $y \geq 3$

D. $x \geq -5$ and $y \in R$

CF1.7 determine, using function notation when appropriate, the algebraic representation of the inverse of a linear or quadratic function, given the algebraic representation of the function and make connections, through investigation using a variety of tools between the algebraic representations of a function and its inverse

INVERSE FUNCTION NOTATION

A function is often written as F, and the inverse of a function is often written as F'. There are many different notations used for functions and their inverses, such as function $f(x)$ and inverse $f^{-1}(x)$. (Note that $f^{-1}(x) \neq \frac{1}{f(x)}$). Because the notations vary, an awareness of the notation being used in a particular problem or situation is essential. The function notation for the inverse of a function is $f^{-1}(x)$, and it is read as "f inverse."

Example

Write the inverse of $f(x) = \frac{1}{3}x + 4$.

Solution

Step 1

Replace $f(x)$ with y.

$y = \frac{1}{3}x + 4$

Step 2

Interchange x and y.

$x = \frac{1}{3}y + 4$

Step 3

Solve for y.

$$\begin{aligned} x &= \frac{1}{3}y + 4 \\ 3x &= y + 12 \\ 3x - 12 &= y \\ y &= 3x - 12 \end{aligned}$$

Step 4

Replace y with $f^{-1}(x)$.

Since $y = 3x - 12$ is a linear function, it can be written using function notation.

$f^{-1}(x) = 3x - 12$

---

12. What is the inverse of the linear function $f(x) = \frac{1}{2}x + 3$?

A. $f^{-1}(x) = 2(x - 3)$

B. $f^{-1}(x) = \frac{1}{2}x - 3$

C. $f^{-1}(x) = 2x - 3$

D. $f^{-1}(x) = \frac{x-3}{2}$

13. What is the inverse of the quadratic function $f(x) = (x - 4)^2 + 5$?

A. $f^{-1}(x) = \sqrt{x-5} + 4$

B. $f^{-1}(x) = \sqrt{x+4} - 5$

C. $y = \pm\sqrt{x-5} + 4$

D. $y = \pm\sqrt{x+4} - 5$

CF1.8 determine, through investigation using technology, the roles of the parameters a, k, d, and c in functions of the form y = af (k(x - d)) + c, and describe these roles in terms of transformations on the graphs of f(x) = x, f(x) = x(²), f(x) = √x, and f(x) = 1/x (i.e., translations; reflections in the axes; vertical and horizontal stretches and compressions to and from the x- and y-axes)

TRANSFORMATIONS OF FUNCTIONS

The effects of changing $y = f(x)$ into $y = af(k(x - d)) + c$ by adding parameters a, k, d, and c are summarized in the following table:

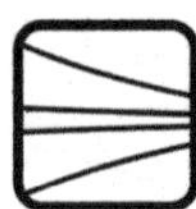

Conditions on Parameter	Effect
$\lvert a \rvert < 1$	Vertical compression to the x-axis by a factor of a
$\lvert a \rvert > 1$	Vertical stretch from the x-axis by a factor of a
$a < 0$	Reflection in the x-axis
$\lvert k \rvert < 1$	Horizontal stretch from the y-axis by a factor of $\frac{1}{k}$
$\lvert k \rvert > 1$	Horizontal compression to the y-axis by a factor of $\frac{1}{k}$
$k < 0$	Reflection in the y-axis
$d < 0$	Horizontal translation of d units to the left
$d > 0$	Horizontal translation of d units to the right
$c < 0$	Vertical translation of c units down
$c > 0$	Vertical translation of c units up

Example

The graph of the function $y = f(x)$ is stretched horizontally about the y-axis by a factor of $\frac{1}{4}$, stretched vertically about the x-axis by a factor of 3, reflected in the x-axis, translated 5 units to the left, and translated 2 units down.

If the transformations are done in the given order, then the equation of the transformed function is

Solution

Step 1
If the graph of $y = f(x)$ is stretched horizontally about the y-axis by a factor of $\frac{1}{4}$, substitute $4x$ for x in the equation $y = f(x)$.
The resulting equation is $y = f(4x)$.

Step 2
If the graph of $y = f(4x)$ is stretched vertically about the x-axis by a factor of 3, substitute $\frac{1}{3}y$ for y in the equation $y = f(4x)$.
The resulting equation is $\frac{1}{3}y = f(4x)$ or $y = 3f(4x)$.

Step 3
Substitute $-y$ for y in the equation $y = 3f(4x)$ to reflect the graph $y = 3f(4x)$ in the x-axis.
The resulting equation becomes $-y = 3f(4x)$, which is equivalent to $y = -3f(4x)$.

Step 4
To translate the graph of $y = -3f(4x)$ 5 units left and 2 units down, substitute $x + 5$ for x and $y + 2$ for y in the equation $y = -3f(4x)$.
Thus, the equation of the transformed function is $y + 2 = -3f(4(x + 5))$ or $y = -3f(4(x + 5)) - 2$.
The equation $y = -3f(4(x + 5)) - 2$ can be written as $y = -3f(4x + 20) - 2$.

---

14. In order to reflect the graph of the function $f(x) = \sqrt{x}$ in the y-axis and translate it 3 units vertically upward, into what must the equation be transformed?

A. $f(x) = \sqrt{-x} + 3$

B. $f(x) = \sqrt{-x + 3}$

C. $f(x) = -\sqrt{x} + 3$

D. $f(x) = -\sqrt{x + 3}$

15. When the function $f(x) = x^2$ is transformed into the function $g(x) = 2(x + 1)^2$, the graph of $g(x)$ can be obtained from the graph of $f(x)$ by applying a

A. vertical stretch by a factor of 2 and a horizontal translation 1 unit to the left

B. horizontal stretch by a factor of 2 and a horizontal translation 1 unit to the right

C. vertical compression by a factor of $\frac{1}{2}$ and a horizontal translation 1 unit to the right

D. horizontal compression by a factor of $\frac{1}{2}$ and a horizontal translation 1 unit to the left

CF1.9 sketch graphs of y = af (k(x - d)) + c by applying one or more transformations to the graphs of f(x) = x, f(x) = x(²), f(x) = √x, and f(x) = 1/x, and state the domain and range of the transformed functions

Sketching Graphs Using Transformations

In order to sketch the graph of $y = af(k(x - d)) + c$ by hand, transformations can be applied to the graphs of $f(x) = x$, $f(x) = x^2$, $f(x) = \sqrt{x}$, and $f(x) = \frac{1}{x}$. All points on the transformed graph must satisfy the given transformations.

For example, consider the following graphs.

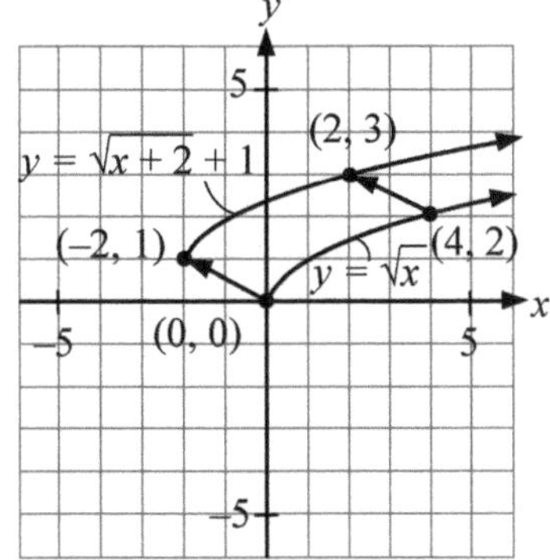

Compared to the graph of $y = \sqrt{x}$, the graph of the function $y = \sqrt{x+2} + 1$ has been translated 2 units left and 1 unit up, and the point (0, 0) has become point (−2, 1). Similarly, the point (4, 2), which is on the graph of $y = \sqrt{x}$, has become the point (2, 3) on the graph of $y = \sqrt{x+2} + 1$ since 2 is 2 units left of 4 and 3 is 1 unit up from 2.

When you are sketching the graph of $y = a(x - h)^2 + k$ by applying transformations to the graph of $y = x^2$, the order of transformations should be as follows:

1. Vertical stretch or compression
2. Reflection in the x-axis (Steps 1 and 2 can be reversed.)
3. Vertical and/or horizontal translations (in either order)

Example

Sketch the graph of $y = -(x + 6)^2 + 5$ by applying transformations to the graph of $y = x^2$.

Solution

Step 1

Compare the equation of the graph $y = -(x + 6)^2 + 5$ with the vertex form $f(x) = a(x - h)^2 + k$ to determine the parameters a, h, and k, as well as the transformations that should be applied.

Since a is negative, the graph of $y = x^2$ will be reflected in the x-axis. Since $h = -6$, the graph will be translated 6 units to the left. Since $k = 5$, the graph will be translated up 5 units.

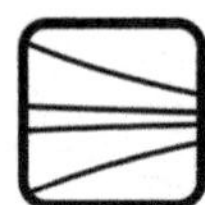

Step 2

Apply the transformations as follows:

1. Reflect the graph of $y = x^2$ in the x-axis. The equation of the resulting graph is $y = -x^2$.
2. Horizontally translate the graph of $y = -x^2$ six units to the left. The equation of the resulting graph is $y = -(x + 6)^2$.
3. Vertically translate the graph of $y = -(x + 6)^2$ five units up. The equation of the resulting graph is $y = -(x + 6)^2 + 5$.

This image shows the translations performed in order on the graph of $y = x^2$ that result in the graph of $y = -(x + 6)^2 + 5$.

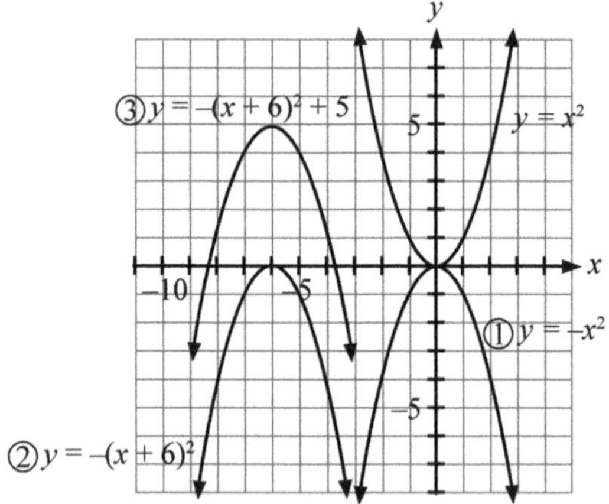

Use the following information to answer the next question.

> The function $f(x) = \sqrt{x}$ is transformed into the function $g(x) = -\sqrt{x + 4}$.

16. What are the domain and range of $g(x)$?

A. $x \leq -4$ and $y \geq 0$

B. $x \geq -4$ and $y \geq 0$

C. $x \leq -4$ and $y \leq 0$

D. $x \geq -4$ and $y \leq 0$

Use the following information to answer the next question.

> The function $f(x) = x^2$ is transformed into the function $g(x) = \frac{1}{2}(x - 3)^2$.

17. Which of the following graphs shows the transformed function, $g(x)$?

A.

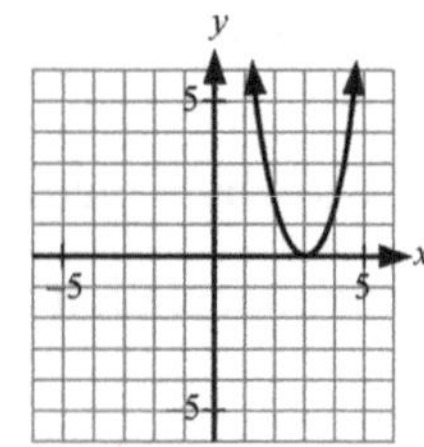

B.

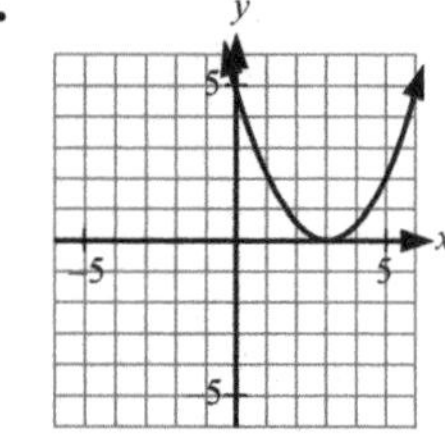

C.

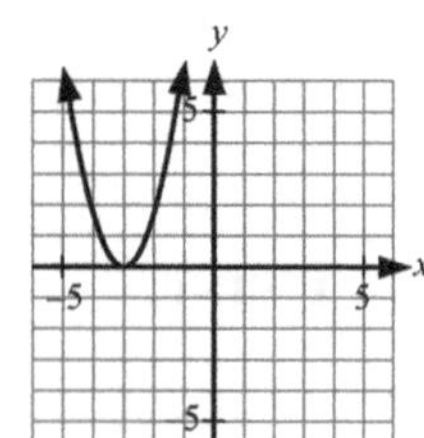

D.

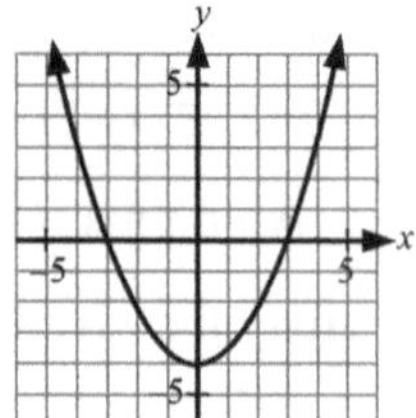

CF2.1 determine the number of zeros (i.e., x-intercepts) of a quadratic function, using a variety of strategies

Zeros of a Quadratic Function

A real number, a, is a zero of a function, $f(x)$, if $f(a) = 0$. Since the y-coordinates of every point on the x-axis are zero, every zero of $f(x)$ will also be an x-intercept of the graph of $f(x)$, and, conversely, every x-intercept of the graph of $f(x)$ will be a zero of the function.

When factoring, the number of factors will indicate the number of zeros. For example, for the quadratic function $f(x) = x^2 - 9$, the equation can be factored to $f(x) = (x + 3)(x - 3)$, indicating two real and distinct zeros.

When analyzing a graph, the x-intercepts will indicate the number of zeros for the function. For example, the given graph touches the x-axis at only one point. Therefore, it has one x-intercept and one zero.

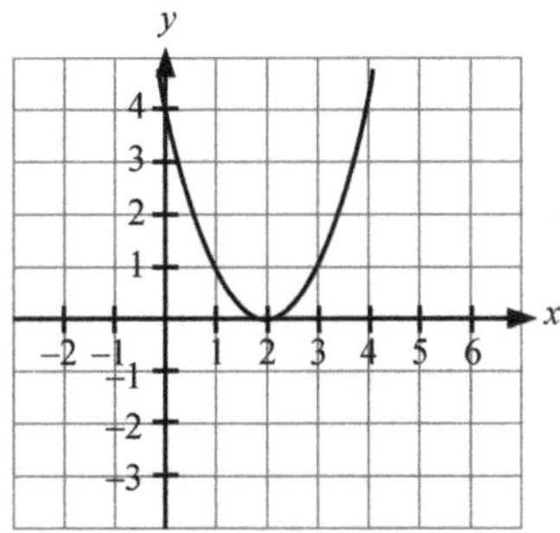

The expression $b^2 - 4ac$ is called the **discriminant** of the quadratic function $f(x) = ax^2 + bx + c$. The value of the discriminant determines the number of real zeros of the function as follows:

- If $b^2 - 4ac < 0$, there are no real zeros (x-intercepts).
- If $b^2 - 4ac = 0$, there is one real zero (x-intercept).
- If $b^2 - 4ac > 0$, there are two real zeros (x-intercepts).

Example

For the quadratic equation $3x^2 - 2x + 4 = 0$, use the discriminant to describe the nature of the roots.

Solution

Step 1
Identify the values of a, b, and c in the quadratic equation of the form $ax^2 + bx + c = 0$, $a \neq 0$.
$a = 3$, $b = -2$, and $c = 4$

Step 2
Determine the value of the discriminant $b^2 - 4ac$.
Substitute the values of a, b, and c into the discriminant $b^2 - 4ac$.
For $3x^2 - 2x + 4 = 0$,

$$\begin{aligned} b^2 - 4ac &= (-2)^2 - 4(3)(4) \\ &= 4 - 48 \\ &= -44 \end{aligned}$$

Since $b^2 - 4ac = -44$, $b^2 - 4ac < 0$ and the given equation has no real roots.

Use the following information to answer the next question.

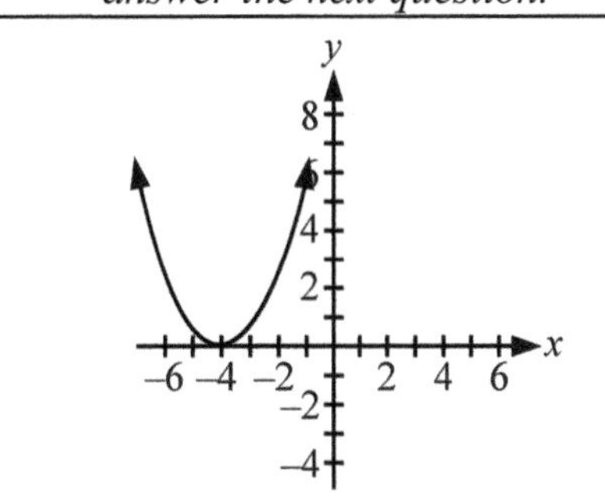

A graph of a quadratic function is given.

18. How many different real zeros does the function have?

A. 0 **B.** 1

C. 2 **D.** 3

Open Response

19. How many real zeros does the quadratic function $y = 3x^2 + 2x + 4$ have?

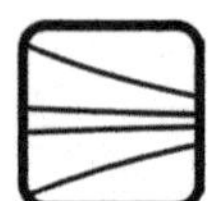

CF2.2 determine the maximum or minimum value of a quadratic function whose equation is given in the form f(x) = ax(²) + bx + c, using an algebraic method

Determining the Maximum or Minimum Value of a Quadratic Function

When the quadratic function $f(x) = ax^2 + bx + c$ is converted into the completed square form $f(x) = a(x - h)^2 + k$, the coordinates of the vertex (h, k) can be quickly identified. Since the vertex is the maximum point if $a < 0$ or the minimum point if $a > 0$, the maximum or minimum value of the function, k, is also identified.

Example

Determine the maximum or minimum value of the quadratic function $f(x) = \frac{1}{2}x^2 - 4x + 2$, and identify whether it is a maximum or a minimum.

Solution

The function $f(x) = \frac{1}{2}x^2 - 4x + 2$ has a minimum because $a > 0$. Complete the square.

$$\begin{aligned} f(x) &= \frac{1}{2}x^2 - 4x + 2 \\ &= \frac{1}{2}(x^2 - 8x) + 2 \\ &= \frac{1}{2}(x^2 - 8x + 16 - 16) + 2 \\ &= \frac{1}{2}(x^2 - 8x + 16) - 8 + 2 \\ &= \frac{1}{2}(x - 4)^2 - 6 \end{aligned}$$

The minimum value is -6.

The maximum or minimum value can also be determined by partially factoring a quadratic formula and using symmetry.

Example

To determine the maximum value of $f(x) = -2x^2 - 24x - 67$, partially factor the function.

$f(x) = -2x(x + 12) - 67$

The values of $f(0)$ and $f(-12)$ are both -67, so by the symmetry of the parabola, the maximum must be at $x = -6$ (midway between $x = 0$ and $x = -12$).

The maximum is calculated as follows:

$$\begin{aligned} f(-6) &= -2(-6)^2 - 24(-6) - 67 \\ f(-6) &= -72 + 144 - 67 \\ f(-6) &= 5 \end{aligned}$$

---

20. By completing the square, it can be determined that the quadratic function $f(x) = -3x^2 + 12x - 4$ has a

A. maximum value of -16

B. minimum value of -16

C. maximum value of 8

D. minimum value of 8

Open Response

21. Find the minimum value of the function $f(x) = 2x^2 - 8x - 3$ by partially factoring the first two terms.

CF2.3 solve problems involving quadratic functions arising from real-world applications and represented using function notation

Solving Real-World Problems Involving Quadratic Functions

Quadratic functions can be used to describe real-world situations, and problems related to quadratic functions can be solved.

Example

A rock is thrown from the roof of a building. Its height, h, in metres above the ground t seconds after it is thrown can be modelled using the equation $h(t) = -5t^2 + 10t + 15$.

How long after the rock is thrown does it reach its maximum height?

Solution

Determine the vertex by completing the square.

$$\begin{aligned} h(t) &= -5t^2 + 10t + 15 \\ &= \left(-5t^2 + 10t\right) + 15 \\ &= -5\left(t^2 - 2t\right) + 15 \\ &= -5\left(t^2 - 2t + 1 - 1\right) + 15 \\ &= -5\left(t^2 - 2t + 1\right) - 1(-5) + 15 \\ &= -5(t - 1)^2 + 20 \end{aligned}$$

The vertex is at (1, 20).

The rock reaches its maximum height 1 s after it is thrown.

Use the following information to answer the next question.

> A theatre owner averages attendance of 200 patrons with a ticket price of \$12. A survey shows that if he decreases the ticket price, the attendance will increase. The quadratic function $P(x) = -10x^2 + 140x + 1\ 800$ predicts his profit, $P(x)$, in dollars for one movie, where x is the number of times he decreases the ticket price by \$0.50.

22. The **maximum** profit the theatre owner can obtain is

A. \$1 849 with a ticket price of \$7.00

B. \$2 290 with a ticket price of \$7.00

C. \$1 849 with a ticket price of \$8.50

D. \$2 290 with a ticket price of \$8.50

Use the following information to answer the next question.

> In metres, the height of an arrow, $h(t)$, shot vertically upward from a height of 1 m above ground level is predicted by the quadratic function $h(t) = -5t^2 + 60t + 1$, where t is the amount of time in seconds since the arrow was shot.

Numerical Response

23. The maximum height of the arrow is __________ m.

CF2.4 determine, through investigation, the transformational relationship among the family of quadratic functions that have the same zeros, and determine the algebraic representation of a quadratic function, given the real roots of the corresponding quadratic equation and a point on the function

The Equation of a Quadratic Function

If a quadratic function has zeros m and n, then the equation of the function must also have the factors $x - m$ and $x - n$. The only transformation that will not change the zeros (x-intercepts) is a vertical stretch or compression relative to the x-axis or a reflection in the x-axis. Since parameter a controls these transformations, the family of all quadratic functions with zeros m and n must have equations of the form $f(x) = a(x - m)(x - n)$.

Example

Determine the equation of the quadratic function that has zeros of $2\sqrt{3}$ and $-2\sqrt{3}$ and passes through the point $(1, 2)$.

Solution

This function can be written in the form $f(x) = a(x - m)(x - n)$, where $m = 2\sqrt{3}$ and $n = -2\sqrt{3}$.

Thus, the equation is given as follows:

$$y = a(x - 2\sqrt{3})(x - (-2\sqrt{3}))$$
$$y = a(x - 2\sqrt{3})(x + 2\sqrt{3})$$
$$y = a(x^2 - 12)$$

Since the graph passes through $(1, 2)$, the values $x = 1$ and $y = 2$ satisfy the equation.

$$\begin{aligned} y &= a(x^2 - 12) \\ 2 &= a(1^2 - 12) \\ 2 &= a(-11) \\ -\frac{2}{11} &= a \end{aligned}$$

The equation of the quadratic function is given as follows:

$$y = -\frac{2}{11}(x^2 - 12)$$
$$y = -\frac{2}{11}x^2 + \frac{24}{11}$$

---

24. If the roots of a quadratic equation are $3 + \sqrt{2}$ and $3 - \sqrt{2}$, the corresponding equation of the quadratic function passing through the point $(1, 4)$ is

A. $f(x) = 2x^2 - 12x + 14$

B. $f(x) = 2x^2 + 12x + 14$

C. $f(x) = x^2 - 6x + 7$

D. $f(x) = x^2 + 6x + 7$

Open Response

25. Determine the equation of the quadratic function that passes through the point $(-5, 9)$ if the roots of the corresponding quadratic equation are 4 and -3.

CF2.5 solve problems involving the intersection of a linear function and a quadratic function graphically and algebraically

THE INTERSECTION OF LINEAR AND QUADRATIC FUNCTIONS

Solving problems where a linear function, $g(x)$, intersects a quadratic function, $f(x)$, involves equating the two functions ($f(x) = g(x)$) and solving for x. Once the x-value or values are known, they are substituted back into either of the functions to determine the y-value or values. This yields the ordered pair or pairs that satisfy both functions.

Example

Determine the point or points of intersection for the linear function $g(x) = 3 - 6x$ and the quadratic function $f(x) = -2x^2 - 8x + 3$.

Solution

Step 1

To find the x-coordinates of the points of intersection, equate the two functions.

$$f(x) = g(x)$$
$$-2x^2 - 8x + 3 = 3 - 6x$$
$$-2x^2 - 2x = 0$$
$$-2x(x + 1) = 0$$

$-2x = 0$

$x = 0$

or

$(x + 1) = 0$

$x = -1$

Step 2

Use $g(x)$ to find the y-values of these x-values.

$g(0) = 3 - 6(0)$
$= 3$

or

$g(-1) = 3 - 6(-1)$
$= 3 + 6$
$= 9$

You can also use $f(x)$ to find the y-values of these x-values.

$f(0) = -2(0)^2 - 8(0) + 3$
$= 3$

or

$f(-1) = -2(-1)^2 - 8(-1) + 3$
$= -2 + 8 + 3$
$= 9$

The points are (0, 3) and (−1, 9).

---

26. The points of intersection of the quadratic function $f(x) = x^2 + 3x - 28$ and the linear function $g(x) = x - 13$ are

A. (3, −5) and (−5, −9)

B. (3, −10) and (−5, −18)

C. (4, −9) and (−7, −20)

D. (−3, −28) and (5, 12)

Use the following information to answer the next question.

A cylindrical water tank is being filled at a constant rate so that the height, $h(t)$, in metres, is rising according to the function $h(t) = \frac{1}{2}t + 6$, in which t is the time in minutes. At the same time, a conical tank is being emptied so that its height, $g(t)$, also in metres, is decreasing according to the function $g(t) = -\frac{1}{12}t^2 - \frac{1}{6}t + \frac{50}{3}$.

27. The number of minutes that pass before the two water levels are at the same height is

A. 6 **B.** 8

C. 10 **D.** 16

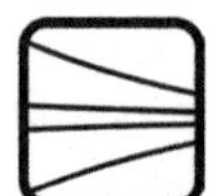

CF3.1 simplify polynomial expressions by adding, subtracting, and multiplying

SIMPLIFYING POLYNOMIAL EXPRESSIONS

The following mathematical processes are often used when simplifying polynomial expressions:

1. Distributive property: $a(x + y) = ax + ay$
2. Product law of exponents: $x^a(x^b) = x^{a+b}$
3. Collecting and simplifying all like terms
4. **FOIL:**
   F—multiply the first term in each binomial together
   O—multiply the two outside terms together
   I—multiply the two inside terms together
   L—multiply the last two terms together
   After multiplying the terms together, gather like terms.

Example

Simplify the expression $x(x^2 + 4x) + 2(x + 7)^2$.

Solution

Step 1
Use the distributive property and product law of exponents.

$$\begin{aligned} &x(x^2 + 4x) + 2(x + 7)^2 \\ &= x^{1+2} + 4x^{1+1} + 2(x + 7)^2 \\ &= x^3 + 4x^2 + 2(x + 7)^2 \end{aligned}$$

Step 2
Use the FOIL method.

$$\begin{aligned} &x^3 + 4x^2 + 2(x + 7)^2 \\ &= x^3 + 4x^2 + 2(x + 7)(x + 7) \\ &= x^3 + 4x^2 + 2(x^2 + 7x + 7x + 49) \\ &= x^3 + 4x^2 + 2(x^2 + 14x + 49) \end{aligned}$$

Step 3
Use the distributive property.

$$\begin{aligned} &x^3 + 4x^2 + 2(x^2 + 14x + 49) \\ &= x^3 + 4x^2 + 2x^2 + 28x + 98 \end{aligned}$$

Step 4
Collect and simplify all like terms.

$$\begin{aligned} &x^3 + 4x^2 + 2x^2 + 28x + 98 \\ &= x^3 + 6x^2 + 28x + 98 \end{aligned}$$

Example

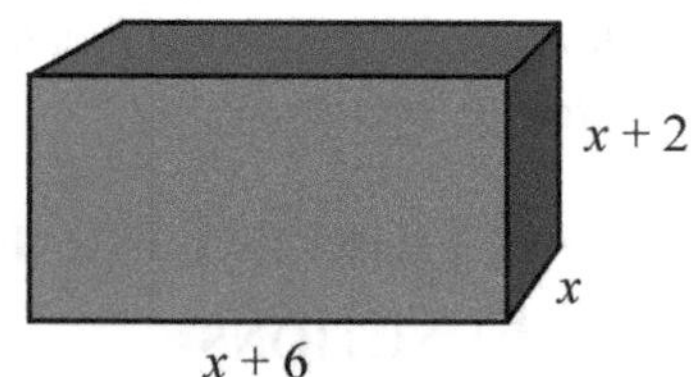

Find the volume of the given box.

Solution

Step 1
Use the distributive property.

$$\begin{aligned} V &= lwh \\ &= (x)(x + 2)(x + 6) \\ &= (x^2 + 2x)(x + 6) \end{aligned}$$

Step 2
Use the FOIL method.

$$\begin{aligned} V &= (x^2 + 2x)(x + 6) \\ &= x^3 + 6x^2 + 2x^2 + 12x \\ &= x^3 + 8x^2 + 12x \end{aligned}$$

Use the following information to answer the next question.

Two squares have side lengths of $3x + 1$ and $x - 2$.

28. Which of the following expressions represents the difference in the area of the two squares?

A. $8x^2 + 5$

B. $8x^2 + 2x + 5$

C. $8x^2 + 2x - 3$

D. $8x^2 + 10x - 3$

Open Response

29. Write and simplify an expression for the volume of a cube with an edge length of $5x - 2$.

CF3.2 verify, through investigation with and without technology, that $\sqrt{ab} = \sqrt{a} \times \sqrt{b}$, $a \geq 0$, $b \geq 0$, and use this relationship to simplify radicals and radical expressions obtained by adding, subtracting, and multiplying

Simplifying Radicals

The radical $\sqrt{a}$ is equivalent to the power $a^{\frac{1}{2}}$ because, by definition, $(\sqrt{a})^2 = a$.

$$\begin{aligned}(\sqrt{a})^2 &= \left(a^{\frac{1}{2}}\right)^2\\ &= a^{\frac{1}{2}} \times a^{\frac{1}{2}}\\ &= a^{\frac{1}{2}+\frac{1}{2}}\\ &= a\end{aligned}$$

The power of a product law states that to take the power of a product, multiply the exponent of each variable inside the brackets by the exponent outside the brackets.

$(xy)^m = x^m y^m$

$$\begin{aligned}\sqrt{a} \times \sqrt{b} &= a^{\frac{1}{2}} \times b^{\frac{1}{2}}\\ &= (ab)^{\frac{1}{2}}\\ &= \sqrt{ab}\end{aligned}$$

Example

Express $\sqrt{27} + \sqrt{75}$ as a single radical.

Solution

Simplify the radicals to see if they are like radical terms. If so, add the numbers outside the radical sign, keeping the radicand and radical sign the same.

$$\begin{aligned}\sqrt{27} + \sqrt{75} &= \sqrt{(9)(3)} + \sqrt{(25)(3)}\\ &= 3\sqrt{3} + 5\sqrt{3}\\ &= 8\sqrt{3}\end{aligned}$$

---

30. What is the simplified form of $(5 + \sqrt{50}) - (8 + \sqrt{4}) + (6 - \sqrt{18})$?

A. $5 + 2\sqrt{2}$ **B.** $3 + 2\sqrt{7}$

C. $3 + \sqrt{2}$ **D.** $1 + 2\sqrt{2}$

Numerical Response

31. When the radical $\sqrt{72}$ is expressed in simplest form $(a\sqrt{b})$, the value of $a + b$ is _________.

CF3.3 simplify rational expressions by adding, subtracting, multiplying, and dividing, and state the restrictions on the variable values

Simplifying Rational Expressions

When simplifying rational expressions, remember that rational expressions are undefined when the denominator is zero. Therefore, any variable that causes a zero denominator is restricted.

To add or subtract rational expressions, there must be a lowest common denominator (LCD).

Example

Simplify $\dfrac{5x}{4x-4} + \dfrac{3}{2x+2}$.

Solution

Step 1

Determine the restrictions on the expression.

$$\frac{5x}{4x-4} + \frac{3}{2x+2} = \frac{5x}{4(x-1)} + \frac{3}{2(x+1)}$$

The restrictions are $x - 1$ and $x + 1 \neq 0$. Thus, $x \neq \pm 1$.

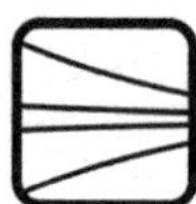

Step 2
Simplify the expression.
Factor the denominators first. The lowest common denominator is $4(x-1)(x+1)$.

$$\frac{5x(x+1)}{4(x-1)(x+1)}+\frac{3(2)(x-1)}{4(x-1)(x+1)}$$
$$=\frac{5x^2+5x+6x-6}{4(x-1)(x+1)}$$
$$=\frac{5x^2+11x-6}{4(x-1)(x+1)}$$

To multiply rational expressions, simplify or factor them first if possible. Division of a rational expression is equivalent to the multiplication of its reciprocal.

Example

Simplify $\frac{a^2+4a+4}{a^2+7a+12}\div\frac{a^2-a-6}{a^2-9}$.

Solution

Step 1
Factor. Reciprocate the second expression.

$$\frac{a^2+4a+4}{a^2+7a+12}\div\frac{a^2-a-6}{a^2-9}$$
$$=\frac{(a+2)(a+2)}{(a+4)(a+3)}\div\frac{(a-3)(a+2)}{(a-3)(a+3)}$$
$$=\frac{(a+2)(a+2)}{(a+4)(a+3)}\times\frac{(a-3)(a+3)}{(a-3)(a+2)}$$

Step 2
Determine the restrictions of the expression.
Since $a+2$, $a-3$, $a+3$, $a+4\neq 0$, the restrictions are $a\neq -2, \pm 3, -4$.

Step 3
Simplify, and multiply.

$$\frac{(a+2)(a+2)}{(a+4)(a+3)}\times\frac{(a-3)(a+3)}{(a-3)(a+2)}$$
$$=\frac{a+2}{a+4}$$

---

32. With the restrictions on the variable, the simplified form of the rational expression $\frac{10x}{2x^2-x}-\frac{6x-12}{5x-10}$ is

A. $\frac{4(14-3x)}{5(2x-1)}, x\neq\frac{1}{2}$

B. $\frac{2x+6}{x^2-3x+5}, x\neq\frac{1}{2}$

C. $\frac{44-12x}{10x-5}, x\neq 0, \frac{1}{2}, 2$

D. $\frac{56-12x}{10x-5}, x\neq 0, \frac{1}{2}, 2$

Use the following information to answer the next multipart question.

33. The length and width of a rectangle are represented by the rational expressions $\frac{2x+4}{x^2-9}$ and $\frac{3x+9}{x^2-x-6}$, respectively.
A smaller square has an area represented by the rational expression $\frac{2x+4}{x^2-4x+3}$.

Open Response

a) State the restrictions on the variable x according to these expressions.

b) Determine the perimeter of the rectangle in simplified form.

c) Determine the rational expression that represents the area of the rectangle, expressed in simplified form.

d) Determine the simplified expression that shows how many times larger the area of the rectangle is than the area of the square.

CF3.4 determine if two given algebraic expressions are equivalent (i.e., by simplifying; by substituting values)

Determining if Algebraic Expressions Are Equivalent

To determine if two expressions are equivalent, it is necessary to either simplify each expression or substitute values into each expression to determine if equal values or expressions can be obtained.

Example

Determine if the expression $\frac{4x^2-8x-60}{x-5}$ is equivalent to the expression $4x + 12$.

Solution

Substitute any value for x in each expression, and determine if equal values are obtained.

Step 1

Evaluate the expression $\frac{4x^2-8x-60}{x-5}$ when $x = 0$.

$$\begin{aligned}\frac{4x^2-8x-60}{x-5} &= \frac{4(0)^2-8(0)-60}{0-5}\\ &= \frac{-60}{-5}\\ &= 12\end{aligned}$$

Step 2

Evaluate the expression $4x + 12$ when $x = 0$.

$$\begin{aligned}4x+12 &= 4(0)+12\\ &= 12\end{aligned}$$

Since equal values are obtained when $x = 0$, the two expressions are equivalent.

---

34. The algebraic expression equivalent to $\frac{3x^2+x-10}{x+2}$ is

A. $(x+2)^2-(x^2-x+9)$

B. $6x^2-3x(2x-1)-4$

C. $\frac{3x^2+8x+5}{x+1}$

D. $\frac{9x^2-25}{3x+5}$

35. Which of the following algebraic expressions is **not** equivalent to $\frac{4x^2-9x-9}{x-3}$?

A. $(2x+3)^2-2(2x^2+4x+3)$

B. $4x^2-2x(2x-2)+3$

C. $\frac{4x-3}{x+5}\times\frac{x^2-25}{x-5}$

D. $\frac{16x^2-9}{4x-3}$

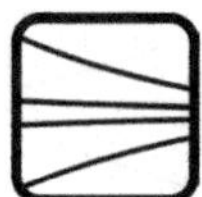

ANSWERS AND SOLUTIONS
CHARACTERISTICS OF FUNCTIONS

1. B	9. A	17. B	25. OR	33. a) OR
2. OR	10. OR	18. B	26. B	b) OR
3. D	11. D	19. OR	27. B	c) OR
4. 13	12. A	20. C	28. D	d) OR
5. B	13. C	21. OR	29. OR	34. D
6. OR	14. A	22. D	30. D	35. C
7. C	15. A	23. 181	31. 8	
8. B	16. D	24. A	32. D	

1. B

A graph that is intersected by a vertical line at two or more points is not a function. Use this vertical line test to determine which of the given graphs are not functions.

In graph B, at almost any place a vertical line is drawn, it will either intersect the graph in two locations or not at all. Therefore, the graph does not represent a function.

Since a vertical line does not intersect the other graphs more than once, the relations in graphs A, C, and D are functions.

2. OR

Step 1
Isolate the y-variable.

$$x + y^2 = 4$$
$$y^2 = 4 - x$$
$$y = \pm\sqrt{4 - x}$$

Step 2
The square root of a negative number is undefined. As such, $x < 4$.
Select any value less than four to substitute for x in order to determine an ordered pair of the relation. For example, a value of zero could be chosen for x.

$$y = \pm\sqrt{4 - 0}$$
$$= \pm 2$$

This gives the two ordered pairs $(0, -2)$ and $(0, 2)$. Since these two points have the same x-coordinate, this relation is not a function.

3. D

Since this is a linear function, it must have an equation of the form $f(x) = mx + b$. With linear functions, m is the slope and b is the y-intercept.

Step 1
Determine the value of b.
The y-intercept is 1 from the graph, so $b = 1$.

Step 2
Calculate the slope of the graph.
Using the points $(0, 1)$ and $(1, -1)$, substitute 0 for x_1, 1 for x_2, 1 for y_1, and -1 for y_2 into the slope formula, which is $m = \frac{y_2 - y_1}{x_2 - x_1}$.

$$m = \frac{y_2 - y_1}{x_2 - x_1}$$
$$= \frac{-1 - 1}{1 - 0}$$
$$= -2$$

Step 3
Determine the equation of the function.
Substitute -2 for m and 1 for b in the function $f(x) = mx + b$.

$$f(x) = mx + b$$
$$f(x) = -2x + 1$$

4. 13

Substitute -2 for x and $g(-2)$ for $g(x)$ in the function $g(x) = -2x^2 - 3x + 15$.

$$g(x) = -2x^2 - 3x + 15$$
$$g(-2) = -2(-2)^2 - 3(-2) + 15$$
$$g(-2) = -2(4) + 6 + 15$$
$$g(-2) = -8 + 6 + 15$$
$$g(-2) = 13$$

5. B

Step 1
Determine the domain of the function.
The radicand must be either positive or zero.

$$9 - x \geq 0$$
$$-x \geq -9$$
$$x \leq 9$$

Step 2
Determine the range of the function.

The function considers only the positive square root of $9 - x$, so the values of y are greater than or equal to zero.

Therefore, the range is $y \geq 0$.

6. **OR**

Step 1
Determine the physical factors that restrict the domain.

The possible speeds of the car define the domain. Physical factors affecting the speed are the road conditions (dry, wet, snow, or ice) and the person driving the car. The speed must be greater than or equal to zero and is likely to be less than or equal to 120 km/h (depending on the speed limit).

A reasonable domain is $0 \leq v \leq 120$.

Step 2
Determine the physical factors that restrict the range.

The kinetic energy values represent the range, and these are also greater than or equal to zero with a maximum value at the maximum speed.

Substitute in the maximum speed of $v = 120$ km/h into the equation.

$$\begin{aligned} E_k &= 46.3v^2 \\ &= 46.3(120)^2 \\ &\approx 6.67 \times 10^5 \text{ J} \end{aligned}$$

Therefore, a reasonable range is $0 \leq E_k \leq 6.67 \times 10^5$.

7. **C**

The operations performed on x must be reversed, but so must the order. Since adding 5 was originally performed last, subtracting 5 must be performed first in the inverse of the function. The reverse of multiplying by 3 is dividing by 3.

8. **B**

The given function can be expressed as $y = (x + 4) \times 6$.

Determine the inverse of this function by first interchanging the variables and then solving for y.

$$\begin{aligned} x &= (y+4) \times 6 \\ \frac{x}{6} &= \frac{(y+4) \times 6}{6} \\ \frac{x}{6} &= y + 4 \\ \frac{x}{6} - 4 &= y + 4 - 4 \\ \frac{x}{6} - 4 &= y \end{aligned}$$

To determine the inverse of a function following the interchanging of variables, the operations on the original function must be reversed (opposite operations performed) as must the order in which each operation was performed.

In this case, dividing by 6 must be done first since multiplying by 6 was the last operation performed on the original function. Then, the reverse of adding 4, which is subtracting 4, must be performed.

9. **A**

To find the points on the inverse function, interchange the x- and y-coordinates of the ordered pairs.

- $(-3, 1) \Rightarrow (1, -3)$
- $(0, -2) \Rightarrow (-2, 0)$
- $(2, 6) \Rightarrow (6, 2)$
- $(4, 22) \Rightarrow (22, 4)$

The corresponding points on the inverse are $(1, -3)$, $(-2, 0)$, $(6, 2)$, and $(22, 4)$.

10. **OR**

Step 1
Perform a horizontal line test on the given function.

The function does not pass the horizontal line test because any horizontal line above $y = 3$ will intersect the graph at two points, indicating that the inverse will have points with the same x-coordinates and will therefore not be a function.

Step 2
Determine the domain of the inverse.

The range of the given function is $y \geq 3$, so the domain of the inverse becomes $x \geq 3$.

Step 3
Determine the range of the inverse.

The domain of the given function is $x \in R$, so the range of the inverse becomes $y \in R$.

11. **D**

Step 1
Determine the domain of the inverse function.

The quadratic function $f(x) = (x - 3)^2 - 5$ has a vertex at the point $(3, -5)$ and opens upward.

The range of the function is $y \geq -5$. The domain of the inverse becomes $x \geq -5$.

Step 2
Determine the range of the inverse function.

The domain of this function is $x \in R$. The range of the inverse becomes $y \in R$.

12. A

Step 1
Replace $f(x)$ with y.

$f(x) = \frac{1}{2}x + 3$

$y = \frac{1}{2}x + 3$

Step 2
Interchange x and y.

$y = \frac{1}{2}x + 3$

$x = \frac{1}{2}y + 3$

Step 3
Solve for y.

$x = \frac{1}{2}y + 3$

$2x = y + 6$

$2x - 6 = y$

$y = 2x - 6$

Step 4
Replace y with $f^{-1}(x)$.
Since $y = 2x - 6$ is a linear function, it can be written using function notation.

$y = 2x - 6$

$f^{-1}(x) = 2x - 6$

$f^{-1}(x) = 2(x - 3)$

13. C

Step 1
Replace $f(x)$ with y.

$f(x) = (x - 4)^2 + 5$

$y = (x - 4)^2 + 5$

Step 2
Interchange x and y.

$y = (x - 4)^2 + 5$

$x = (y - 4)^2 + 5$

Step 3
Solve for y.

$x = (y - 4)^2 + 5$

$x - 5 = (y - 4)^2$

$\pm\sqrt{x - 5} = y - 4$

$\pm\sqrt{x - 5} + 4 = y$

$y = \pm\sqrt{x - 5} + 4$

Since the inverse is not a function, y cannot be replaced by $f^{-1}(x)$.

14. A

Step 1
To reflect the graph $y = \sqrt{x}$ in the y-axis, substitute $-x$ for x in the equation $y = \sqrt{x}$.

$y = \sqrt{x}$

$y = \sqrt{-x}$

Step 2
To translate the graph of $y = \sqrt{-x}3$ units upward $(c = 3)$, substitute $y - 3$ for y in the equation $y = \sqrt{-x}$.

$y = \sqrt{-x}$

$y - 3 = \sqrt{-x}$

Step 3
Solve for y in the equation $y - 3 = \sqrt{-x}$.

$y - 3 = \sqrt{-x}$

$y = \sqrt{-x} + 3$

15. A

Step 1
Determine the necessary changes to obtain the equation $g(x) = 2(x + 1)^2$ from the equation $f(x) = x^2$ by comparing $g(x)$ to the general equation of $y = af(k(x - d)) + c$.
When comparing the equation $g(x)$ to the equation $y = af(k(x - d)) + c$, it can be seen that the value of a is 2, the value of d is -1, and the other variables remain unchanged.

Step 2
Describe the transformations needed to obtain the graph of $g(x) = 2(x + 1)^2$ from the graph of $f(x) = x^2$.
In the equation $f(x) = x^2$, 2 is substituted for a, which vertically stretches the graph of $f(x) = x^2$ about the x-axis by a factor of 2.
To obtain the graph of the equation $g(x) = 2(x + 1)^2$, translate the graph 1 unit to the left, because -1 is substituted for d.

16. D

Step 1
Determine the domain of $g(x)$.
The domain of $f(x) = \sqrt{x}$ is $x > 0$.
To obtain the graph of $g(x) = -\sqrt{x + 4}$, the graph of $f(x) = \sqrt{x}$ is reflected in the x-axis (which doesn't impact the domain) and translated horizontally 4 units left (which does impact the domain). As such, the domain of $g(x)$ is $x \geq -4$.

Step 2
Determine the range of $g(x)$.
The range of $f(x) = \sqrt{x}$ is $y > 0$.
To obtain the graph of $g(x) = -\sqrt{x+4}$, the graph of $f(x) = \sqrt{x}$ is reflected in the x-axis (which does impact the range) and translated horizontally 4 units left (which doesn't impact the range). As such, the range of $g(x)$ is $y \leq 0$.

17. B

When the function $g(x) = \frac{1}{2}(x-3)^2$ is compared to the function of the form $y = af(k(x-d)) + c$, it can be seen that $a = \frac{1}{2}$ and $d = 3$. Therefore, there is a vertical compression to the x-axis by a factor of $\frac{1}{2}$, which makes the parabola wider, and a horizontal translation 3 units right.

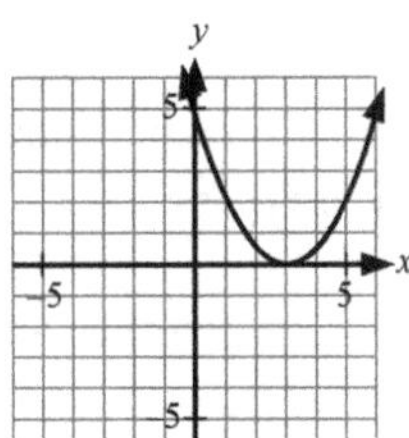

18. B

The zeros are also the x-intercepts. Since there is only one x-intercept, there is only one real zero.

19. OR

The nature of the zeros of a quadratic function can be determined by finding the value of the discriminant, $b^2 - 4ac$, given a quadratic of the form $ax^2 + bx + c$.

Determine the value of the discriminant.

$$\begin{aligned} &b^2 - 4ac \\ &= (2)^2 - 4(3)(4) \\ &= 4 - 48 \\ &= -44 \end{aligned}$$

Since the discriminant is less than zero, the function has no real zeros.

20. C

The function $f(x) = -3x^2 + 12x - 4$ has a maximum value since parameter $a < 0$.
Complete the square.

$$\begin{aligned} f(x) &= -3x^2 + 12x - 4 \\ &= -3(x^2 - 4x) - 4 \\ &= -3(x^2 - 4x + 4 - 4) - 4 \\ &= -3(x^2 - 4x + 4) + 12 - 4 \\ &= -3(x-2)^2 + 8 \end{aligned}$$

The vertex of the graph of the function is located at (2, 8). As such, the maximum value of the function is 8.

21. OR

The graph of the given function is a parabola opening upwards, which means the function will indeed have a minimum value, at its vertex.

The partially factored form of $f(x) = 2x^2 - 8x - 3$ is $f(x) = 2x(x-4) - 3$. The values of $f(0)$ and $f(4)$ are both -3. Since the graph of a quadratic function is a parabola symmetrical about a vertical line passing through its vertex, the x-coordinate of the vertex must be at $x = 2$, which is halfway between $x = 0$ and $x = 4$.

Determine the minimum value of the function.

$$\begin{aligned} f(2) &= 2(2)^2 - 8(2) - 3 \\ &= 8 - 16 - 3 \\ &= -11 \end{aligned}$$

The minimum value is -11.

22. D

Step 1
Complete the square.

$$\begin{aligned} P(x) &= -10x^2 + 140x + 1\ 800 \\ &= -10(x^2 - 14x) + 1\ 800 \\ &= -10(x^2 - 14x + 49 - 49) + 1\ 800 \\ &= -10(x^2 - 14x + 49) + 490 + 1\ 800 \\ &= -10(x-7)^2 + 2\ 290 \end{aligned}$$

Step 2
Determine the maximum profit and the ticket price.
The vertex is located at (7, 2 290). This means that the maximum profit is \$2 290 when $x = 7$.
Since x is the number of \$0.50 decreases in the ticket price, the theatre owner must decrease the original price (\$12) by \$3.50 (7 × \$0.50), giving a ticket price of \$8.50(\$12 – \$3.50).

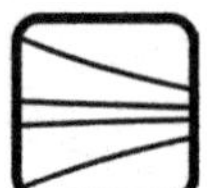

23. 181

Complete the square.

$$\begin{aligned} h(t) &= -5t^2 + 60t + 1 \\ &= -5(t^2 - 12t) + 1 \\ &= -5(t^2 - 12t + 36 - 36) + 1 \\ &= -5(t^2 - 12t + 36) + 180 + 1 \\ &= -5(t-6)^2 + 181 \end{aligned}$$

The maximum value of $h(t)$ is 181. Therefore, 181 m is the maximum height the arrow can reach.

24. A

Since the roots of the quadratic equation are the zeros of the corresponding quadratic function, the equation of the function must be

$f(x) = a(x - (3 + \sqrt{2}))(x - (3 - \sqrt{2}))$.

Step 1
Simplify the equation.

$$\begin{aligned} f(x) &= a(x - 3 - \sqrt{2})(x - 3 + \sqrt{2}) \\ &= a(x^2 - 3x + \sqrt{2}x - 3x + 9 \\ &\quad - 3\sqrt{2} - \sqrt{2}x + 3\sqrt{2} - 2) \\ &= a(x^2 - 6x + 7) \end{aligned}$$

Step 2
Since the point (1, 4) must satisfy the equation, substitute $x = 1$ and $y = 4$ into the equation.

$$\begin{aligned} 4 &= a((1)^2 - 6(1) + 7) \\ 4 &= a(2) \\ 2 &= a \end{aligned}$$

Step 3
Write the equation of the function.

$$\begin{aligned} f(x) &= 2(x^2 - 6x + 7) \\ &= 2x^2 - 12x + 14 \end{aligned}$$

25. OR

Since the roots of the corresponding quadratic equation are the zeros of the function, the equation of the function must be $f(x) = a(x-4)(x-(-3))$.

Step 1
Expand the equation.

$$\begin{aligned} f(x) &= a(x-4)(x+3) \\ &= a(x^2 - x - 12) \end{aligned}$$

Step 2
The point (–5, 9) must satisfy this equation, so substitute those values into the equation.

$$\begin{aligned} 9 &= a((-5)^2 - (-5) - 12) \\ 9 &= a(25 + 5 - 12) \\ 9 &= a(18) \\ \frac{1}{2} &= a \end{aligned}$$

Step 3
Substitute $\frac{1}{2}$ for a.

$$\begin{aligned} f(x) &= \frac{1}{2}(x^2 - x - 12) \\ &= \frac{1}{2}x^2 - \frac{1}{2}x - 6 \end{aligned}$$

The equation of the quadratic function is

$f(x) = \frac{1}{2}x^2 - \frac{1}{2}x - 6$.

26. B

Step 1
To find the x-coordinates of the points of intersection, equate the two functions and solve for x.

$$\begin{aligned} f(x) &= g(x) \\ x^2 + 3x - 28 &= x - 13 \\ x^2 + 2x - 15 &= 0 \\ (x-3)(x+5) &= 0 \\ x = 3 \text{ or } x &= -5 \end{aligned}$$

Step 2
Substitute 3 for x in either function. Use $f(x)$.

$$\begin{aligned} f(3) &= (3)^2 + 3(3) - 28 \\ &= -10 \end{aligned}$$

Substitute –5 for x in either function. Use $f(x)$.

$$\begin{aligned} f(-5) &= (-5)^2 + 3(-5) - 28 \\ &= -18 \end{aligned}$$

The points are (3, –10) and (–5, –18).

27. B

The two heights are at the same level when $h(t) = g(t)$. Equate the two equations, then solve them.

$$\frac{1}{2}t + 6 = -\frac{1}{12}t^2 - \frac{1}{6}t + \frac{50}{3}$$

Step 1
Multiply both sides by 12.

$6t + 72 = -t^2 - 2t + 200$

Step 2
Add $t^2 + 2t - 200$ to both sides.

$t^2 + 8t - 128 = 0$

Step 3
Factor the resulting equation.

$(t-8)(t+16) = 0$

Step 4
Equate each factor to zero.

$(t-8) = 0$
$t = 8$

or

$(t+16) = 0$
$t = -16$

Since $t > 0$, the two heights are equal at 8 minutes.

28. D

Subtract the area of one of the squares from the area of the other square.

$$\begin{aligned}&(3x+1)^2-(x-2)^2\\&=(9x^2+6x+1)-(x^2-4x+4)\\&=9x^2+6x+1-x^2+4x-4\\&=(9x^2-x^2)+(6x+4x)+(1-4)\\&=8x^2+10x-3\end{aligned}$$

29. OR

The volume of a cube is the cube of its side length, Therefore, $V=(5x-2)^3$. Simplify.

$$\begin{aligned}V&=(5x-2)^3\\&=(5x-2)(5x-2)^2\\&=(5x-2)(25x^2-20x+4)\\&=125x^3-100x^2+20x-50x^2+40x-8\\&=125x^3-150x^2+60x-8\end{aligned}$$

30. D

Step 1
Simplify the radicals.

$$\begin{aligned}&(5+\sqrt{50})-(8+\sqrt{4})+(6-\sqrt{18})\\&=(5+\sqrt{25}\sqrt{2})-(8+2)+(6-\sqrt{9}\sqrt{2})\\&=(5+5\sqrt{2})-(10)+(6-3\sqrt{2})\end{aligned}$$

Step 2
Drop the brackets, and join like terms.

$$\begin{aligned}&(5+5\sqrt{2})-(10)+(6-3\sqrt{2})\\&=5+5\sqrt{2}-10+6-3\sqrt{2}\\&=1+2\sqrt{2}\end{aligned}$$

31. 8

Step 1
Determine the simplified form of $\sqrt{72}$.

$$\begin{aligned}\sqrt{72}&=\sqrt{36\times 2}\\&=\sqrt{36}\times\sqrt{2}\\&=6\sqrt{2}\end{aligned}$$

Step 2
Determine the value of $a+b$.
$a=6,\ b=2.$

$$\begin{aligned}a+b&=6+2\\&=8\end{aligned}$$

32. D

Step 1
Factor the expression.

$$\begin{aligned}&\frac{10x}{2x^2-x}-\frac{6x-12}{5x-10}\\&=\frac{10x}{x(2x-1)}-\frac{6(x-2)}{5(x-2)}\end{aligned}$$

Step 2
Determine the restrictions on the expression.

$x\neq 0,\ x\neq\frac{1}{2},\ x\neq 2$

These restrictions occur because x cannot equal zero. $(x,\ 2x-1,\ x-2\neq 0)$

Step 3
Simplify the expression.

$$\begin{aligned}\frac{10x}{x(2x-1)}-\frac{6(x-2)}{5(x-2)}&=\frac{10}{2x-1}-\frac{6}{5}\\&=\frac{10}{2x-1}\times\frac{5}{5}-\frac{6}{5}\times\frac{2x-1}{2x-1}\\&=\frac{50}{5(2x-1)}-\frac{12x-6}{5(2x-1)}\\&=\frac{50-12x+6}{5(2x-1)}\\&=\frac{56-12x}{10x-5}\end{aligned}$$

33. a) OR

Step 1
Factor the first expression.

$$\frac{2x+4}{x^2-9}=\frac{2(x+2)}{(x-3)(x+3)}$$

Step 2
Factor the second expression.

$$\frac{3x+9}{x^2-x-6}=\frac{3(x+3)}{(x-3)(x+2)}$$

Step 3
Factor the third expression.

$$\frac{2x+4}{x^2-4x+3}=\frac{2(x+2)}{(x-3)(x-1)}$$

Step 4
Determine the restrictions on the variable.

If these expressions were only rational expressions, the restrictions would be $x\neq -2, -3, 1$, and 3, since the denominator of a rational expression cannot be zero. These x-values would result in at least one of the expressions having a zero for the denominator. However, these expressions represent the sides of a rectangle and the side length must be a positive number. If $x\leq 3$, then at least one of the rational expressions will be negative. Therefore, the restriction for the variable for these expressions is $x>3$.

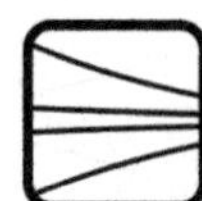

b) OR

Step 1

To determine the perimeter, substitute the length, $\frac{2x+4}{x^2-9}$, and the width, $\frac{3x+9}{x^2-x-6}$, into the equation $P = 2l + 2w$.

$$P = 2l + 2w$$
$$= 2\left(\frac{2x+4}{x^2-9}\right) + 2\left(\frac{3x+9}{x^2-x-6}\right)$$
$$= 2\left(\frac{2(x+2)}{(x-3)(x+3)}\right) + 2\left(\frac{3(x+3)}{(x-3)(x+2)}\right)$$
$$= \frac{4(x+2)}{(x-3)(x+3)} + \frac{6(x+3)}{(x-3)(x+2)}$$

Step 2

Find the lowest common denominator, and add the resulting expressions.

The lowest common denominator is $(x-3)(x+3)(x+2)$.

$$\frac{4(x+2)}{(x-3)(x+3)} + \frac{6(x+3)}{(x-3)(x+2)}$$
$$= \frac{4(x+2)}{(x-3)(x+3)}\left(\frac{x+2}{x+2}\right) + \frac{6(x+3)}{(x-3)(x+2)}\left(\frac{x+3}{x+3}\right)$$
$$= \frac{4x^2+16x+16}{(x-3)(x+3)(x+2)} + \frac{6x^2+36x+54}{(x-3)(x+3)(x+2)}$$
$$= \frac{10x^2+52x+70}{(x-3)(x+3)(x+2)}$$

The perimeter of the rectangle is $\frac{10x^2+52x+70}{(x-3)(x+3)(x+2)}$.

c) OR

Multiply the expressions that represent the sides of the rectangle, and simplify.

$$A = lw$$
$$A = \frac{2x+4}{x^2-9} \times \frac{3x+9}{x^2-x-6}$$
$$A = \frac{2(x+2)}{(x-3)(x+3)} \times \frac{3(x+3)}{(x-3)(x+2)}$$
$$A = \frac{2(x+2) \times 3(x+3)}{(x-3)(x+3)(x-3)(x+2)}$$
$$A = \frac{6}{(x-3)^2}$$

The rational expression that represents the area of the rectangle is $\frac{6}{(x-3)^2}$.

d) OR

Step 1

Determine the area of the rectangle.

$$A = lw$$
$$A = \left(\frac{2x+4}{x^2-9}\right)\left(\frac{3x+9}{x^2-x-6}\right)$$
$$A = \left(\frac{2(x+2)}{(x-3)(x+3)}\right)\left(\frac{3(x+3)}{(x-3)(x+2)}\right)$$
$$A = \frac{6}{(x-3)^2}$$

Step 2

Determine how many times larger the area of the rectangle is than the area of the square by dividing the area of the rectangle by the area of square.

Area of rectangle ÷ area of square

$$= \frac{6}{(x-3)^2} \div \frac{2x+4}{x^2-4x+3}$$
$$= \frac{6}{(x-3)^2} \div \frac{2(x+2)}{(x-1)(x-3)}$$
$$= \frac{6}{(x-3)^2} \times \frac{(x-1)(x-3)}{2(x+2)}$$
$$= \frac{6(x-1)(x-3)}{2(x-3)^2(x+2)}$$
$$= \frac{3(x-1)}{(x-3)(x+2)}$$

The area of the rectangle is $\frac{3(x-1)}{(x-3)(x+2)}$ times larger than the area of the square.

34. D

Step 1

Simplify the given expression.

$$\frac{3x^2+x-10}{x+2}$$
$$= \frac{(3x-5)(x+2)}{x+2}$$
$$= 3x - 5$$

Step 2

Simplify the expressions to choose from.

Simplify $(x+2)^2-\left(x^2-x+9\right)$.

$(x+2)^2-\left(x^2-x+9\right)$
$=x^2+4x+4-x^2+x-9$
$=5x-5$

Simplify $6x^2-3x(2x-1)-4$.

$6x^2-3x(2x-1)-4$
$=6x^2-6x^2+3x-4$
$=3x-4$

Simplify $\frac{3x^2+8x+5}{x+1}$.

$\frac{3x^2+8x+5}{x+1}$
$=\frac{(3x+5)(x+1)}{x+1}$
$=3x+5$

Simplify $\frac{9x^2-25}{3x+5}$.

$\frac{9x^2-25}{3x+5}$
$=\frac{(3x+5)(3x-5)}{3x+5}$
$=3x-5$

The equivalent expression is $\frac{9x^2-25}{3x+5}$.

35. C

Step 1

Simplify the expression $\frac{4x^2-9x-9}{x-3}$.

$\frac{4x^2-9x-9}{x-3}$
$=\frac{(4x+3)(x-3)}{x-3}$
$=4x+3$

Step 2

Simplify $4x^2-2x(2x-2)+3$.

$4x^2-2x(2x-2)+3$
$=4x^2-4x^2+4x+3$
$=4x+3$

Simplify $(2x+3)^2-2\left(2x^2+4x+3\right)$.

$(2x+3)^2-2\left(2x^2+4x+3\right)$
$=4x^2+12x+9-4x^2-8x-6$
$=4x+3$

Simplify $\frac{16x^2-9}{4x-3}$.

$\frac{16x^2-9}{4x-3}$
$=\frac{(4x-3)(4x+3)}{4x-3}$
$=4x+3$

Simplify $\frac{4x-3}{x+5}\times\frac{x^2-25}{x-5}$.

$\frac{4x-3}{x+5}\times\frac{x^2-25}{x-5}$
$=\frac{4x-3}{x+5}\times\frac{(x-5)(x+5)}{x-5}$
$=4x-3$

Therefore, the expression that is not equivalent to $\frac{4x^2-9x-9}{x-3}$ is $\frac{4x-3}{x+5}\times\frac{x^2-25}{x-5}$.

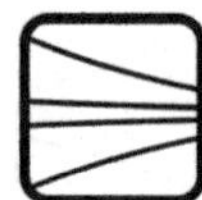

UNIT TEST — CHARACTERISTICS OF FUNCTIONS

1. Which of the following tables represents a relation that is also a function?

A.

x	y
−2	6
−1	9
0	12
3	4
3	−6
4	3

B.

x	y
−5	−8
−5	−3
−5	0
−5	2
−5	4
−5	7

C.

x	y
−4	12
−3	3
0	2
0	5
3	7
4	9

D.

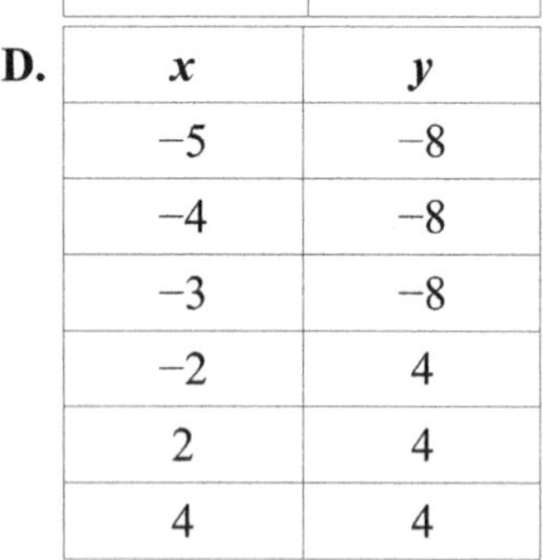

x	y
−5	−8
−4	−8
−3	−8
−2	4
2	4
4	4

Use the following information to answer the next question.

The graph of the quadratic function $f(x)$ is shown.

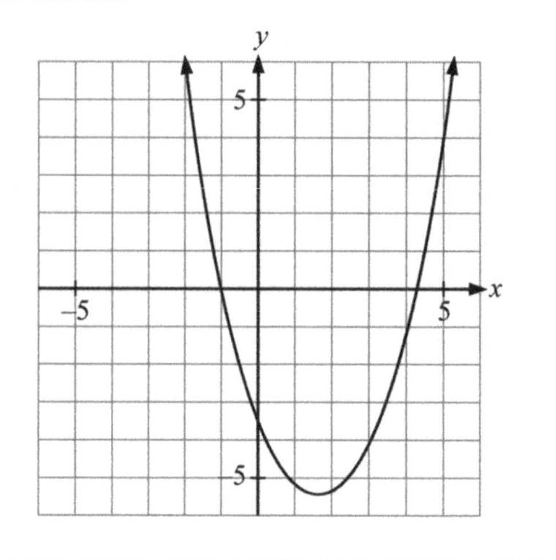

2. Which of the following statements about $f(x)$ is **true**?

A. $f(0) = 0$ **B.** $f(0) = 4$

C. $f(-1) = 0$ **D.** $f(-4) = 2$

Use the following information to answer the next question.

The height of a ball thrown into the air, h, in metres as a function of time, t, in seconds is given by the function $h = -5(t - 2)^2 + 20$.

Open Response

3. Describe the physical factors that restrict the domain and range of any object thrown, and determine the domain and range of the given function.

4. If a function involves the operations of squaring, adding, and dividing the variable x, what are the operations that must be performed in the inverse?

   A. Square, subtract, and divide

   B. Square, subtract, and multiply

   C. Square root, add, and multiply

   D. Square root, subtract, and multiply

Use the following information to answer the next question.

The graph of a linear function is shown.

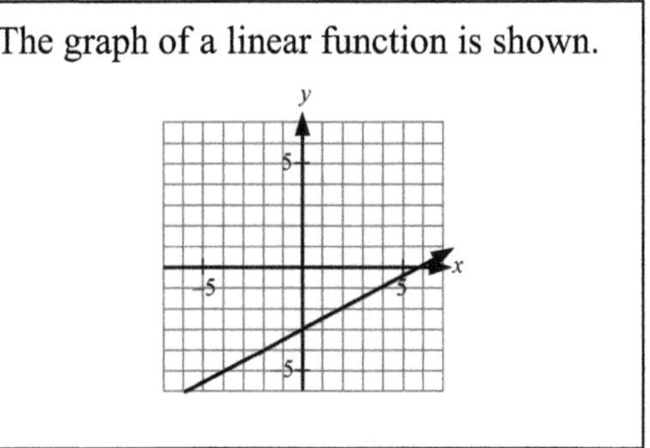

5. Which of the following graphs shows the inverse of this function?

   A.

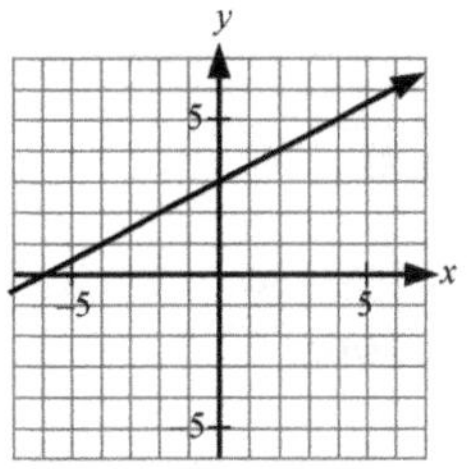

   B.

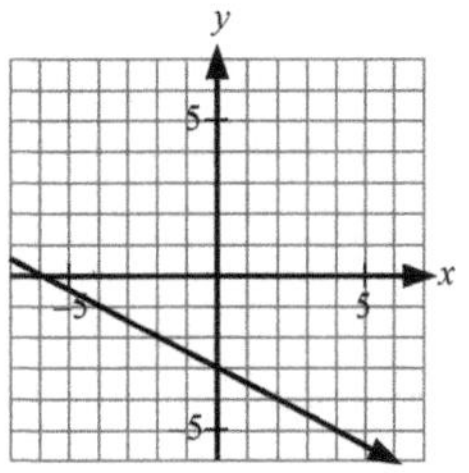

   C.

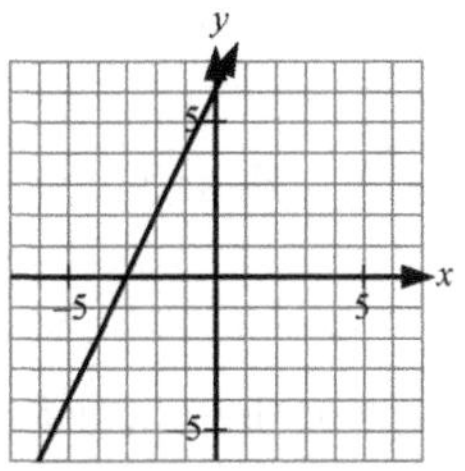

   D.

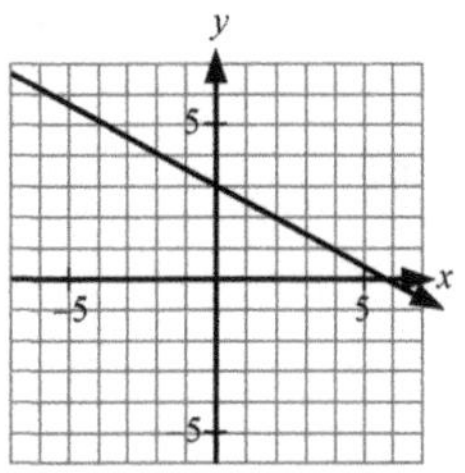

Use the following information to answer the next multipart question.

6. The graph of a quadratic relation is given.

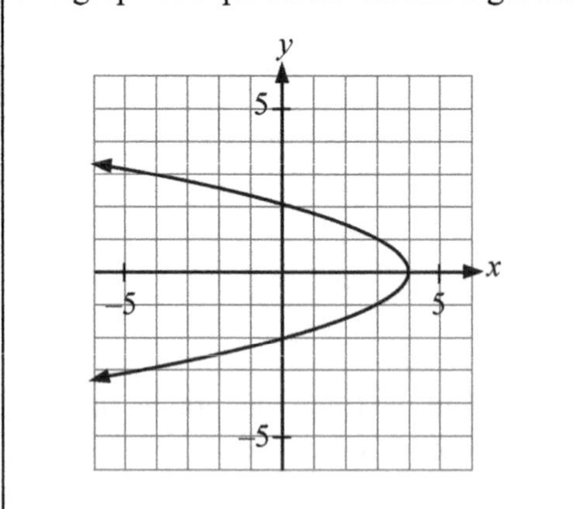

Open Response

a) Determine if the inverse of the given relation is a function.

b) What are the domain and range of the inverse of the given quadratic relation?

A. The domain is $x \in R$, and the range is $y \leq 4$.

B. The domain is $x \in R$, and the range is $y \geq 4$.

C. The domain is $x \leq 4$, and the range is $y \in R$.

D. The domain is $x \geq 4$, and the range is $y \in R$.

7. What is the inverse of the linear function $f(x) = 4x - 7$?

A. $f^{-1}(x) = 4x + 28$

B. $f^{-1}(x) = \frac{1}{4}x + 7$

C. $f^{-1}(x) = x + \frac{7}{4}$

D. $f^{-1}(x) = \frac{x+7}{4}$

8. When the function $f(x) = x^2$ is transformed into the function $g(x) = (3x)^2 - 5$, the graph of $g(x)$ can be obtained by applying to the graph of $f(x)$ a horizontal

A. stretch from the y-axis by a factor of 3 and a vertical translation 5 units up

B. stretch from the y-axis by a factor of 3 and a horizontal translation 5 units left

C. compression to the y-axis by a factor of $\frac{1}{3}$ and a vertical translation 5 units down

D. compression to the y-axis by a factor of $\frac{1}{3}$ and a horizontal translation 5 units right

Use the following information to answer the next question.

The function $f(x) = \frac{1}{x}$ is transformed into the function $g(x) = \frac{1}{x-4} + 2$.

9. Which of the following graphs represents the transformed function, $g(x)$?

A.

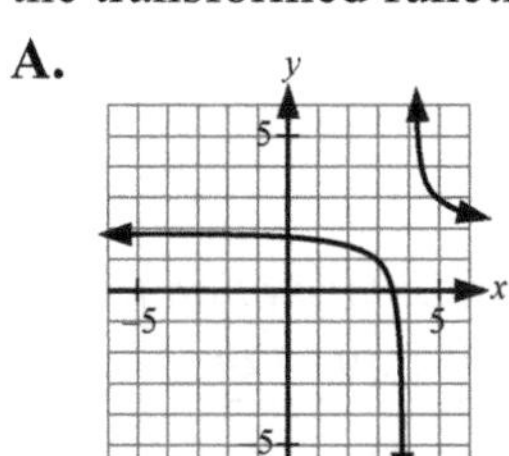

B.

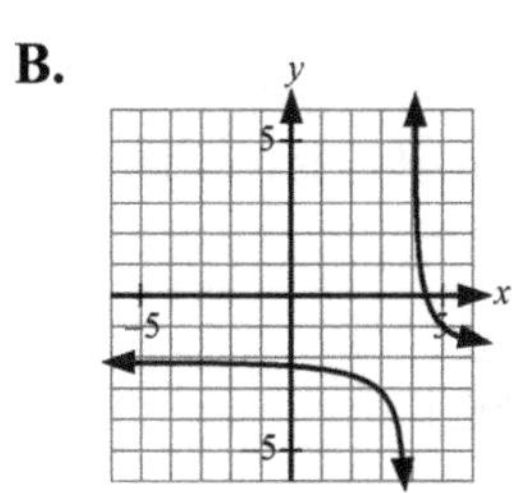

C.

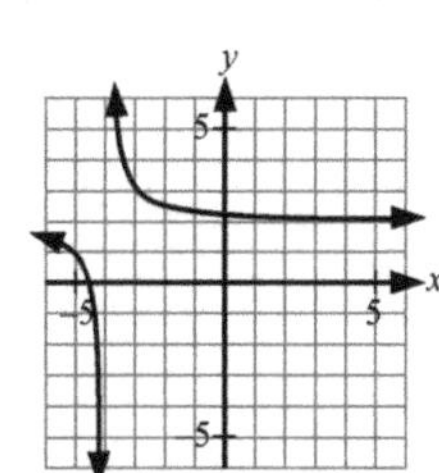

D.

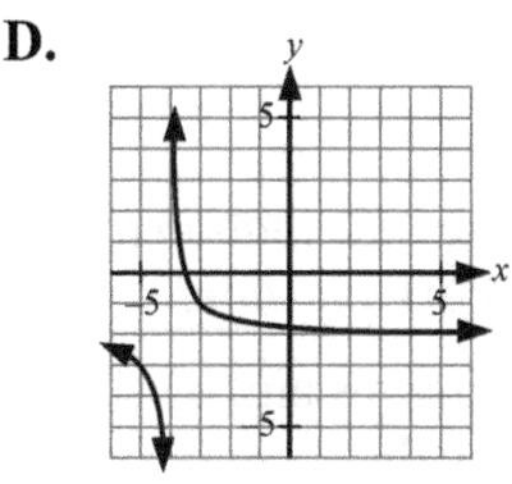

Use the following information to answer the next question.

The function $f(x) = x^2$ is transformed into the function $g(x) = -2(x+4)^2 - 3$.

Open Response

10. Describe and sketch the transformations that turn $f(x)$ into $g(x)$. State the domain and range of $g(x)$.

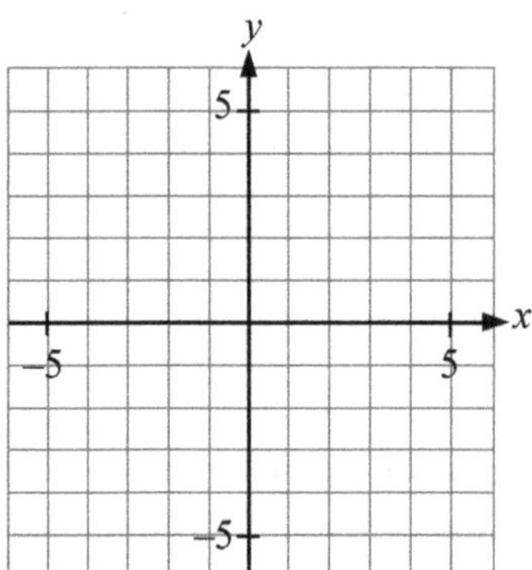

Numerical Response

11. The number of different real zeros of the quadratic function $y = (3x+2)(x-2)$ is _________.

12. What is the maximum value of the quadratic function $f(x) = -4x^2 - 24x + 8$?

A. -34 **B.** 8

C. 17 **D.** 44

Use the following information to answer the next multipart question.

13. The quadratic function $h(t) = \frac{1}{2}t^2 - 8t + 34$ approximates the height, $h(t)$, in metres, of a part of a ride on a ferris wheel. In this case, t is the time in seconds after the ride has started.

Open Response

a) Determine the minimum height of the Ferris wheel.

b) If the middle of the ferris wheel is 20 m above the ground, determine when the rider is at this height.

c) Explain why only the bottom half of one rotation of the entire ride can be predicted by this quadratic function, and state the domain of the function given that it models the height of a moving part on a ferris wheel.

d) The middle of the Ferris wheel is 20 m above the ground. Determine the equation of a quadratic function that could be used to predict the top half of the ride. Explain and state the domain for which this would be valid.

Use the following information to answer the next question.

A quadratic function $f(x)$ passes through the point (6, 4). The roots of the corresponding quadratic equation are 2 and 5. The function $g(x)$ is a reflection of $f(x)$ about the x-axis.

Open Response

14. Determine the equation of the function $g(x)$.

Use the following information to answer the next question.

A hunter is practising his aim by shooting clay disks. The clay disks are fired so that the height, $h(t)$, in metres as a function of time, t, in seconds is $h(t) = -5t^2 + 26t - 28$. The hunter aims his rifle so that the path of the bullet will have a height, $g(t)$, also in metres, given by the function $g(t) = t + 2$.

15. At what height might the hunter hit the clay disks?

A. 2 m or 3 m **B.** 3 m or 4 m

C. 3 m or 5 m **D.** 4 m or 5 m

Use the following information to answer the next question.

A rectangle has side lengths that are given by the expressions $3x^2 - 2x + 7$ and $2x^2 + 8x - 5$.

16. What expression represents the perimeter of the rectangle?

A. $10x^2 + 12x + 4$

B. $10x^2 + 12x + 2$

C. $10x^2 + 6x + 2$

D. $5x^2 + 6x + 2$

Use the following information to answer the next question.

A square has a side length of $4x - 2$. A smaller rectangle has side lengths given by the expressions $x - 2$ and $2x + 1$.

Open Response

17. Determine the expression that represents the difference in the areas of the square and the rectangle.

Use the following information to answer the next question.

A rectangle has a length of $(3 + \sqrt{27})$ cm and a width of $(5 - \sqrt{6})$ cm.

18. In square centimetres, the area of this rectangle expressed in simplest form is

A. $15 - 9\sqrt{2}$ cm^2

B. $16 + 6\sqrt{3} - 2\sqrt{6}$ cm^2

C. $15 - 3\sqrt{6} + 15\sqrt{3} - 9\sqrt{2}$ cm^2

D. $15 - 3\sqrt{6} + 5\sqrt{27} - \sqrt{162}$ cm^2

Numerical Response

19. Expressed to the nearest tenth, the sum of the restrictions on the variable in the rational expression

$$\frac{x-2}{x^2 - 7x + 10} + \frac{2x+1}{(3x-4)(2x+1)}$$

is __________.

20. Which of the following algebraic expressions is equivalent to

$$\frac{8x-5}{x+4} \times \frac{x^2-16}{x-4}?$$

A. $4(x^2 + x + 1) - (2x - 1)^2$

B. $2x^2 - 2x(x - 4x) - 5$

C. $\frac{8x^2 + 21x + 10}{x+2}$

D. $\frac{64x^2 - 25}{8x - 5}$

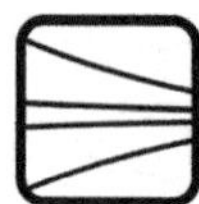

ANSWERS AND SOLUTIONS — UNIT TEST

1. D	**6. a) OR**	**10. OR**	**c) OR**	**17. OR**
2. C	**b) A**	**11. 2**	**d) OR**	**18. C**
3. OR	**7. D**	**12. D**	**14. OR**	**19. 7.8**
4. D	**8. C**	**13. a) OR**	**15. D**	**20. B**
5. C	**9. A**	**b) OR**	**16. A**	

1. D

In order for a relation to be a function, each x-value must have its own y-value.

Table A does not represent a function. The x-value of 3 has two separate y-values: 4 and −6. Thus, each x-value does not have its own y-value.

Table B does not represent a function. The x-value of −5 has six separate y-values: −8, −3, 0, 2, 4, and 7. Thus, each x-value does not have its own y-value.

Table C does not represent a function. The x-value of 0 has two separate y-values: 2 and 5. Thus, each x-value does not have its own y-value.

Table D is the only set of values in which all the x-coordinates are different. Therefore, it is the only function.

2. C

The function $f(x) = y$ means that the point (x, y) is part of the graph of $f(x)$.

The statements $f(0) = 0$, $f(0) = 4$, $f(-1) = 0$, and $f(-4) = 2$ correspond to the points (0, 0), (0, 4), (−1, 0), and (−4, 2). To evaluate the given statements, check to see if the corresponding points (0, 0), (0, 4), (−1, 0), and (−4, 2) are on the graph of $f(x)$.

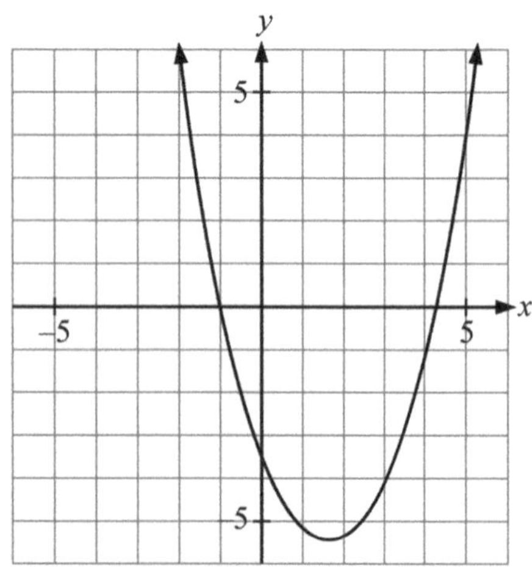

The only point on the the graph is (−1, 0). Therefore, the statement $f(-1) = 0$ is true.

3. OR

Step 1
Determine the physical factors that restrict the domain and range.
The physical factors that restrict the domain and range are related to who throws the object, where the ball is thrown from, and the angle the object makes relative to the ground when projected. A child will likely produce a smaller domain and range than an adult. The ground also provides a physical restriction on the domain and range. The greater the angle relative to the ground, the greater the height or range of the ball.

Step 2
Determine the domain and range of the given function.

The function $h = -5(t-2)^2 + 20$ is quadratic with a vertex at (2, 20).
The maximum height reached is 20 m at the vertex. When $t = 0$ and $t = 4$ s, $h = 0$, so the ball starts from ground level and reaches the ground again at 4 s.

$$\begin{aligned} h &= -5(t-2)^2 + 20 \\ 0 &= -5(t-2)^2 + 20 \\ -20 &= -5(t-2)^2 \\ 4 &= (t-2)^2 \\ \pm 2 &= t - 2 \\ 2 \pm 2 &= t \end{aligned}$$

Therefore, the domain is $0 \le t \le 4$ s, and the range is $0 \le h \le 20$ m.

4. D

The inverse of squaring is taking the square root, the inverse of adding is subtracting, and the inverse of dividing is multiplying. Therefore, the operations that must be performed are taking the square root, subtracting, and multiplying.

5. C

The graph of the inverse is a reflection of the original graph in the line $y = x$.

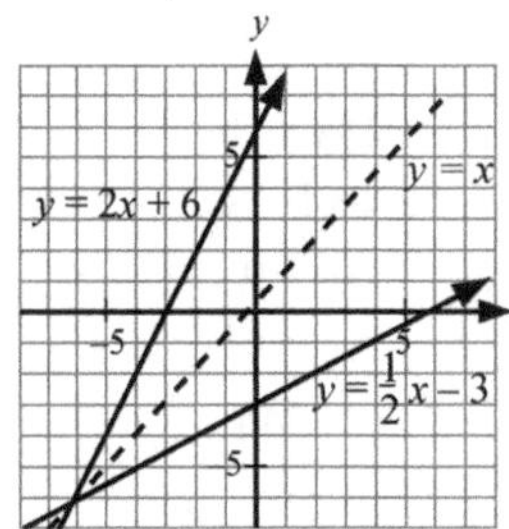

6. a) OR

Perform a horizontal line test on the given relation.

The relation passes the horizontal line test because a horizontal line will not intersect the graph at two or more points. This indicates that the inverse will not have two or more points with the same x-coordinate. Therefore, the inverse is a function.

b) A

Step 1
Determine the domain of the inverse relation.

The range of the given relation is $y \in R$. Therefore, the domain of the inverse becomes $x \in R$.

Step 2
Determine the range of the inverse relation.
The domain of the given relation is $x \leq 4$. Therefore, the range of the inverse becomes $y \leq 4$.

7. D

Step 1
Replace $f(x)$ with y.

$$f(x) = 4x - 7$$
$$y = 4x - 7$$

Step 2
Interchange x and y.

$$y = 4x - 7$$
$$x = 4y - 7$$

Step 3
Solve for y.

$$x = 4y - 7$$
$$x + 7 = 4y$$
$$\frac{x+7}{4} = y$$
$$y = \frac{x+7}{4}$$

Step 4
Replace y with $f^{-1}(x)$.

Since $y = \dfrac{x+7}{4}$ is a linear function, it can be written using function notation.

$$y = \frac{x+7}{4}$$
$$f^{-1}(x) = \frac{x+7}{4}$$

8. C

Step 1
Determine the necessary changes to obtain the equation $g(x) = (3x)^2 - 5$ from the equation $f(x) = x^2$ when compared to the general equation of $y = af(k(x - d)) + c$.
When comparing the equation $g(x)$ to the equation $y = af(k(x - d)) + c$, it can be seen that the value of k is 3, the value of c is -5, and the other variables remain unchanged.

Step 2
Describe the transformations needed to obtain the graph of $g(x) = (3x)^2 - 5$ from the graph of $f(x) = x^2$.

In the equation $f(x) = x^2$, 3 is substituted for k, which horizontally compresses the graph of $f(x) = x^2$ about the y-axis by a factor of $\frac{1}{3}$.

The resulting graph is then translated 5 units down, because -5 is substituted for c to obtain the graph of the equation $g(x) = (3x)^2 - 5$.

9. A

When $g(x) = \dfrac{1}{x-4} + 2$ is compared to the form $y = af(k(x - d) + c$, it can be seen that $d = 4$ and $c = 2$.

Therefore, the graph of $f(x) = \dfrac{1}{x}$ is translated horizontally 4 units right and vertically 2 units up.

The graph of $f(x) = \dfrac{1}{x}$ is given.

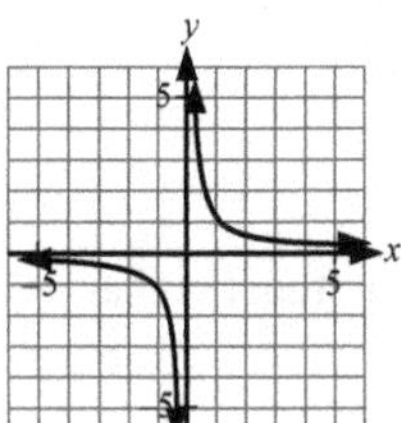

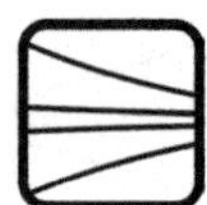

The graph that corresponds to a transformation of horizontally 4 units right and vertically 2 units up is graph A.

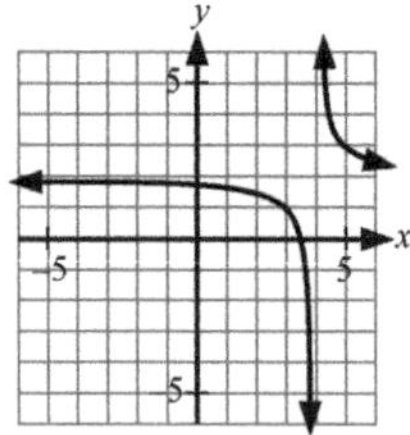

10. OR

When $g(x) = -2(x+4)^2 - 3$ is compared to the function of the form $y = af(k(x-d)) + c$, it can be observed that $a = -2$, $k = 1$, $d = -4$, and $c = -3$.

The graph of $f(x)$ is reflected in the x-axis, stretched vertically from the x-axis by a factor of 2, and translated horizontally 4 units left and vertically 3 units down.

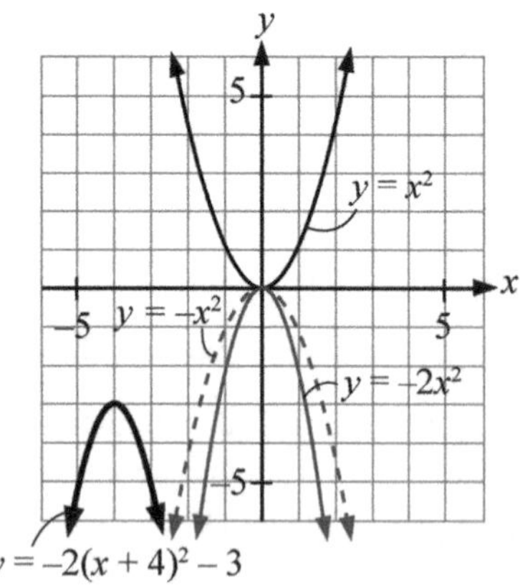

The domain of $g(x)$ is $x \in R$, and its range is $y \le -3$.

11. 2

The given quadratic function has two unique factors, and each factor will yield one real zero.

Determine the zeros of the function $y = (3x+2)(x-2)$.

$$3x + 2 = 0$$
$$3x = -2$$
$$x = -\frac{2}{3}$$
$$x - 2 = 0$$
$$x = 2$$

Therefore, the function has two different real zeros.

12. D

Since the leading coefficient is negative, the quadratic function has a maximum value.

Complete the square.

$$\begin{aligned} f(x) &= -4x^2 - 24x + 8 \\ &= -4(x^2 + 6x) + 8 \\ &= -4(x^2 + 6x + 9 - 9) + 8 \\ &= -4(x^2 + 6x + 9) + 36 + 8 \\ &= -4(x+3)^2 + 44 \end{aligned}$$

The maximum value is 44.

13. a) OR

Since the leading coefficient of the function is positive, the function has a minimum.

Complete the square.

$$\begin{aligned} h(t) &= \frac{1}{2}t^2 - 8t + 34 \\ &= \frac{1}{2}(t^2 - 16t) + 34 \\ &= \frac{1}{2}(t^2 - 16t + 64 - 64) + 34 \\ &= \frac{1}{2}(t^2 - 16t + 64) - 32 + 34 \\ &= \frac{1}{2}(t-8)^2 + 2 \end{aligned}$$

The vertex is at (8, 2), which means the lowest point is 2 m above the ground, and it is reached 8 s after the ride starts.

b) OR

Equate $h(t)$ to 20 in the completed square form, and solve.

$$20 = \frac{1}{2}(t-8)^2 + 2$$
$$18 = \frac{1}{2}(t-8)^2$$
$$36 = (t-8)^2$$
$$\pm 6 = t - 8$$
$$8 \pm 6 = t$$
$$2 = t \text{ or } 14 = t$$

The rider is 20 m in the air when the ferris wheel is going down at 2 s and going up at 14 s.

c) OR

A parabola does not have a maximum if it has a minimum. The rider on the ferris wheel will oscillate between the maximum and minimum heights allowed by the ride. A parabola does not show this oscillating behaviour.

The middle of the ferris wheel is 20 m above the ground. The rider is 20 m in the air at 2 s and at 14 s.

The given function models the height of the ferris wheel part for a domain of $2\text{ s} \le t \le 14\text{ s}$.

d) OR

Step 1
Determine how long it takes the Ferris wheel to reach its maximum height.
The completed square form of the function is $h(t) = \frac{1}{2}(t-8)^2 + 2$. The vertex is (8, 2), which means the lowest point is 2 m above the ground, and it is reached 8 s after the ride starts.
The times that correspond to the height of the middle of the ride (20 m) are 2 s and 14 s. This means it takes $14 - 2 = 12$ s for the ride to make half a rotation.
The maximum height occurs 12 seconds after the Ferris wheel is at its lowest point (8 s).
The Ferris wheel reaches its maximum height at $8 + 12 = 20$ s.

Step 2
Determine the maximum height.
The minimum height is 2 m and the middle is at 20 m. From the bottom of the ride to the middle of the ride is $20 - 2 = 18$ m. The maximum height will be $20 + 18 = 38$ m. The vertex of the second parabola must be at the point (20, 38).

Step 3
Determine the equation.
The top half of the ride must open downwards and be congruent to the original. This means that the parameters are $a = -\frac{1}{2}$, $k = 20$ and $p = 38$.

The equation is $y = -\frac{1}{2}(t-20)^2 + 38$.

Step 4
Determine the domain of the top half of the ride.
The top half of the ride occurs 14 seconds after the ride starts. The Ferris wheel takes 12 seconds to make half a rotation. Therefore, the top half of the ride ends at $14 + 12 = 26$ s. The domain of the top half of the ride is $14\text{ s} \le t \le 26\text{ s}$.

14. OR

Step 1
Determine the equation for the function $f(x)$.
Since the roots of the corresponding quadratic equation are the zeros of the function, the equation of the function must be $f(x) = a(x-2)(x-5)$.
Simplify the equation.
$$\begin{aligned} f(x) &= a(x-2)(x-5) \\ &= a(x^2 - 7x + 10) \end{aligned}$$

Step 2
Determine the value of a for the function $g(x)$.
Since $g(x)$ is a reflection of $f(x)$ about the x-axis, the function $g(x)$ is also of the form $g(x) = a(x^2 - 7x + 10)$.
The point (6, 4) must satisfy the original function, $f(x)$. When reflected in the x-axis, the graph of the new function, $g(x)$, must pass through the point (6, −4).
Substitute the variables into the equation, and simplify.
$$\begin{aligned} -4 &= a((6)^2 - 7(6) + 10) \\ -4 &= a(36 - 42 + 10) \\ -4 &= a(4) \\ -1 &= a \end{aligned}$$

Step 3
Write the equation of the function $g(x)$.
$$\begin{aligned} g(x) &= -1(x^2 - 7x + 10) \\ &= -x^2 + 7x - 10 \end{aligned}$$

15. D

Step 1
The bullet will hit the clay disks when the two heights are equal; that is, when $h(t) = g(t)$. Equate, and simplify.
$$\begin{aligned} (h)t &= g(t) \\ -5t^2 + 26t - 28 &= t + 2 \\ 5t^2 - 25t + 30 &= 0 \\ t^2 - 5t + 6 &= 0 \end{aligned}$$

Step 2
Factor the equation $t^2 - 5t + 6 = 0$.
$$\begin{aligned} t^2 - 5t + 6 &= 0 \\ (t-2)(t-3) &= 0 \end{aligned}$$

Step 3
Determine the zeros of the equation by equating each factor to zero.
$$\begin{aligned} (t-2) &= 0 \\ t &= 2 \\ (t-3) &= 0 \\ t &= 3 \end{aligned}$$

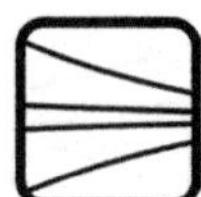

Step 4
Determine the two heights.
$g(t) = t + 2$
$g(2) = (2) + 2$
$g(2) = 4$ m
$g(t) = t + 2$
$g(3) = (3) + 2$
$g(3) = 5$ m
Therefore, the heights are 4 m or 5 m.

16. A

Determine the perimeter of the rectangle using the equation for perimeter, $P = 2l + 2w$, in which l is the length and w is the width of a rectangle.

$$\begin{aligned} P &= 2l + 2w \\ &= \begin{pmatrix} 2(3x^2 - 2x + 7) \\ + 2(2x^2 + 8x - 5) \end{pmatrix} \\ &= \begin{pmatrix} 6x^2 - 4x + 14 \\ + 4x^2 + 16x - 10 \end{pmatrix} \\ &= (6x^2 + 4x^2) + (-4x + 16x) + (14 - 10) \\ &= 10x^2 + 12x + 4 \end{aligned}$$

17. OR

Step 1
Determine the area of the square.

$$\begin{aligned} A &= s^2 \\ &= (4x - 2)^2 \\ &= 16x^2 - 16x + 4 \end{aligned}$$

Step 2
Determine the area of the smaller rectangle.

$$\begin{aligned} A &= b \times h \\ &= (x - 2)(2x + 1) \\ &= 2x^2 - 3x - 2 \end{aligned}$$

Step 3
Determine the expression that represents the difference in the areas of the square and the rectangle by subtracting the area of the smaller rectangle from the area of the square.
Difference in area

$$\begin{aligned} &= (16x^2 - 16x + 4) - (2x^2 - 3x - 2) \\ &= 16x^2 - 16x + 4 - 2x^2 + 3x + 2 \\ &= 14x^2 - 13x + 6 \end{aligned}$$

18. C

The formula for the area of a rectangle is length multiplied by width.

$$\begin{aligned} A &= lw \\ &= (3 + \sqrt{27})(5 - \sqrt{6}) \\ &= (3 + \sqrt{9}\sqrt{3})(5 - \sqrt{6}) \\ &= (3 + 3\sqrt{3})(5 - \sqrt{6}) \\ &= 15 - 3\sqrt{6} + 15\sqrt{3} - 3\sqrt{18} \\ &= 15 - 3\sqrt{6} + 15\sqrt{3} - 3\sqrt{9}\sqrt{2} \\ &= 15 - 3\sqrt{6} + 15\sqrt{3} - 9\sqrt{2}\text{ cm}^2 \end{aligned}$$

19. 7.8

Step 1
Express the denominators in factored form.

$$\begin{aligned} &\frac{x - 2}{x^2 - 7x + 10} + \frac{2x + 1}{(3x - 4)(2x + 1)} \\ &= \frac{x - 2}{(x - 2)(x - 5)} + \frac{2x + 1}{(3x - 4)(2x + 1)} \end{aligned}$$

Step 2
Determine the restrictions on the variable.

The restrictions are $x \neq 2, 5, \frac{4}{3}$, and $-\frac{1}{2}$.

Step 3
Determine the sum of all the restrictions.
The sum of the restrictions can be determined when all the restrictions are added together.

$$\begin{aligned} 2 + 5 + \frac{4}{3} + \left(-\frac{1}{2}\right) &= 7 + \frac{8}{6} - \frac{3}{6} \\ &= 7\frac{5}{6} \\ &\approx 7.8 \end{aligned}$$

20. B

Step 1
Simplify the given expression.

$$\begin{aligned} \frac{8x - 5}{x + 4} \times \frac{x^2 - 16}{x - 4} &= \frac{8x - 5}{x + 4} \times \frac{(x - 4)(x + 4)}{x - 4} \\ &= \frac{(8x - 5)(x - 4)(x + 4)}{(x - 4)(x + 4)} \\ &= 8x - 5 \end{aligned}$$

Step 2

Simplify $4(x^2 + x + 1) - (2x - 1)^2$.

$4(x^2 + x + 1) - (2x - 1)^2$
$= 4x^2 + 4x + 4 - (4x^2 - 4x + 1)$
$= 4x^2 + 4x + 4 - 4x^2 + 4x - 1$
$= 4x^2 - 4x^2 + 4x + 4x + 4 - 1$
$= 8x + 3$

Simplify $2x^2 - 2x(x - 4x) - 5$.

$2x^2 - 2x(x - 4x) - 5$
$= 2x^2 - 2x^2 + 8x - 5$
$= 8x - 5$

Simplify $\dfrac{8x^2 + 21x + 10}{x + 2}$.

$\dfrac{8x^2 + 21x + 10}{x + 2}$
$= \dfrac{(8x + 5)(x + 2)}{x + 2}$
$= 8x + 5$

Simplify $\dfrac{64x^2 - 25}{8x - 5}$.

$\dfrac{64x^2 - 25}{8x - 5}$
$= \dfrac{(8x - 5)(8x + 5)}{8x - 5}$
$= 8x + 5$

The equivalent expression is $2x^2 - 2x(x - 4) - 5$.

NOTES

Exponential Functions

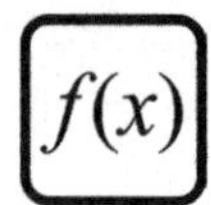

EXPONENTIAL FUNCTIONS

Table of Correlations

	Specific Expectation	Practice Questions	Unit Test Questions	Practice Test 1	Practice Test 2
EF1.0	Representing Exponential Functions				
EF1.1	*graph, with and without technology, an exponential relation, given its equation in the form y = ax (a>0, a ≠ 1), define this relation as the function f(x) = ax, and explain why it is a function*	1, 2	1	14a, 14b, 14c	7a, 7b
EF1.2	*determine, through investigation using a variety of tools and strategies, the value of a power with a rational exponent (i.e.,* $x^{m/n}$*, where x>0 and m and n are integers)*	5	2		
EF1.3	*simplify algebraic expressions containing integer and rational exponents and evaluate numeric expressions containing integer and rational exponents and rational bases*	6, 7	3	15	8
EF1.4	*determine, through investigation, and describe key properties relating to domain and range, intercepts, increasing/ decreasing intervals, and asymptotes for exponential functions represented in a variety of ways*	3, 4	4	16	9
EF2.0	Connecting Graphs and Equations of Exponential Functions				
EF2.1	*distinguish exponential functions from linear and quadratic functions by making comparisons in a variety of ways*	8, 9	5	17	10a, 10b, 10c
EF2.2	*determine, through investigation using technology, the roles of the parameters a, k, d, and c in functions of the form y = af (k(x - d)) + c, and describe these roles in terms of transformations on the graph of f(x) = a (a>0, a≠1) (i.e., translations; reflections in the axes; vertical and horizontal stretches and compressions to and from the x- and y-axes)*	10, 11	6	18	
EF2.3	*sketch graphs of y = af (k(x - d)) + c by applying one or more transformations x to the graph of f(x) = a (a>0, a≠1), and state the domain and range of the transformed functions*	12, 13, 14	7	19	11
EF2.4	*determine, through investigation using technology, that the equation of a given exponential function can be expressed using different bases and explain the connections between the equivalent forms in a variety of ways*	15, 16	8	20	12
EF2.5	*represent an exponential function with an equation, given its graph or its properties*	17, 18	9	21	13
EF3.0	Solving Problems Involving Exponential Functions				
EF3.1	*collect data that can be modelled as an exponential function, through investigation with and without technology, from primary sources, using a variety of tools or from secondary sources and graph the data*	19	10a, 10b		
EF3.2	*identify exponential functions, including those that arise from real-world applications involving growth and decay given various representations (i.e., tables of values, graphs, equations), and explain any restrictions that the context places on the domain and range*	20a, 20b, 21a, 21b	11		
EF3.3	*solve problems using given graphs or equations of exponential functions arising from a variety of real-world applications by interpreting the graphs or by substituting values for the exponent into the equations*	22, 23	12, 13a, 13b, 13c	22a, 22b	14

EF1.1 graph, with and without technology, an exponential relation, given its equation in the form y = ax (a>0, a ≠ 1), define this relation as the function f(x) = ax, and explain why it is a function

EF1.4 determine, through investigation, and describe key properties relating to domain and range, intercepts, increasing/decreasing intervals, and asymptotes for exponential functions represented in a variety of ways

Representing Exponential Functions

Any function of the form $f(x) = a^x$ where $a > 0$, $a \neq 1$ is called an **exponential function**. All exponential functions of this form have a y-intercept of 1 since $f(0) = a^0 = 1$ for all permissible values of a.

When the base a has a value between 0 and 1 $(0 < a < 1)$, the graph will have the general shape shown by the graph of $f(x) = \left(\frac{1}{2}\right)^x$. As the value of x increases, the value of y decreases and approaches zero as x gets very large over the entire domain of the function. Functions of this type are described as exponential decay.

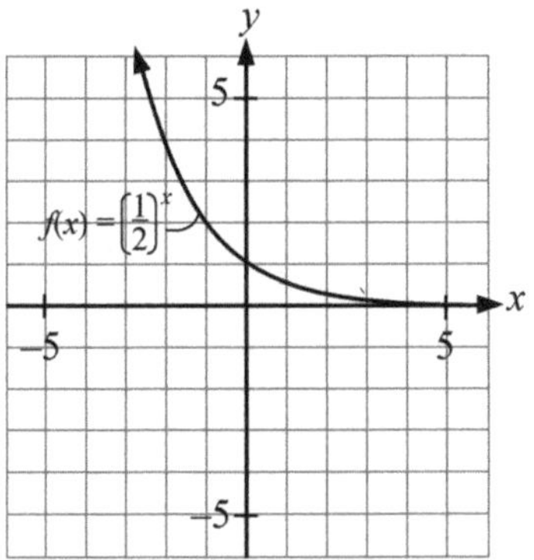

When the base value is larger than $1(a > 1)$, the graph will have the general shape shown by the graph of $f(x) = 2^x$. As the value of x increases, the value of y also increases over the entire domain. This type of function is described as exponential growth.

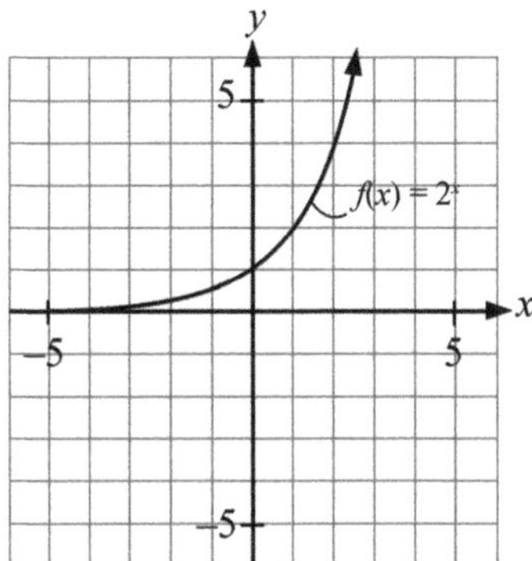

Both graphs have the x-axis $(y = 0)$ as a horizontal asymptote, a domain of $x \in R$, and a range of $y > 0$. As well, both satisfy the vertical line test for functions, where no vertical line intersects the graph at two or more points, indicating that no two points have the same x-coordinate.

Example

Draw the graph of the relation $y = 2^x$, examine the graph on a graphing calculator, and confirm that the given relation is a function.

Solution

Step 1

Sketch $y = 2^x$.

Substitute some values for x in 2^x to define the values of y, and display the results in a table of values.

x	−2	−1	0	1	2
y	$\frac{1}{4}$	$\frac{1}{2}$	1	2	4

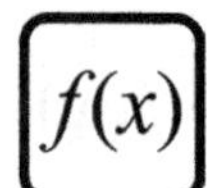

Step 2

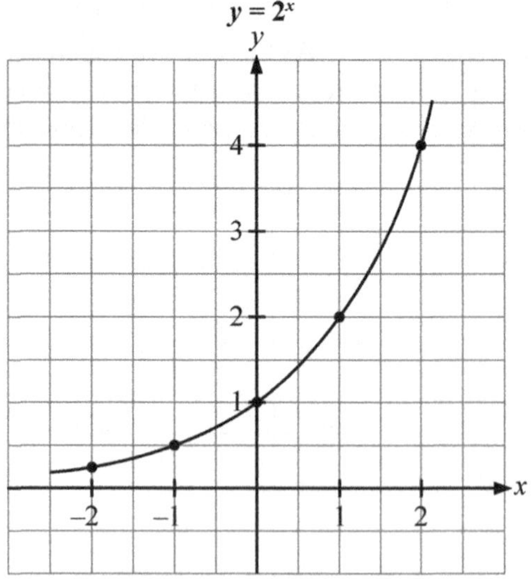

Use the values from the table to draw the graph of the relation $y = 2^x$.

Step 3

Graph $y = 2^x$ on your TI-83 or similar graphing calculator.

Follow these instructions:

1. Press WINDOW. Set the settings as x:[−3, 3, 1], y:[−2, 6, 1].
2. Press Y =, and enter the equation into $Y_1 =$ as $Y_1 = 2^\wedge x$.
3. Press GRAPH to see the screen shown.

Step 4

Confirm that the given relation is a function.

The relation $y = 2^x$ is a function and can be written as $f(x) = 2^x$ based on the following reasons:

- For every x-value in the table or on the graph, there is only one corresponding y-value. This can be observed by tracing along the graph on your graphing calculator using the trace feature.
- If a vertical line ($x = a$, where $a \in \mathbb{R}$) were to be drawn through any location on the graph, it would pass through one single point only.

Therefore, it can be concluded that the relation $y = a^x$, where $a > 0$ and $a \neq 1$, is a function and can be written as $f(x) = a^x$.

$f(x)$

1. Which of the following graphs **best** represents the function $f(x) = 3^x$?

A.
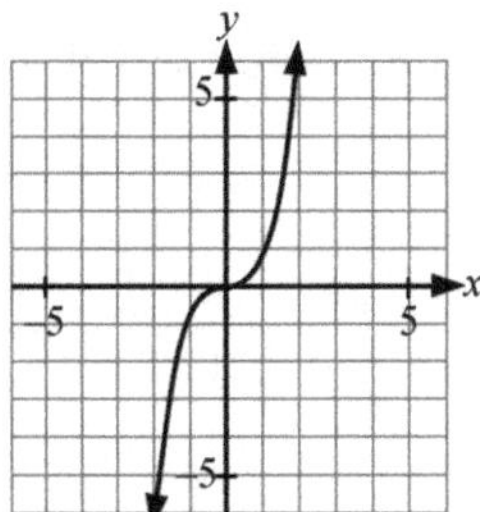

B.
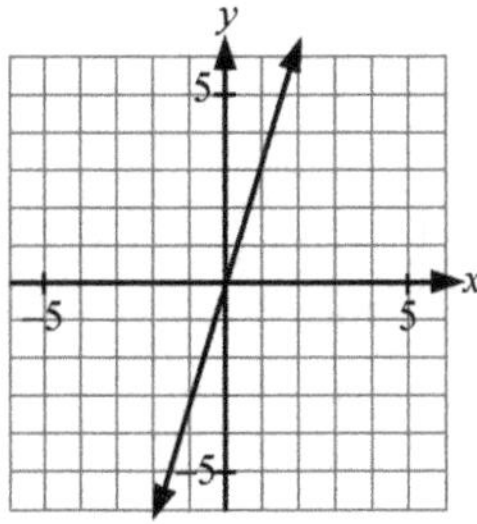

C.
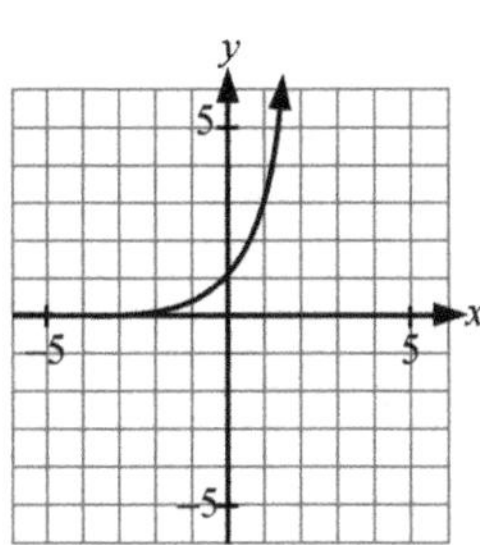

D.
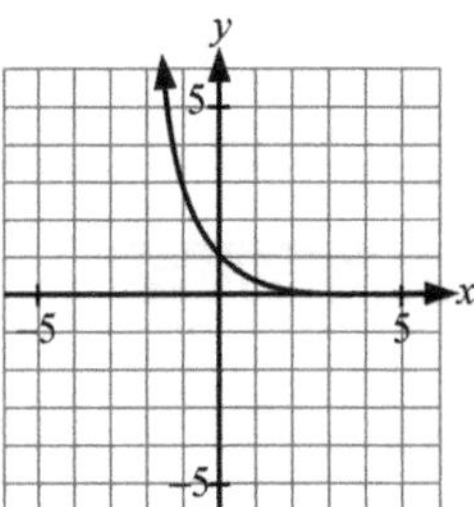

Open Response

2. On the given grid, sketch and label the graphs of $f(x) = \left(\frac{1}{4}\right)^x$ and $g(x) = 4^x$.

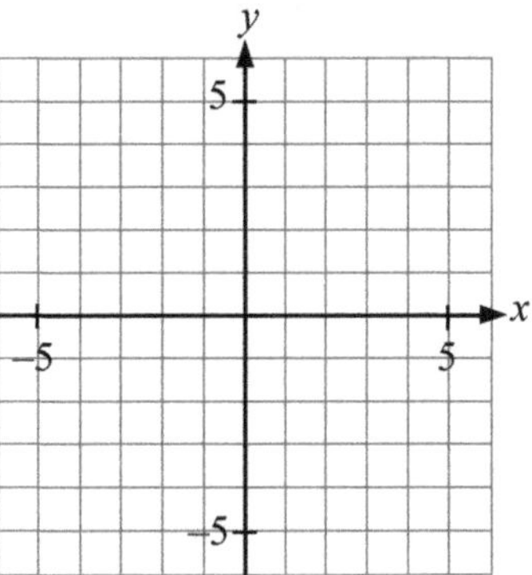

3. Which of the following functions contain function values that increase over the entire domain of the function?

A. $f(x) = 4^x$

B. $f(x) = x^2$

C. $f(x) = 3^{-x}$

D. $f(x) = \left(\frac{3}{4}\right)^x$

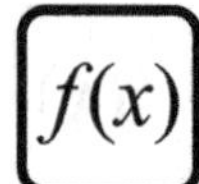

Open Response

4. On the given grid, sketch and label the graphs of $f(x)=\left(\frac{1}{3}\right)^x$ and $g(x)=3^x$, and state the similarities and differences of the two functions.

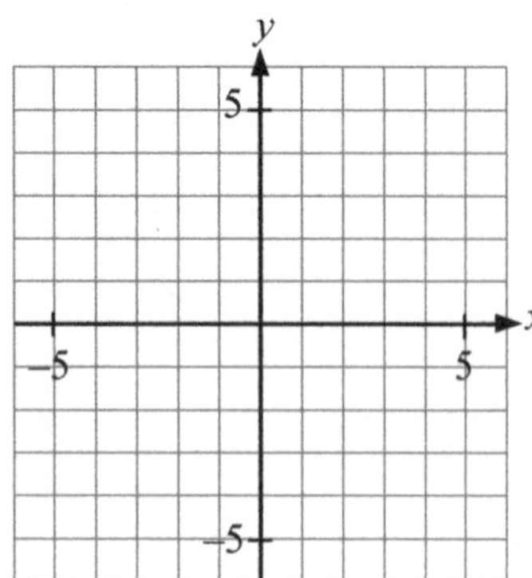

EF1.2 determine, through investigation using a variety of tools and strategies, the value of a power with a rational exponent (i.e., $x^{m/n}$, where $x>0$ and m and n are integers)

The Rational Exponent

By the laws of exponents, $x^{\frac{1}{2}}\times x^{\frac{1}{2}}=x^{\frac{1}{2}+\frac{1}{2}}=x^1=x$. By definition, $\sqrt{x}$ is a number, such that $\sqrt{x}\times\sqrt{x}=x$. Since $x^{\frac{1}{2}}$ behaves like $\sqrt{x}$, they must be equivalent to each other; thus, $x^{\frac{1}{2}}=\sqrt{x}$.

Likewise, since $x^{\frac{1}{3}}\times x^{\frac{1}{3}}\times x^{\frac{1}{3}}=x^{\frac{1}{3}+\frac{1}{3}+\frac{1}{3}}=x^1=x$, $x^{\frac{1}{3}}$ behaves like the cube root of x; therefore, $x^{\frac{1}{3}}=\sqrt[3]{x}$.

In general, it can be shown that $x^{\frac{1}{n}}=\sqrt[n]{x}$.

It can also be shown that $x^{\frac{m}{n}}=\left(x^{\frac{1}{n}}\right)^m=\left(\sqrt[n]{x}\right)^m$ and $x^{\frac{m}{n}}=\left(x^m\right)^{\frac{1}{n}}=\sqrt[n]{x^m}$.

Example

Simplify both $64^{\frac{1}{3}}$ and $9^{\frac{3}{2}}$.

Solution

Determine the value of $64^{\frac{1}{3}}$.

$$\begin{aligned}64^{\frac{1}{3}}&=\sqrt[3]{64}\\&=4\end{aligned}$$

Determine the value of $9^{\frac{3}{2}}$.

$$\begin{aligned}9^{\frac{3}{2}}&=(\sqrt{9})^3\\&=(3)^3\\&=27\end{aligned}$$

Numerical Response

5. The value of $32^{\frac{1}{5}}$ is __________.

$f(x)$

EF1.3 simplify algebraic expressions containing integer and rational exponents and evaluate numeric expressions containing integer and rational exponents and rational bases

Simplifying and Evaluating Exponential Expressions

When simplifying and/or evaluating algebraic expressions containing exponents, the laws of exponents must be used.

- Product law—$x^m \times x^n = x^{m+n}$
- Quotient law—$\dfrac{x^m}{x^n} = x^{m-n}$
- Power law—$(x^m)^n = x^{mn}$

Example

Evaluate the expression $\left(\dfrac{6^2}{6}\right)^3$.

Solution

Step 1
Use the power law.

$$\left(\frac{6^2}{6}\right)^3 = \frac{6^{2\times3}}{6^{1\times3}} = \frac{6^6}{6^3}$$

Step 2
Use the quotient law.

$$\frac{6^6}{6^3} = 6^{6-3} = 6^3 = 216$$

Example

Simplify the expression $(x^5y^2)^2$.

Solution

Use the power law to simplify the expression.

$$(x^5y^2)^2 = x^{5\times2}y^{2\times2} = x^{10}y^4$$

Example

Evaluate the expression $(2^2 \times 2^4)^{-\frac{1}{2}}$.

Solution

Step 1
Use the product law.

$$(2^2 \times 2^4)^{-\frac{1}{2}} = (2^{2+4})^{-\frac{1}{2}} = (2^6)^{-\frac{1}{2}}$$

Step 2
Use the negative exponent law.

$$(2^6)^{-\frac{1}{2}} = \left(\frac{1}{2^6}\right)^{\frac{1}{2}}$$

Step 3
Use the power law.

$$\left(\frac{1}{2^6}\right)^{\frac{1}{2}} = \frac{1^{\frac{1}{2}}}{(2^6)^{\frac{1}{2}}} = \frac{1}{2^{6\times\frac{1}{2}}} = \frac{1}{2^3} = \frac{1}{8}$$

---

6. The simplified form of $x^4 \div x^{\frac{1}{3}}$ is

   A. $x^{\frac{13}{3}}$ **B.** $x^{\frac{11}{3}}$

   C. $x^{\frac{4}{3}}$ **D.** $x^{\frac{3}{4}}$

Use the following information to answer the next question.

When simplified, $\left(\dfrac{27}{64}\right)^{\frac{2}{3}}$ has the form $\dfrac{a}{b}$.

Numerical Response

7. The value of $a + b$ is _________.

EF2.1 distinguish exponential functions from linear and quadratic functions by making comparisons in a variety of ways

Distinguishing Between Different Types of Functions

A linear function has an equation of the form $f(x) = mx + b$, where m is the slope and b is the y-intercept. The graph of a linear function is a straight line. For linear functions, the first differences are constant. The domain and range of every linear function whose graph is an oblique line is $x \in R$ and $y \in R$, respectively.

A quadratic function has an equation of the form $f(x) = ax^2 + bx + c$ or $f(x) = a(x - p)^2 + q$, where $a \neq 0$. The graph of every quadratic function is a parabola. For quadratic functions, the second differences are non-zero constants. The domain is $x \in R$, but the range is $y \leq q$ if $a < 0$ or $y \geq q$ if $a > 0$.

A simple exponential function's equation can be written in the form $f(x) = a^x$, where $a > 0$ and $a \neq 1$. The graph of every exponential function of this form has the x-axis ($y = 0$) as a horizontal asymptote and a y-intercept of 1. It also either increases over the entire domain if $a > 1$ or decreases over the entire domain if $0 < a < 1$.

When finite differences are used on an exponential function, no differences are constant; however, the ratio of consecutive function values is constant. The domain is $x \in R$, and the range is $y > 0$.

Example

Compare the linear function $f(x) = 2x$, the quadratic function $f(x) = x^2$, and the exponential function $f(x) = 2^x$ by examining their respective graphs and tables of values.

Solution

The graphs of $f(x) = 2x$, $f(x) = x^2$, and $f(x) = 2^x$ are shown.

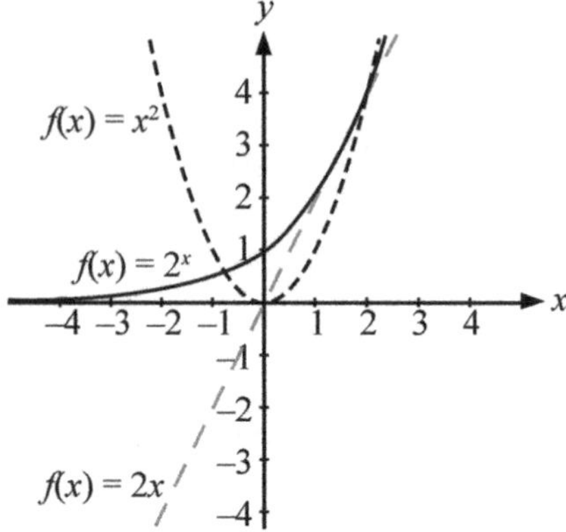

- The graph of $f(x) = 2x$ is a straight line with a rate of change or slope of 2, a y-intercept of 0, and a range of $f(x) \in \mathbb{R}$.
- The graph of $f(x) = x^2$ is a parabola opening upward with a vertex or minimum point at (0, 0), a y-intercept of 0, and a range of $y \geq 0$.
- The graph of $f(x) = 2^x$ is a curve that is relatively flat on the left side of the y-axis and rapidly increases or gets steeper on the right side of the y-axis. The graph has a y-intercept of 1 and a range of $y > 0$.

A table of values of $f(x) = 2x$ is shown. Since the first differences are constant at 2, this is a linear function.

x	y	D_1	D_2	R
–3	–6			
		2		$\frac{2}{3}$
–2	–4		0	
		2		$\frac{1}{2}$
–1	–2		0	
		2		0
0	0		0	
		2		undefined
1	2		0	
		2		2
2	4		0	
		2		$\frac{3}{2}$
3	6			

A table of values of $f(x) = x^2$ is shown. Since the second differences are constant at 2 (and not zero), this is a quadratic function.

x	y	D_1	D_2	R
–3	9			
		–5		$\frac{4}{9}$
–2	4		2	
		–3		$\frac{1}{4}$
–1	1		2	
		–1		0
0	0		2	
		1		undefined
1	1		2	
		3		4
2	4		2	
		5		$\frac{9}{4}$
3	9			

A table of values of $f(x) = 2^x$ is shown. Since the ratios of successive y-values are constant at 2, this is an exponential function.

x	y	D_1	D_2	R
–3	$\frac{1}{8}$			
		$\frac{1}{8}$		2
–2	$\frac{1}{4}$		$\frac{1}{8}$	
		$\frac{1}{4}$		2
–1	$\frac{1}{2}$		$\frac{1}{4}$	
		$\frac{1}{2}$		2
0	1		$\frac{1}{2}$	
		1		2
1	2		1	
		2		2
2	4		2	
		4		2
3	8			

First differences (D_1) are differences between successive y-values, second differences (D_2) are differences between successive first differences, and ratios (R) are values found by dividing successive y-values.

Use the following information to answer the next question.

The given table represents the progression of a function.

x	y
–2	16
–1	8
0	4
1	2
2	1

8. The given table of values is **most likely** from

A. a linear function

B. a quadratic function

C. an exponential-decay function

D. an exponential-growth function

9. A function with a domain of $x \in R$ and a range of $y \geq 0$ could be
A. linear
B. quadratic
C. exponential decay
D. exponential growth

EF2.2 determine, through investigation using technology, the roles of the parameters a, k, d, and c in functions of the form y = af (k(x - d)) + c, and describe these roles in terms of transformations on the graph of f(x) = a (a>0, a≠1) (i.e., translations; reflections in the axes; vertical and horizontal stretches and compressions to and from the x- and y-axes)

Transformations of Exponential Functions

The following transformations can be performed on exponential functions:

- If the equation $y = f(x)$ is changed to $y = af(x)$ by multiplying $f(x)$ on the right side of the equation by a, the graph of $f(x)$ will be vertically stretched from the x-axis if $|a| > 1$ or vertically compressed toward the x-axis if $|a| < 1$. The vertical stretch or compression factor is $|a|$. Also, if $a < 0$, the graph of $f(x)$ will be reflected in the x-axis.
- If the equation $y = f(x)$ is changed to $y = f(kx)$ by replacing x with kx, the graph of $f(x)$ will be horizontally stretched from the y-axis if $|k| < 1$ or horizontally compressed toward the y-axis if $|k| > 1$. The horizontal stretch or compression factor is $\frac{1}{|k|}$. Also, if $k < 0$, there will be a reflection in the y-axis.
- If the equation $y = f(x)$ is changed to $y = f(x - d)$ by replacing the variable x with $x - d$, the graph of $f(x)$ will be translated horizontally d units left if $d < 0$ and d units right if $d > 0$.
- If the equation $y = f(x)$ is changed to $y = f(x) + c$ by adding c to the right side of the equation, the graph of $f(x)$ will be translated vertically c units down if $c < 0$ and c units up if $c > 0$.
- When $y = f(x)$ is changed to $y = af(k(x - d)) + c$, all horizontal and vertical stretches, compressions, and reflections must be performed first, followed by any translations.

Example

Describe the transformations required to change the graph of $y = 4^x$ into the graph of $y = 3(4)^{-2x+4} - 5$.

Solution

In order to express $y = 3(4)^{-2x+4} - 5$ in the form $y = af(k(x - d)) + c$, the exponent $-2x + 4$ must be expressed in factored form as $-2(x - 2)$.

You can write $y = 3(4)^{-2(x-2)} - 5$ as $y = 3f(-2(x - 2)) - 5$, so the values of the parameters are $a = 3$, $k = -2$, $d = 2$, and $c = -5$.

The transformations required to change the graph of $y = 4^x$ into the graph of $y = 3(4)^{-2x+4} - 5$ are a vertical stretch from the x-axis by a factor of 3, a reflection in the y-axis, and a horizontal compression to the y-axis by a factor of $\frac{1}{2}$. These three transformations may be done in any order but must be performed before the final translations of the graph: 2 units to the right and 5 units down.

$f(x)$

10. In order to stretch the graph of the function $y = \left(\frac{1}{2}\right)^x$ horizontally by a factor of 3 from the y-axis and translate it vertically up 4 units, the equation of the function must be change to

A. $y = \left(\frac{1}{2}\right)^{3x}$

B. $y = \left(\frac{1}{2}\right)^{\frac{1}{3}x}$

C. $y = \left(\frac{1}{2}\right)^{3x} + 4$

D. $y = \left(\frac{1}{2}\right)^{\frac{1}{3}x} + 4$

Open Response

11. Describe the transformations needed to change the graph of $y = 3^x$ into the graph of $y = -\frac{1}{2}(3)^{3x-6} - 2$.

EF2.3 sketch graphs of y = af (k(x - d)) + c by applying one or more transformations x to the graph of f(x) = a (a>0, a≠1), and state the domain and range of the transformed functions

Sketching Graphs Using Transformations of Exponential Functions

To sketch the graphs of exponential functions of the form $y = af(k(x-d)) + c$, transformations can be applied to the graph of $f(x) = a^x (a > 0,\ a \neq 1)$. All points on the transformed graph must satisfy the given transformations.

For example, consider the following graphs:

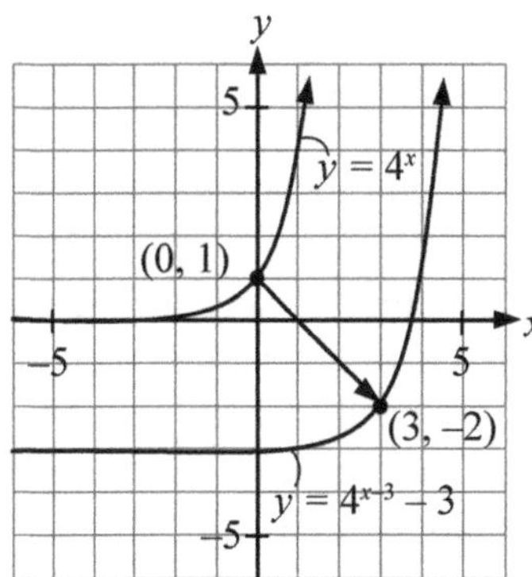

Compared to the graph of $y = 4^x$, the graph of the function $y = 4^{x-3} - 3$ has been translated 3 units right and 3 units down. Similarly, the point (0, 1), which is on the graph of $y = 4^x$, has become the point (3, −2) on the graph of $y = 4^{x-3} - 3$, since 3 is 3 units right of 0 and −2 is 3 units down from 1.

The order of transformations should be as follows:

1. Vertical and horizontal stretches or compressions (in either order)
2. Reflections in either axes (steps 1 and 2 can be reversed)
3. Vertical and horizontal translations (in either order)

Example

Certain transformations to the graph of the function $f(x) = \left(\frac{1}{2}\right)^x$ will result in the graph of the transformed function $g(x) = \frac{1}{3}\left(\frac{1}{2}\right)^{2x} + 3$.

State the domain and range of the transformed function $g(x)$, and draw the graph of $g(x)$ by graphing $f(x)$ and each individual transformation. Identify $f(x)$, and label each transformation with its appropriate equation.

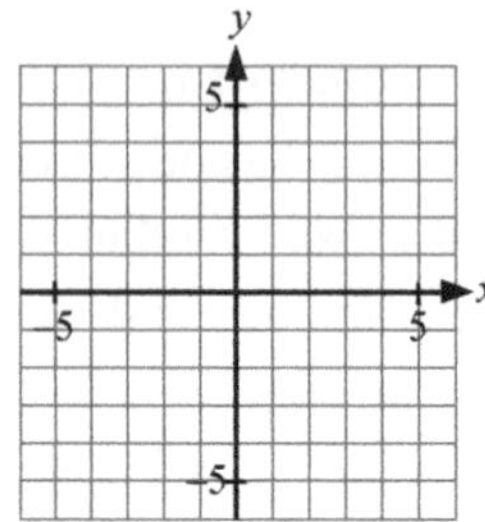

Solution

Step 1

Identify the transformations.

The transformations are a vertical compression to the x-axis by a factor of $\frac{1}{3}$, a horizontal compression to the y-axis by a factor of $\frac{1}{2}$, and a vertical translation 3 units up.

Step 2

State the domain and range.

The domain and range of $g(x)$ are $x \in R$ and $y > 3$, respectively.

Step 3

Graph all the transformations.

This image shows the transformations to the graph of $f(x)$ that result in the graph of $g(x)$.

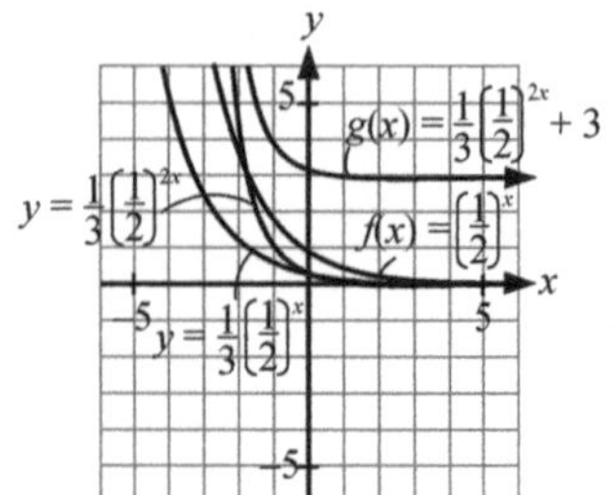

12. Which of the following graphs is the graph of the function $f(x) = 2^{x+1} - 3$?

A.

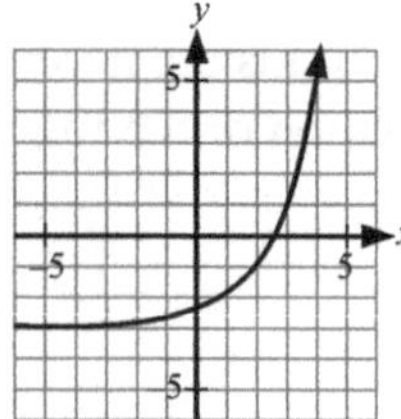

B.

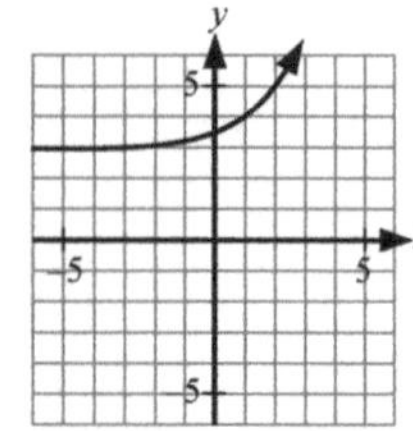

C.

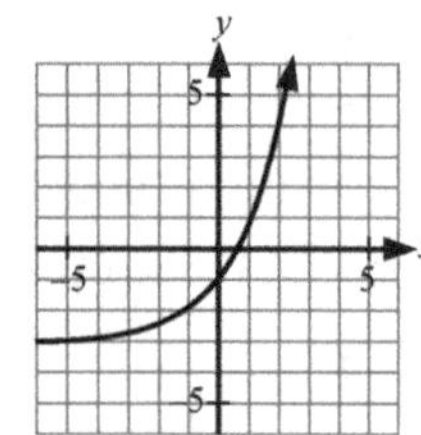

D.

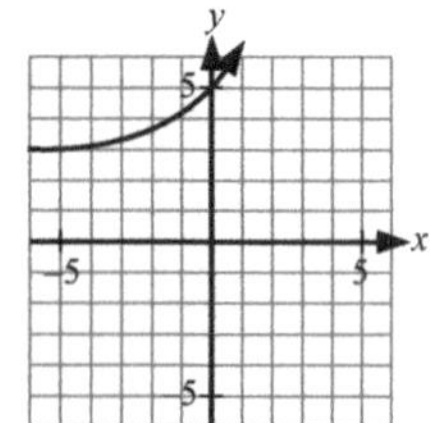

13. Which of the following graphs represents the function $f(x) = -3^x + 2$?

A.

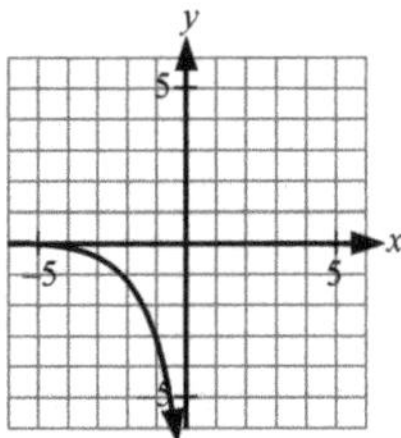

B.

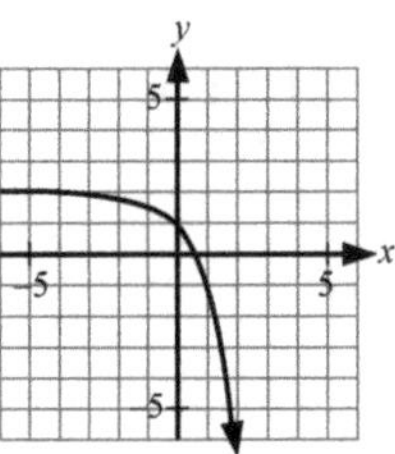

C.

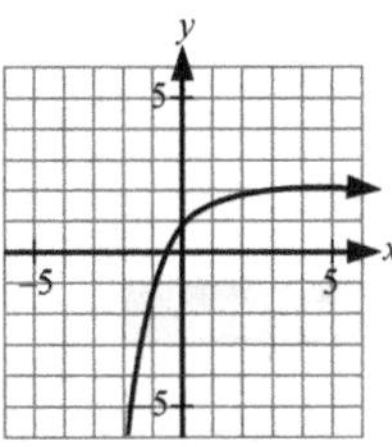

D.

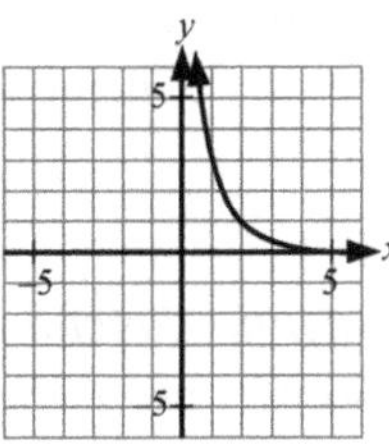

Use the following information to answer the next question.

The functions $f(x) = 3^x$ and $g(x) = -2(3)^{x-3} - 5$ are given, where $f(x)$ has been transformed into $g(x)$.

Open Response

14. Sketch and label each transformation involved in transforming the graph of $f(x)$ to the graph of $g(x)$. State the domain and range of the transformed function, $g(x)$.

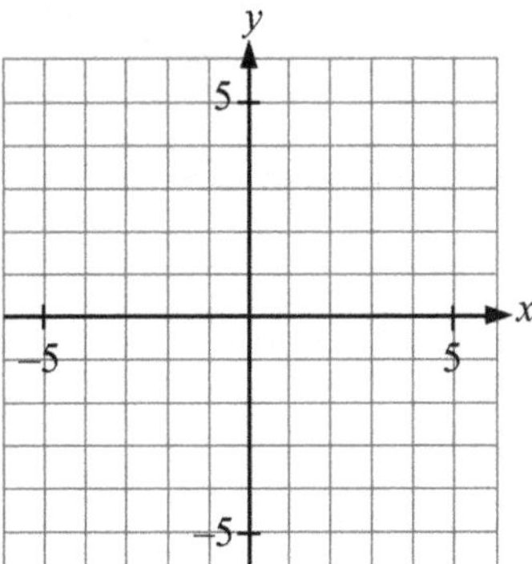

EF2.4 determine, through investigation using technology, that the equation of a given exponential function can be expressed using different bases and explain the connections between the equivalent forms in a variety of ways

Equivalent Forms of Exponential Functions

Since the bases of exponential functions are numbers, and any number can be written in several equivalent forms, it is possible to write any exponential function in an equivalent form with a different base.

Example

Express $f(x) = 8^x$ in base 2.

Solution

Equate base 8 with base 2.

$8 = 2^3$

Solve.

$$\begin{aligned} f(x) &= 8^x \\ &= (2^3)^x \\ &= 2^{3x} \end{aligned}$$

Example

Express $f(x) = \left(\frac{1}{3}\right)^x$ in base 3.

Solution

Equate base $\frac{1}{3}$ with base 3.

$\frac{1}{3} = 3^{-1}$

Solve.

$$\begin{aligned} f(x) &= \left(\frac{1}{3}\right)^x \\ &= (3^{-1})^x \\ &= 3^{-x} \end{aligned}$$

Example

Express $f(x) = 27^x$ in base 9.

Solution

Step 1

Equate base 27 with base 9.

$27 = 9^{\frac{3}{2}}$

Step 2

Solve.

$$\begin{aligned} f(x) &= 27^x \\ &= \left(9^{\frac{3}{2}}\right)^x \\ &= 9^{\frac{3}{2}x} \end{aligned}$$

---

15. Which of the following functions is **not** equivalent to $f(x) = \left(\frac{1}{4}\right)^x$?

A. $f(x) = 4^{-x}$

B. $f(x) = 2^{-2x}$

C. $f(x) = 8^{-\frac{3}{2}x}$

D. $f(x) = \left(\frac{1}{2}\right)^{2x}$

Numerical Response

16. If $f(x) = 128^x$ is written in an equivalent form as $f(x) = 32^{kx}$, the value of k is. (Record your answer to the nearest hundredth.)

EF2.5 represent an exponential function with an equation, given its graph or its properties

Representing an Exponential Function with an Equation Given Its Graph or Its Properties

Like other functions, exponential functions can be represented with various equations. The equation of the function can be derived from a graph or from certain given properties, such as the equation of an asymptote and/or certain points on the graph.

When coming up with alternative forms for an exponential equation, recall that exponential equations can be written using different bases. For example, $y = 4^x$ can also be written as $y = 2^{2x}$ since $2^2 = 4$.

Example

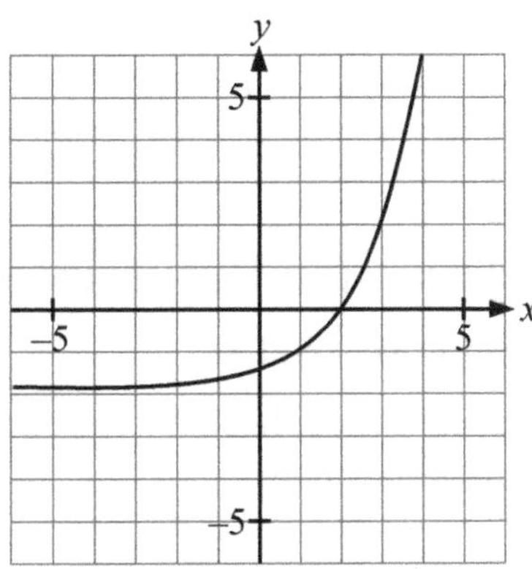

The given graph has an equation of the form $f(x) = (2)^{x-d} + c$.

What is the value of $\frac{c}{d}$?

Solution

Step 1
Determine the value of c.

The graph of $y = 2^x$ has a horizontal asymptote at the x-axis ($y = 0$). For the given graph, the value of c is -2 because the horizontal asymptote is the line $y = -2$, and this value corresponds to a vertical translation of two units down.

Step 2
Determine the value of d.

The given graph has clearly defined points at $(1, -1)$ and $(2, 0)$. Determine the points on the graph of $y = 2^x$ that can be transformed so that they coincide with $(1, -1)$ and $(2, 0)$ after the transformations.

Consider $(0, 1)$ and $(1, 2)$ on the graph of $y = 2^x$. These points can be mapped to the given graph as follows:

- $(0, 1) \rightarrow (1, -1)$—right 1 unit and down 2 units
- $(1, 2) \rightarrow (2, 0)$—right 1 unit and down 2 units

The steps are illustrated in the given graph.

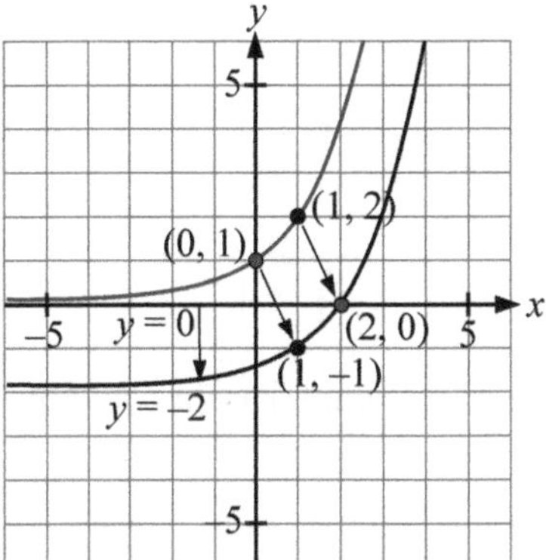

Since the graph has been translated 1 unit to the right, $d = 1$.

Alternatively, knowing the value of c, the value of d could be determined by substituting the coordinates of one of the known points, such as $(1, -1)$, into the equation $f(x) = (2)^{x-d} - 2$ as follows:

$$\begin{aligned} f(x) &= (2)^{x-d} - 2 \\ -1 &= (2)^{1-d} - 2 \\ 1 &= (2)^{1-d} \\ 2^0 &= (2)^{1-d} \\ 0 &= 1 - d \\ d &= 1 \end{aligned}$$

Step 3

Determine the value of $\frac{c}{d}$.

$$\begin{aligned} \frac{c}{d} &= \left(-\frac{2}{1}\right) \\ &= -2 \end{aligned}$$

17. Which of the following functions has a base of 3, a y-intercept of 4, and a range of $y > 1$?

A. $f(x) = 4(3)^{x+1}$

B. $f(x) = (3)^x + 3$

C. $f(x) = 4(3)^x + 1$

D. $f(x) = (3)^{x+1} + 1$

Use the following information to answer the next question.

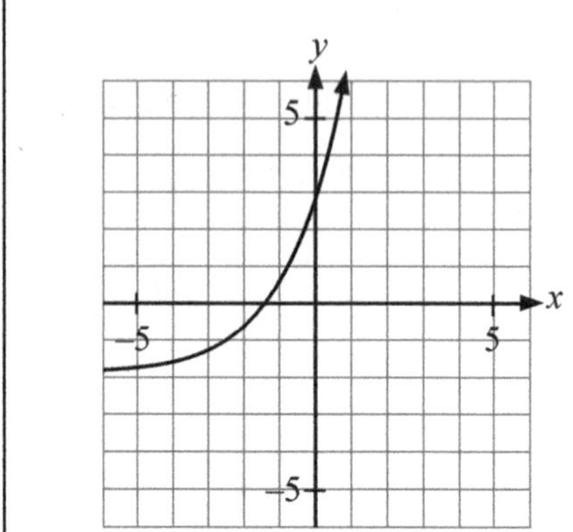

The given graph has an equation in the form $f(x) = a(2)^x + c$.

Numerical Response

18. The value of $a + c$ is ________.

EF3.1 collect data that can be modelled as an exponential function, through investigation with and without technology, from primary sources, using a variety of tools or from secondary sources and graph the data

Collecting and Representing Exponential Data

Data from real-life applications can be modelled as an exponential function.

Example

The data in the given table shows a deer population growing exponentially in a particular region over a 10-year period.

Year	Number of Deer
0	4 000
1	4 800
2	5 730
3	6 900
4	8 295
5	9 900
6	11 950
7	14 320
8	17 200
9	20 630
10	25 000

Graph the data, and find the approximate rate of growth.

Solution

Step 1
Graph the data.
The plotted data is shown on the given graph, in which x is the year number and y is the number of deer.

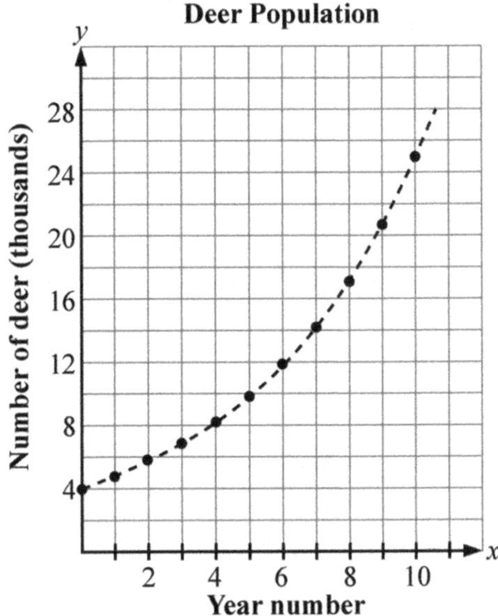

Step 2
Determine the approximate rate of growth.
To determine the approximate rate of growth, divide the successive y-values and round to the nearest thousandth.

$\frac{4\ 800}{4\ 000} = 1.200, \frac{5\ 730}{4\ 800} = 1.194,$
$\frac{6\ 900}{5\ 730} = 1.204, \frac{8\ 295}{6\ 900} = 1.202,$
$\frac{9\ 900}{8\ 295} = 1.193, \frac{11\ 950}{9\ 900} = 1.207,$
$\frac{14\ 320}{11\ 950} = 1.198, \frac{17\ 200}{14\ 320} = 1.201,$
$\frac{20\ 630}{17\ 200} = 1.199, \frac{25\ 000}{20\ 630} = 1.211$

Upon examination of the ratios, the approximate rate of growth of the deer population was 1.20 deer/year.

How would the shape of the curve change if there had been wolves in this region?

Solution

The curve would increase less rapidly or be flatter, since the wolves would eat a certain amount of deer each year, resulting in annual population values that were less than the original values in the table of values.

The ratio of growth would be less than 1.20 deer/year.

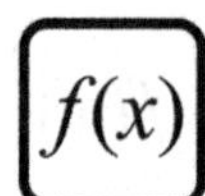

Use the following information to answer the next question.

Jennifer knew that the population of humans grows exponentially. She found population figures for the Hawaiian county of Maui from the Internet, some of which are recorded in the given table.
To graph the data, she let 1980 represent a time of 0 years.

Year	Population
1980	70 991
1984	79 385
1987	80 877
1990	100 504
1993	106 280
1996	117 013
2000	128 241
2004	138 347

19. Including the curve of best fit, which of the following graphs correctly represents the given data?

A.

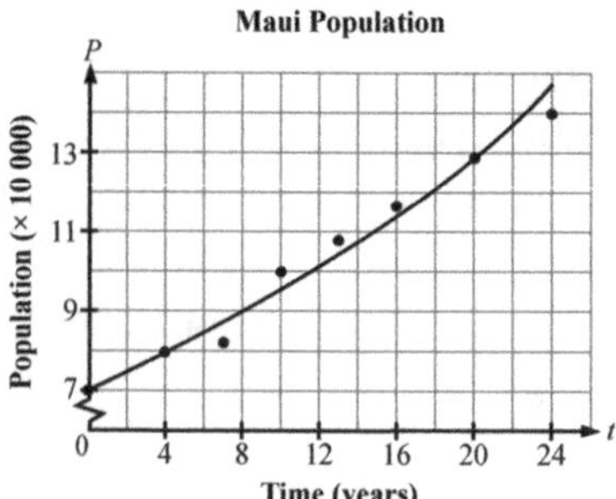

B.

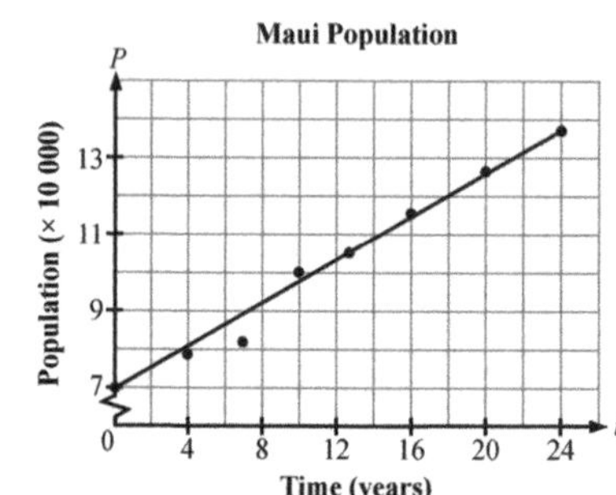

C.

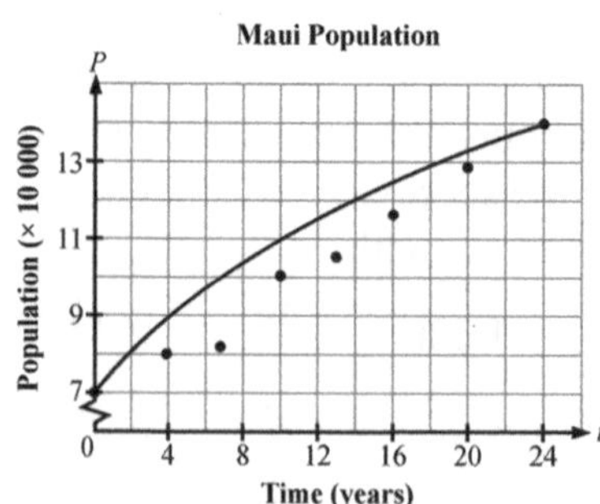

D.

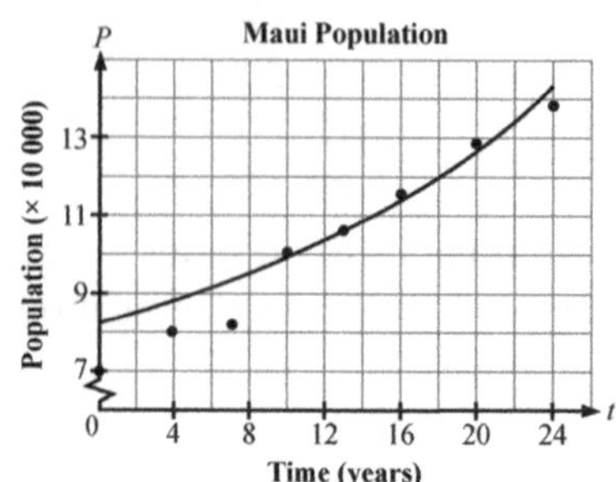

EF3.2 identify exponential functions, including those that arise from real-world applications involving growth and decay given various representations (i.e., tables of values, graphs, equations), and explain any restrictions that the context places on the domain and range

Identify Exponential Functions in Real-World Problems

Exponential function equations are often broken down into two different forms:

1. **Exponential growth:** Equations, graphs, and tables of values of exponential functions are often used to model real-life examples in which quantities increase or grow at an exponential rate. A common example in which an exponential function is used to model exponential growth is population growth.
2. **Exponential decay:** Equations, graphs, and tables of values of exponential functions can also be used to model real-life examples in which quantities decrease or decay at an exponential rate. Common examples in which exponential functions are used to model exponential decay are depreciating assets or investments and radioactive half-lives.

A general formula that defines a quantity exponentially growing or decaying is given by $N_t = N_0 \times R^{\frac{t}{p}}$, in which the following apply:

- N_t: The quantity at time, t
- N_0: The initial size or value (when $t = 0$)
- R: The growth rate. When $R > 1$, it is an exponential growth. For example, when the quantity doubles in size, $R = 2$; when it triples, $R = 3$; when it increases by 25%, $R = 1.25$; and so on. When R has a value of $0 < R < 1$, it is an exponential decay. For example, when a quantity decreases to half its original value, $R = \frac{1}{2}$; when it depreciates by 25%, $R = 0.75$; and so on.
- t: The elapsed time
- p: The period of time it takes the quantity to grow by a rate, R. For example, if it takes 3 hours for a population to double, $p = 3$.

Example

A petri dish contains 25 bacteria. The number of bacteria, N, doubles every hour.

Construct a table of values, a graph, and an equation to represent the time, t, for the first 4 hours. Highlight the growth factor, r, and explain any restrictions on the domain and range.

Solution

Step 1

Construct a table of values.

t (h)	0	1	2	3	4
N	25	50	100	200	400
Ratio (r)		$\frac{50}{25} = 2$	$\frac{100}{50} = 2$	$\frac{200}{100} = 2$	$\frac{400}{200} = 2$

Step 2

Sketch the graph.

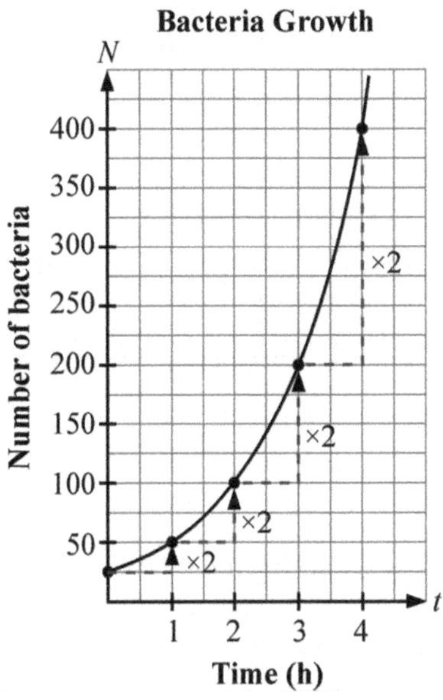

Step 3

Determine the exponential function.

Using the general formula of an exponential function, $N_t = N_0 \times R^{\frac{t}{p}}$, substitute 25 for N_0, 2 for R, and 1 for p.

$$N_t = N_0 \times R^{\frac{t}{p}}$$

$$N_t = 25 \times (2)^{\frac{t}{1}}$$

$$N_t = 25(2)^t$$

Step 4

State any restrictions on the domain and range.

The domain of the scenario is $t \geq 0$ up to a value of t, at which point the bacteria stops growing in the dish because of lack of food. The range is $N \geq 25$ up to a value of N, at which point the number of bacteria reaches its maximum.

Example

A lab technician had an 80 mg sample of a radioactive substance called iodine-131 with a half-life of 8 days. (Half-life means the time it takes for a radioactive substance to decay to $\frac{1}{2}$ its original mass.)

Construct a table of values, a graph, and an equation to represent the amount of mass, m, remaining over time, t, in the first 32 days. Highlight the decay factor, r, and explain any restrictions on the domain and range.

Solution

Step 1

Construct a table of values.

t (d)	0	8	16	24	32
m	80	40	20	10	5
Ratio (r)		$\frac{40}{80} = \frac{1}{2}$	$\frac{20}{40} = \frac{1}{2}$	$\frac{10}{20} = \frac{1}{2}$	$\frac{5}{10} = \frac{1}{2}$

Step 2

Sketch a graph from the table of values.

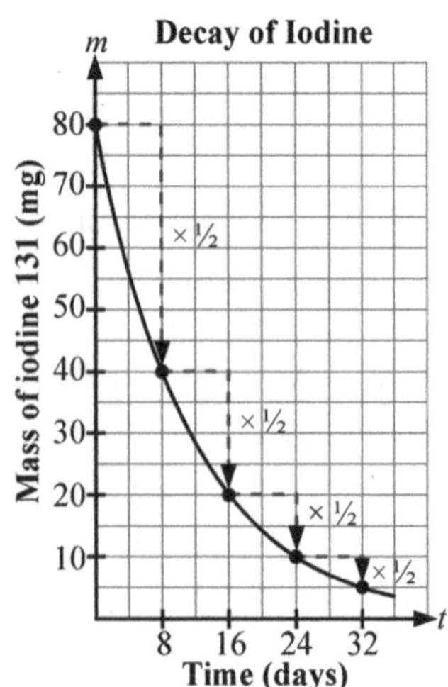

Step 3

Determine the equation of the exponential function.

Using the general formula of an exponential function, $N_t = N_0 \times R^{\frac{t}{p}}$, substitute 80 for N_0, $\frac{1}{2}$ for R, and 8 for p.

$$N_t = N_0 \times R^{\frac{t}{p}}$$

$$N_t = 80 \times \left(\frac{1}{2}\right)^{\frac{t}{8}}$$

$$N_t = 80\left(\frac{1}{2}\right)^{\frac{t}{8}}$$

Note: The exponent in the equation is $\frac{t}{8}$.

A value is placed in the denominator when the growth or decay time is not given as a unit value (e.g., 4 min $\rightarrow \frac{t}{4}$, 16.5 years $\rightarrow \frac{t}{16.5}$, 175 m $\rightarrow \frac{d}{175}$).

Step 4

State the restrictions on the domain and range.

The domain of this scenario is $t \geq 0$ up to the time that only one molecule of iodine is left ($t \doteq$ infinity). Therefore, the domain is $t \geq 0$. The range is $0 < m \leq 80$, since the mass would realistically never get to 0 mg and also would never become a negative amount.

Use the following information to answer the next multipart question.

20. A certain island has 30 spiders.
The population of spiders quadruples every nine days.

a) The exponential function representing the island's spider population is

A. $N_t = 30 \times 4^{\frac{t}{9}}$

B. $N_t = 30 \times 9^{\frac{t}{4}}$

C. $N_t = 30 \times \left(\frac{1}{4}\right)^{\frac{t}{9}}$

D. $N_t = 30 \times \left(\frac{1}{9}\right)^{\frac{t}{4}}$

Open Response

b) Does the population of spiders represent exponential growth or decay?

Use the following information to answer the next multipart question.

21. Boon noticed that when he sucked on a large jawbreaker in his mouth, it dissolved slowly at first and then more quickly at the end. He decided to collect some data using his knowledge of geometry. The given table of values shows the volume of the jawbreaker, V, in cubic centimetres, over time, t, in minutes.

Time (min)	Volume (cm³)
0	33.5
1	28.1
2	23.6
3	19.7
4	16.7
5	14.0

Open Response

a) State the restrictions on the domain (time) and range (volume). Give reasons for your answer.

b) Written as a percentage, the volume of the jawbreaker decays exponentially over time by a factor of

A. 84% **B.** 80%

C. 8.4% **D.** 8.0%

EF3.3 solve problems using given graphs or equations of exponential functions arising from a variety of real-world applications by interpreting the graphs or by substituting values for the exponent into the equations

Solving Problems Using Exponential Equations and Graphs

Exponential graphs and their corresponding functions, which arise from scientific and financial investigations, can be interpreted and analyzed to make accurate predictions.

Example

The number of cellphone customers with a particular phone company increased by 20% every 6 months from 1996 to 2000. The given graph shows this exponential growth between the number of customers, N, and the time, t, in months from January 1, 1996.

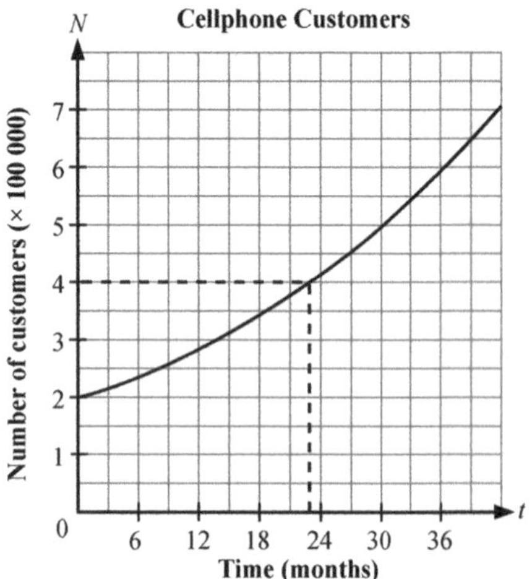

How many cellphone customers were with the company on January 1, 1996?

Solution

The y-intercept (value at $t = 0$) describes the number of cellphone customers on January 1, 1996.

This value is 200 000 customers.

How long does it take for the number of cellphone customers to double?

Solution

If the number of cellphone customers at $t = 0$ was 200 000, find the approximate time, t, when there will be 400 000 customers. According to the dotted line on the graph, this occurs at about $t = 23$.

Therefore, it takes about 23 months for the number of cellphone customers to double.

Write the exponential equation that represents the scenario portrayed by the given graph.

Solution

Since the given graph portrays a growth curve, the growth factor has to be larger than 1. Since 100% is a growth ratio of 1 (which means no change), then 120% (100% + 20% increase) is a growth ratio of 1.20, which is the ratio represented by the graph. Whenever a population increases by i%, the growth ratio is $\frac{(100\% + i\%)}{100}$.

This growth ratio occurs every 6 months. Since the original number of customers was 200 000, use the general formula of an exponential function, $N_t = N_0 \times R^{\frac{t}{p}}$. Substitute 200 000 for N_0, 1.20 for R, and 6 for p.

$$N_t = N_0 \times R^{\frac{t}{p}}$$

$$N_t = 200\ 000 \times (1.20)^{\frac{t}{6}}$$

$$N_t = 200\ 000(1.20)^{\frac{t}{6}}$$

Determine the number of cellphone customers there would be on January 1, 2000.

Solution

The number of years between the starting time of January 1, 1996 to January 1, 2000 is 4 years or $4 \times 12 = 48$ months.

Therefore, you need to find the number of customers, N, at a time, $t = 48$. This can be found by substituting 48 for t and solving for N_t in the equation $N_t = 200\ 000(1.20)^{\frac{t}{6}}$.

$$\begin{aligned} N_t &= 200\ 000(1.20)^{\frac{t}{6}} \\ N_{48} &= 200\ 000(1.20)^{\frac{48}{6}} \\ &= 200\ 000(1.20)^8 \\ &= 859\ 963.392\ldots \\ &\approx 859\ 963 \text{ customers} \end{aligned}$$

Use a graphing calculator to determine the month and year when there would be 650 000 customers.

Solution

To graph the function $N = 200\ 000(1.20)^{\frac{t}{6}}$, press the $[\mathrm{Y}_1 =]$ key and enter $\mathrm{Y}_1 = 200\ 000(1.20)\ ^\wedge\ (\mathrm{X}/6)$.

Set your window to the following settings:

```
WINDOW
 Xmin=-5
 Xmax=50
 Xscl=5
 Ymin=0
 Ymax=1000000
 Yscl=100000
 Xres=1
```

Then, press GRAPH to get the following screen:

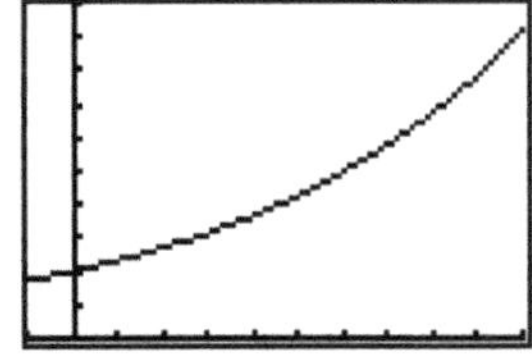

Using the TRACE feature, scroll to the right until the y-value is as close as possible to $y = 650\ 000$. The cursor should be at about $x = 38.882\ 979$ when $y = 651\ 874.18$, as shown in the given diagram.

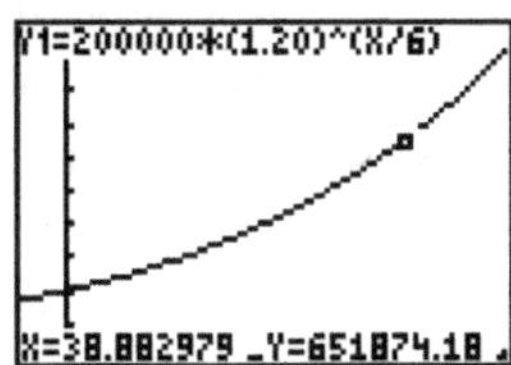

According to the graph, there would be 650 000 cellphone customers at about 38.88 months after January 1, 1996. Since there are 36 months in 3 years, this value occurs 3 years and 2.88 months after January 1, 1996, which would be at the end of March 1999.

Use the following information to answer the next question.

> The exponential equation $R = 3.7(1.171)^n$, can be used to represent the number of rats, R, in millions, in a certain region, after n number of years since 1997.

22. If the rat population continues to grow at the given rate, then what will be the approximate number of rats in that region in the year 2010?

A. 12.6 million **B.** 14.4 million

C. 28.8 million **D.** 32.3 million

Use the following information to answer the next question.

A radioactive isotope technetium-99 is commonly used in various medical diagnoses. Given that a patient is injected with 10 mg of this isotope, the graph shows the amount of the isotope, m, in milligrams, remaining in her body over the next 24 hours, t.

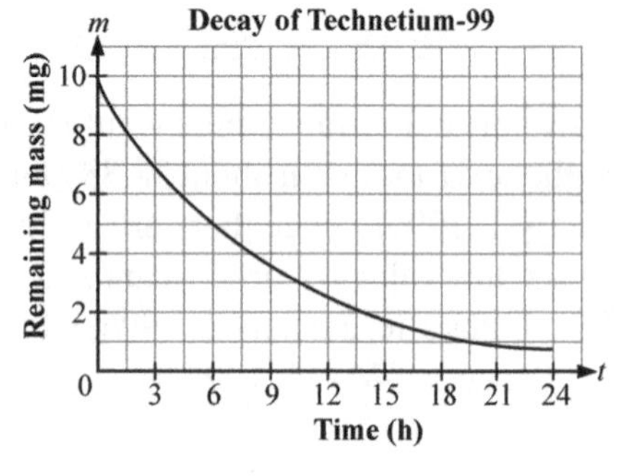

Numerical Response

23. To the nearest 0.1 h, the half-life of the radioactive isotope is _________.

$f(x)$

ANSWERS AND SOLUTIONS
EXPONENTIAL FUNCTIONS

1. C	**6. B**	**11. OR**	**16. 1.40**	**b) OR**
2. OR	**7. 25**	**12. C**	**17. D**	**21. a) OR**
3. A	**8. C**	**13. B**	**18. 3**	**b) A**
4. OR	**9. B**	**14. OR**	**19. A**	**22. C**
5. 2	**10. D**	**15. C**	**20. a) A**	**23. 6.0**

1. C

The function $f(x) = 3^x$ is an exponential-growth function. The graph will have the x-axis as a horizontal asymptote. Graph C is the only graph with these characteristics.

2. OR

The graphs of $f(x) = \left(\frac{1}{4}\right)^x$ and $g(x) = 4^x$ are shown on the grid.

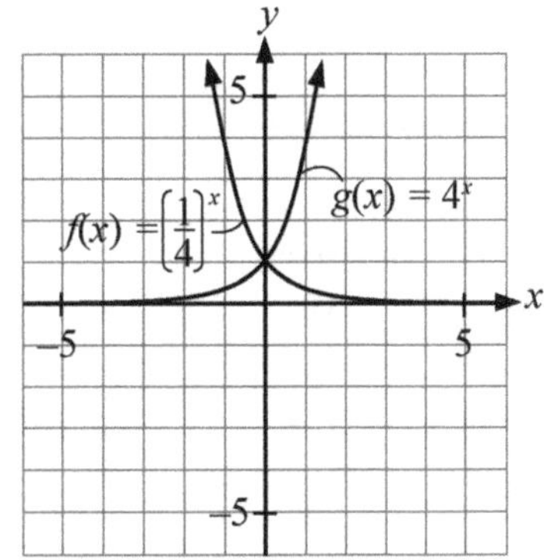

3. A

The function $f(x) = 4^x$ is an exponential growth function. Its function values increase over the entire domain.

4. OR

Both functions have the same domain ($x \in R$), the same range ($y > 0$), the same y-intercept ($y = 1$), and the same asymptote (the x-axis). The difference is that $f(x) = \left(\frac{1}{3}\right)^x$ represents exponential decay since y decreases as x increases, while $g(x) = 3^x$ represents exponential growth with y increasing as x increases.

The graphs of the two functions are correctly sketched and labelled on the grid.

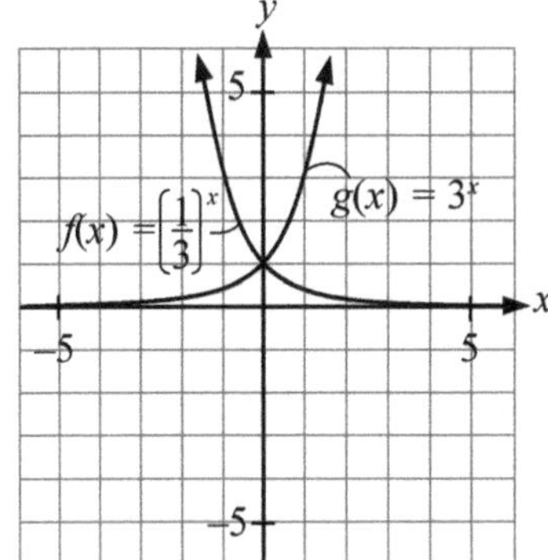

5. 2

Since $2^5 = 32$, the value of $32^{\frac{1}{5}}$ can be calculated.

$$\begin{aligned} 32^{\frac{1}{5}} &= \sqrt[5]{32} \\ &= 2 \end{aligned}$$

6. B

Simplify $x^4 \div x^{\frac{1}{3}}$ by applying the quotient law of exponents.

$$\begin{aligned} x^4 \div x^{\frac{1}{3}} &= x^{4-\frac{1}{3}} \\ &= x^{\frac{12}{3}-\frac{1}{3}} \\ &= x^{\frac{11}{3}} \end{aligned}$$

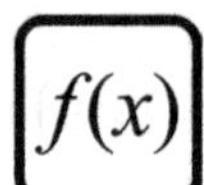

7. 25

Step 1

Simplify the expression $\left(\frac{27}{64}\right)^{\frac{2}{3}}$.

$$\begin{aligned}\left(\frac{27}{64}\right)^{\frac{2}{3}} &= \left(\sqrt[3]{\frac{27}{64}}\right)^2 \\ &= \left(\frac{3}{4}\right)^2 \\ &= \frac{9}{16}\end{aligned}$$

Step 2

Determine the value of $a + b$.

Since $\left(\frac{27}{64}\right)^{\frac{2}{3}} = \frac{9}{16}$ has the form $\frac{a}{b}$ when simplified, $a = 9$ and $b = 16$.

$$\begin{aligned}a + b &= 9 + 16 \\ &= 25\end{aligned}$$

8. C

Using the table of values, determine the first differences.

$8 - 16 = -8$
$4 - 8 = -4$
$2 - 4 = -2$
$1 - 2 = -1$

The first differences are not constant, so it is not a linear function.

Using the first differences, determine the second differences.

$(-4) - (-8) = 4$
$(-2) - (-4) = 2$
$(-1) - (-2) = 1$

The second differences are not constant, so it is not a quadratic function.

The ratio of consecutive terms is a constant $\frac{1}{2}$.

The function is exponential, and the values are decreasing. This means it is an exponential-decay function.

9. B

The domain and range of every linear function whose graph is an oblique line (a line that is not parallel or vertical to the x- and y-axis) is $x \in R$ and $y \in R$. For an exponential function, the range does not include 0. Therefore, of the given functions, only the quadratic has a range that may be greater than or equal to zero.

10. D

Step 1

Determine the change needed to perform the horizontal stretch.

To perform a horizontal stretch by a factor of 3, the parameter is $k = \frac{1}{3}$.

Step 2

Determine the change needed to perform a vertical translation.

For a vertical translation of 4 units up, $c = 4$.

Step 3

State the equation of the function after the transformations.

$$\begin{aligned}y &= \left(\frac{1}{2}\right)^x \\ f(x) &= \left(\frac{1}{2}\right)^x \\ f\left(\frac{1}{3}x\right) + 4 &= \left(\frac{1}{2}\right)^{\frac{1}{3}x} + 4\end{aligned}$$

11. OR

In order to express $y = -\frac{1}{2}(3)^{3x-6} - 2$ in the form $y = af(k(x - d)) + c$, express the exponent $3x - 6$ in factored form, as $3(x - 2)$.

Write $y = -\frac{1}{2}(3)^{3(x-2)} - 2$ as $y = -\frac{1}{2}f(3(x - 2)) - 2$. The value of the parameters are $a = -\frac{1}{2}$, $k = 3$, $d = 2$, and $c = -2$.

The transformations needed to change the graph of $y = 3^x$ into the graph of $y = -\frac{1}{2}(3)^{3x-6} - 2$ are a vertical compression to the x-axis by a factor of $\frac{1}{2}$, a reflection in the x-axis, and a horizontal compression to the y-axis by a factor of $\frac{1}{3}$.

These three transformations may be done in any order, but they must be performed before the final translations of the graph 2 units to the right and 2 units down.

12. C

The graph of $f(x) = 2^{x+1} - 3$ is the graph of $y = 2^x$ translated left 1 unit and down 3 units.

The original y-intercept of $(0, 1)$ will now be at $(-1, -2)$. The new y-intercept is -1, and the horizontal asymptote is the line $y = -3$.

The graph of $f(x) = 2^{x+1} - 3$ should look like the given graph.

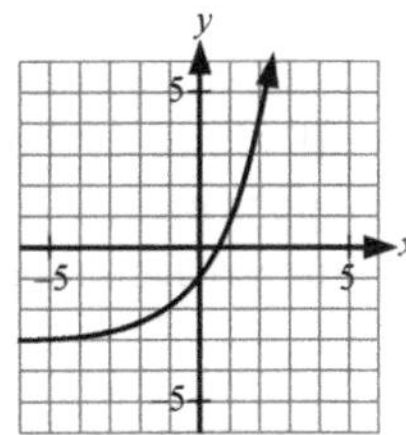

13. B

The graph of $f(x) = -3^x + 2$ is the graph of $y = 3^x$ reflected in the x-axis and translated vertically up 2 units. The y-intercept is at (0, 1), the horizontal asymptote is the line $y = 2$, and the range is $y < 2$.

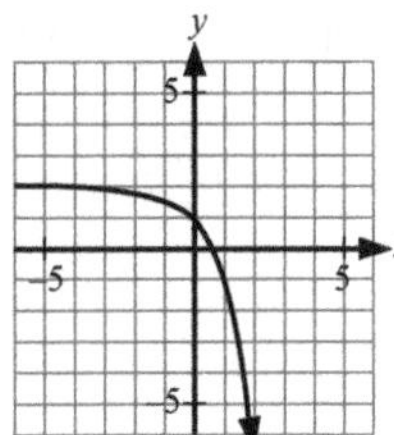

14. OR

Step 1
Identify the transformations.
The transformations involved include a reflection in the x-axis, a vertical stretch from the x-axis by a factor of 2, and translations horizontally 3 units right and vertically 5 units down.

Step 2
State the domain and range of $g(x)$.
The domain and range of $g(x)$ are $x \in R$ and $y < -5$, respectively.

Step 3
Graph all the transformations.

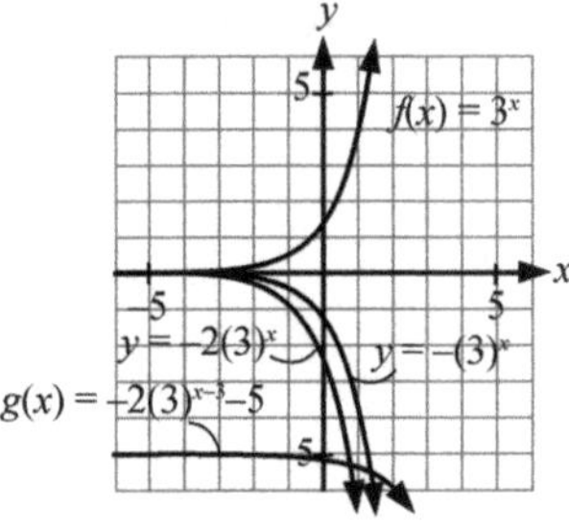

15. C

Step 1
Rewrite the expression $\left(\frac{1}{4}\right)^x$ with a negative exponent. Remember $\frac{1}{x} = x^{-1}$.

$\left(\frac{1}{4}\right)^x = 4^{-x}$

This means $f(x) = \left(\frac{1}{4}\right)^x$ is equivalent to $f(x) = 4^{-x}$.

Step 2
Rewrite the expression 4^{-x} as a power with a base of 2.

$$\begin{aligned} 4^{-x} &= (2^2)^{-x} \\ &= 2^{-2x} \end{aligned}$$

This means $f(x) = \left(\frac{1}{4}\right)^x$ is equivalent to $f(x) = 2^{-2x}$.

Step 3
Rewrite the expression $\left(\frac{1}{4}\right)^x$ as a power with a base of $\frac{1}{2}$.

$$\begin{aligned} \left(\frac{1}{4}\right)^x &= \left(\frac{1^2}{2^2}\right)^x \\ &= \left(\frac{1}{2}\right)^{2x} \end{aligned}$$

This means $f(x) = \left(\frac{1}{4}\right)^x$ is equivalent to $f(x) = \left(\frac{1}{2}\right)^{2x}$.

Since the other functions are all equivalent to $f(x) = \left(\frac{1}{4}\right)^x$, by elimination $f(x) = 8^{-\frac{3}{2}x}$ is not equivalent to $f(x) = \left(\frac{1}{4}\right)^x$.

16. 1.40

The value of k is the solution to the equation $128 = 32^k$.

Step 1
Express both sides as powers of 2.

$$\begin{aligned} 128 &= 32^k \\ 2^7 &= (2^5)^k \\ 2^7 &= 2^{5k} \end{aligned}$$

Step 2
Equate the exponents, and solve for k.

$$7 = 5k$$
$$\frac{7}{5} = k$$
$$1.40 = k$$

17. D

Step 1
Interpret the required range in terms of transformations to the graph of an exponential function of the form $y = b^x$, $b > 1$.
Eliminate any functions that do not have a range of $y > 1$.
Since the desired exponential function has a range of $y > 1$, the function has been vertically translated up 1 unit ($y = b^x$ has a range of $y > 0$).

The function $f(x) = 4(3)^{x+1}$ has not been vertically translated, so its range is $y > 0$, not $y > 1$.

The function $f(x) = (3)^x + 3$ has been vertically translated up 3 units, so the range is $y > 3$, not $y > 1$.

The functions $f(x) = 4(3)^x + 1$ and $f(x) = (3)^{x+1} + 1$ have both been translated up 1 unit, and both functions will have a range of $y > 1$.

Step 2
Determine which of the remaining two functions have a y-intercept of 4.
If the desired function has a y-intercept of 4, $f(0) = 4$.

Using the function $f(x) = 4(3)^x + 1$, determine the value of $f(0)$.

$$\begin{aligned} f(x) &= 4(3)^x + 1 \\ f(0) &= 4(3)^0 + 1 \\ &= 4(1) + 1 \\ &= 4 + 1 \\ &= 5 \end{aligned}$$

Using the function $f(x) = (3)^{x+1} + 1$, determine the value of $f(0)$.

$$\begin{aligned} f(x) &= (3)^{x+1} + 1 \\ f(0) &= (3)^{0+1} + 1 \\ &= (3)^1 + 1 \\ &= 3 + 1 \\ &= 4 \end{aligned}$$

Therefore, $f(x) = (3)^{x+1} + 1$ is the correct function.

18. 3

Step 1
Determine the value of c.

The graph of $y = 2^x$ has a horizontal asymptote at the x-axis $(y = 0)$. Since the horizontal asymptote for the given graph is the line $y = -2$, and this value corresponds to the vertical translation, the value of c is -2.

Step 2
Determine the value of a.
There is no horizontal translation performed on this function, since parameter $d = 0$ in the function $f(x) = a(2)^{x-d} + c$. Because of this, the vertical distance between the y-intercept and the horizontal asymptote is equal to the value of parameter a.
The y-intercept of the graph is at 3, which is 5 units above the asymptote; therefore, the value of a is 5.

Step 3
Determine the value of $a + c$.

$$\begin{aligned} a + c &= 5 + (-2) \\ &= 3 \end{aligned}$$

19. A

The points on all four graphs are the same.

However, in order to show exponential growth, the graph should start at about the original population of 70 991 and curve upwards slightly, to about 140 000, and pass through the middle of all data points. The graph with the curve of best fit is shown in alternative A.

In alternative B, it is a line not a curve that represents the points incorrectly.

In alternative C, the curve of best fit is curving the wrong way, and does not represent the exponential growth of the data.

In alternative D, the curve of best fit starts too high on the y-axis, not representing the data values for 1980, 1984, and 1987 appropriately

20. a) A

Step 1
Determine the exponential equation that defines the problem.
Define the variables whose values are given in the problem with respect to the general formula

$N_t = N_0 \times R^{\frac{t}{p}}$.

- At time 0, the population is 30; therefore, $N_0 = 30$.
- If the population quadruples, then the growth rate is 4; therefore, $R = 4$.
- Since it takes 9 days for the population to quadruple, the period is 9; therefore, $p = 9$.

Step 2
Substitute the values $N_0 = 30$, $R = 4$, and $p = 9$ into the general formula $N_t = N_0 \times R^{\frac{t}{p}}$.

$$N_t = N_0 \times R^{\frac{t}{p}}$$
$$N_t = 30 \times 4^{\frac{t}{9}}$$

b) OR

The population of spiders represents exponential growth since the population of spiders increases by a factor of four every nine days.

21. a) OR

The jawbreaker is the largest when the boy puts it in his mouth at $t = 0$ minutes. This value is 33.5 cm^3.

The jawbreaker is smallest when it is completely dissolved at 0 cm^3. Realistically, this would occur some time after 5 minutes, to say about 15 minutes, which can be called t_f (final time). Therefore, the restrictions of the domain (time) and range (volume) are as follows:
Domain: 0 to t_f minutes or $0 \le t \le 15$
Range: 0 to 33.5 cm^3 or $0 \le V \le 33.5$

b) A

To determine the decay factor, find the ratio between successive volume values, V, in the data table, as shown below.

t	0	1	2	3	4	4
V	33.5	28.1	23.6	19.7	16.7	14.0
Ratio (R)	$\frac{28.1}{33.5} = 0.839$	$\frac{23.6}{28.1} = 0.840$	$\frac{19.7}{23.6} = 0.835$	$\frac{16.7}{19.7} = 0.848$	$\frac{14.0}{16.7} = 0.838$	

The decay ratio seems consistent at 0.84, to two decimal places. As a percentage, this decay factor is $0.84 \times 100\% = 84\%$.

22. C

Step 1
Determine the number of years from 1997 to 2010.
$2\ 010 - 1\ 997 = 13$

Step 2
Substitute 13 for n into the given equation.

$$\begin{aligned} R &= 3.7(1.171)^n \\ &= 3.7(1.171)^{13} \\ &= 3.7(7.784\ 659\ 762) \\ &= 28.8 \end{aligned}$$

In the year 2010, the approximate number of rats in a certain region will be 28.8 million.

23. 6.0

If the original mass of the isotope is 10 mg at $t = 0$ h, then the half-life is the time taken for this mass to decay to half its original amount, namely $\frac{10}{2} = 5$ mg. According to the graph, the mass of 5 mg occurs at $t = 6.0$ h.

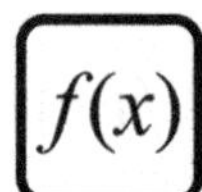

UNIT TEST — EXPONENTIAL FUNCTIONS

1. Which of the following graphs represents the function $f(x) = \left(\frac{4}{5}\right)^x$?

A.

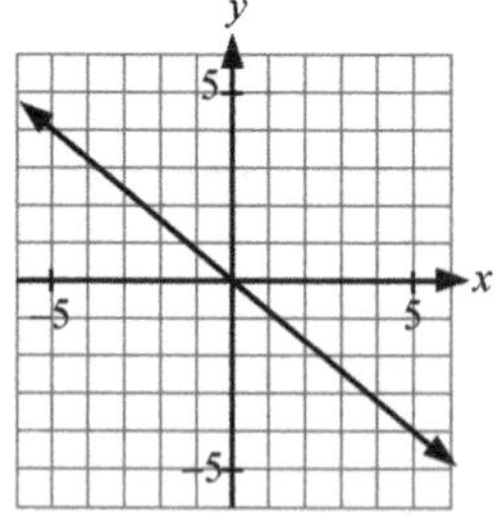

B.

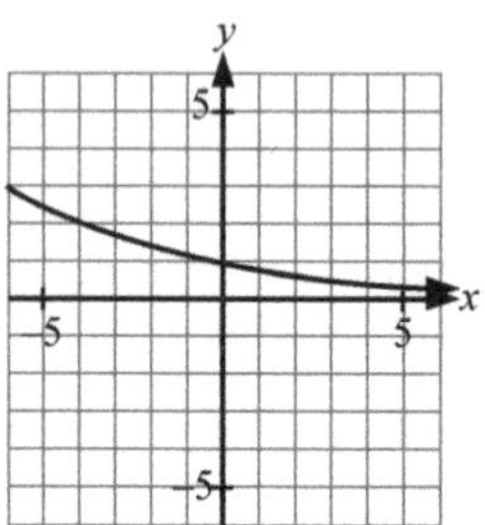

C.

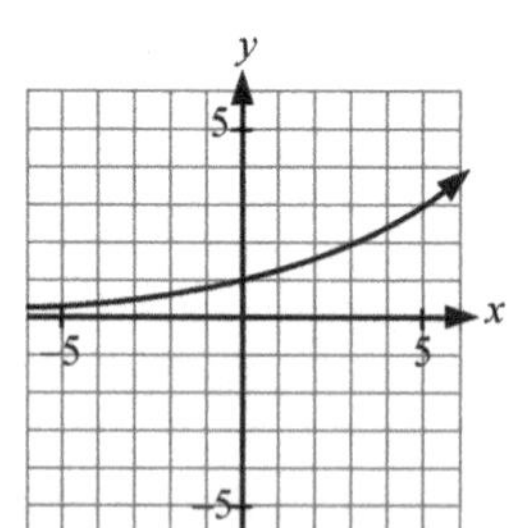

D.

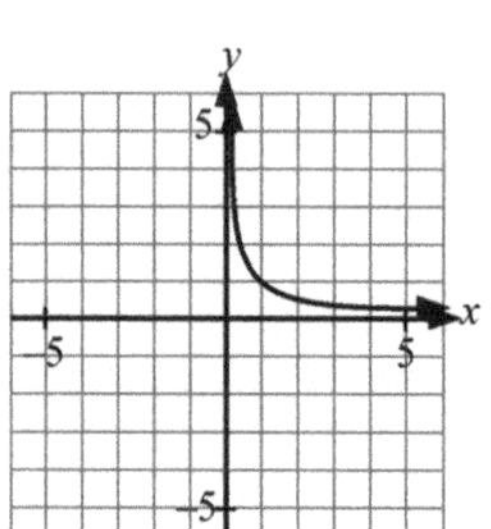

2. The expression $x^{-\frac{4}{3}}$ is equivalent to

A. $\sqrt[4]{x^3}$ **B.** $-\sqrt[3]{x^4}$

C. $-\frac{1}{\sqrt[4]{x^3}}$ **D.** $\frac{1}{\sqrt[3]{x^4}}$

3. The simplified form of $(x^4y^8)^{-\frac{1}{2}}$ is

A. $-x^2y^4$ **B.** $x^{\frac{7}{2}}y^{\frac{15}{2}}$

C. $\frac{1}{x^2y^4}$ **D.** $\frac{1}{x^8y^{16}}$

4. The range and y-intercept of the function $f(x) = 5^x$ are

A. $y \in R$ and $y = 1$

B. $y \in R$ and $y = 0$

C. $y > 0$ and $y = 0$

D. $y > 0$ and $y = 1$

Open Response

5. Describe the differences between the graphs and ranges of the functions $f(x) = 3^x$, $h(x) = 3x^2$, and $g(x) = 3x$.

6. In order to vertically stretch the graph of the function $y = 5^x$ about the x-axis by a factor of $\frac{1}{4}$ and reflect it in the y-axis, the equation of the function must be changed to

A. $y = \frac{1}{4}(5)^{-x}$

B. $y = 4(5)^{-x}$

C. $y = -(5)^{\frac{1}{4}x}$

D. $y = -(5)^{4x}$

$f(x)$

Open Response

7. Identify the transformations to the graph of $f(x) = 2^x$ that will result in the graph of $g(x) = -\frac{1}{2}(2)^{x-1}$. State the domain and range of the transformed function $g(x)$, and draw the graph of $g(x)$ by graphing $f(x)$ and each individual transformation to arrive at the graph of $g(x)$. Identify $f(x)$, and label each transformation with its appropriate equation.

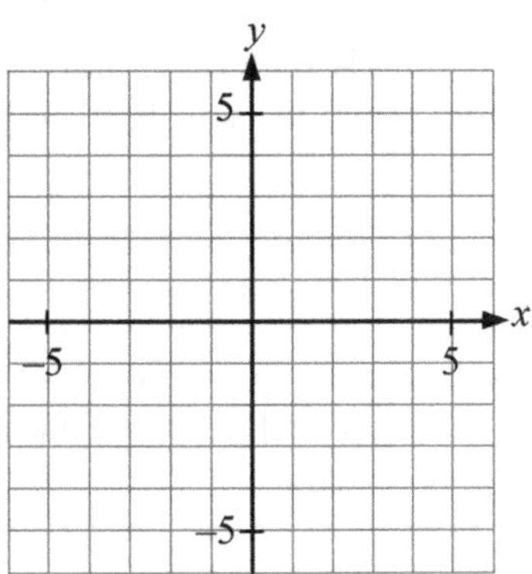

8. Which of the following functions is **not** equivalent to $f(x) = 16^x$?

A. $f(x) = 4^{2x}$

B. $f(x) = \left(\frac{1}{2}\right)^{-8x}$

C. $f(x) = 2^{4x}$

D. $f(x) = \left(\frac{1}{4}\right)^{-2x}$

9. The equation for an exponential function that has a base of $\frac{1}{2}$, a y-intercept at 4, and a range of $y < 5$ is

A. $f(x) = -4\left(\frac{1}{2}\right)^x + 5$

B. $f(x) = -\left(\frac{1}{2}\right)^x + 5$

C. $f(x) = \left(\frac{1}{2}\right)^{-x} + 5$

D. $f(x) = -\left(\frac{1}{2}\right)^{x+5}$

Use the following information to answer the next multipart question.

10. When a golf ball is dropped from the top of a ladder at a height of 4.00 m, the height to which it rebounds from the floor, models an exponential function. The data for the rebound heights, h, for the first 5 bounces, n, is given in this table.

n	1	2	3	4	5
h	2.80	2.00	1.38	0.97	0.68

a) Which of the following graphs correctly represents the data?

A.

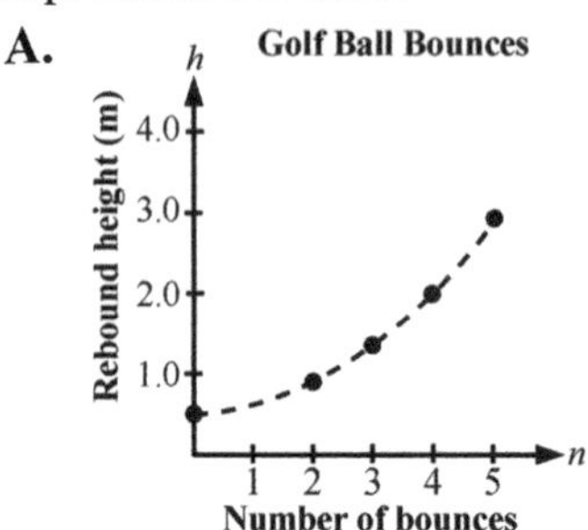

B.

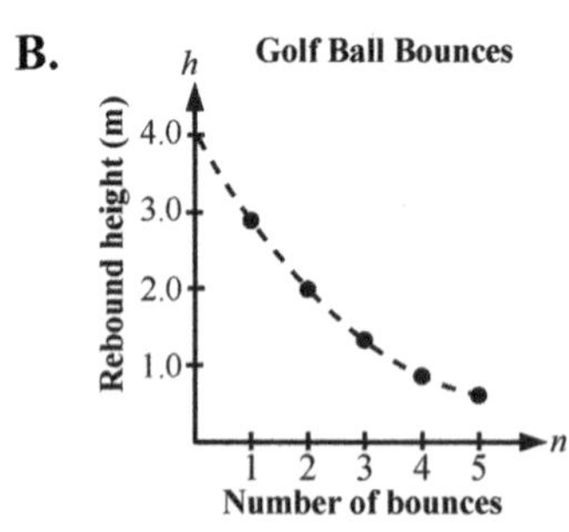

C.

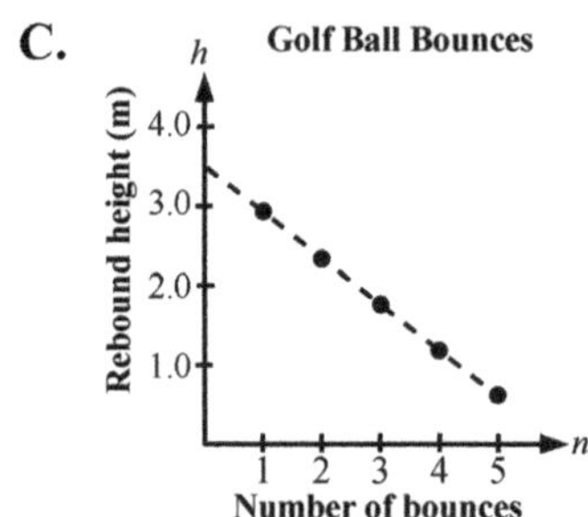

D.

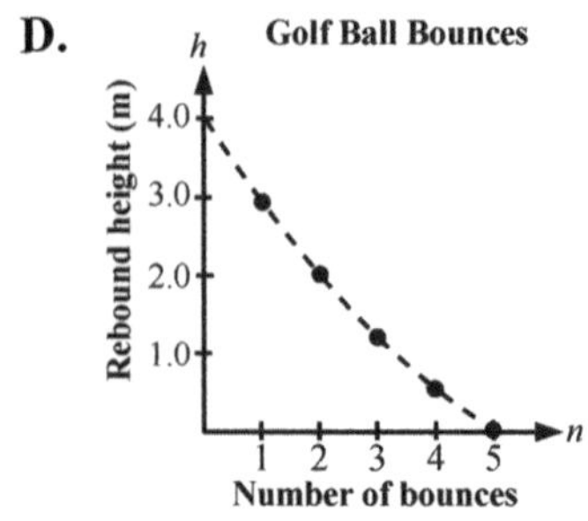

b) If a tennis ball is dropped from the same height and its rebound height decreases exponentially, the graph depicting the rebound height of the ball after each bounce would decline

A. at an inconsistent rate, making it impossible to compare to the graph representing the golf ball's data

B. at the same rate as the graph representing the golf ball's data

C. more quickly than the graph representing the golf ball's data

D. less quickly than the graph representing the golf ball's data

Use the following information to answer the next question.

The mass of a certain radioactive substance is currently 300 g, and its half-life is 7 years.

11. The exponential function of the mass of the given radioactive substance is

A. $N_t = 300(7)^{\frac{t}{2}}$

B. $N_t = 300(2)^{\frac{t}{7}}$

C. $N_t = 300\left(\frac{1}{2}\right)^{\frac{t}{7}}$

D. $N_t = 300\left(\frac{1}{7}\right)^{\frac{t}{2}}$

$f(x)$

Use the following information to answer the next question.

The half-life of iodine-131 is every 8.04 days; that is, after 8.04 days, half of the iodine-131 decays. The amount, N_t, of iodine-131, in kilograms, with an initial mass of 12 600 kg, remaining after t days is given by the formula:

$$N_t = 12\ 600\left(\frac{1}{2}\right)^{\frac{t}{8.04}}$$

12. The approximate mass of iodine-131 remaining after 30 days, to the nearest whole kilogram, is

A. 131 kg **B.** 475 kg

C. 949 kg **D.** 3 378 kg

Use the following information to answer the next multipart question.

13. A newly married couple invests \$20 000 into a variety of stocks in 1989.
The exponential function describing the value, $V(t)$, in dollars over time, t, in years since Jan. 1, 1989 is
$V(t) = 20\ 000(1.065)^t$.

Open Response

a) According to the equation, what is the couple's annual average rate of return as a percentage?

b) According to the function, what should the value of the stock be in 2000?

c) Enter the function on a graphing calculator, set an appropriate window, and determine from the graph in what year they should expect their stock to triple in value.

ANSWERS AND SOLUTIONS — UNIT TEST

1. B	**5. OR**	**9. B**	**12. C**
2. D	**6. A**	**10. a) B**	**13. a) OR**
3. C	**7. OR**	**b) C**	**b) OR**
4. D	**8. B**	**11. C**	**c) OR**

1. B

The function $f(x)=\left(\frac{4}{5}\right)^x$ is an exponential decay function. Since $0<a<1$ in $f(x)=a^x$, the graph will decrease from left to right, go through the point (0, 1), and have the x-axis ($y=0$) as a horizontal asymptote.

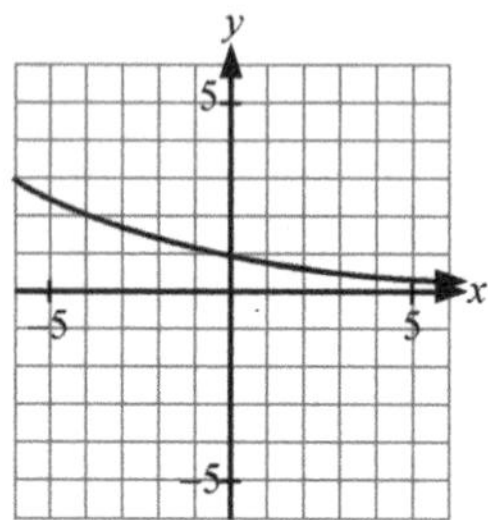

2. D

Step 1
Apply the negative exponent property.

$x^{-\frac{4}{3}}$ can be written as $\frac{1}{x^{\frac{4}{3}}}$.

Step 2
Apply the rational exponent property.

$\frac{1}{x^{\frac{4}{3}}}$ is equivalent to $\frac{1}{\sqrt[3]{x^4}}$.

3. C

Apply the laws of exponents to the given expression.

$$\begin{aligned}&(x^4y^8)^{-\frac{1}{2}}\\&=\frac{1}{(x^4y^8)^{\frac{1}{2}}}\\&=\frac{1}{(x^4)^{\frac{1}{2}}(y^8)^{\frac{1}{2}}}\\&=\frac{1}{x^{4\times\frac{1}{2}}y^{8\times\frac{1}{2}}}\\&=\frac{1}{x^2y^4}\end{aligned}$$

4. D

Step 1
Determine the range of the function.
The range of an exponential function of the form $f(x)=a^x$ is $y>0$. Therefore, the range of $f(x)=5^x$ is $y>0$.

Step 2
Determine the y-intercept of the function.
The y-intercept of an exponential function of the form $f(x)=a^x$ is 1. Therefore, the y-intercept of $f(x)=5^x$ is 1.

5. OR

- The function $f(x)=3^x$ is an exponential growth function whose graph has a horizontal asymptote at $y=0$. Its range is $y>0$.
- The function $h(x)=3x^2$ is a quadratic function whose graph opens upward. Its range is $y\geq 0$.
- The function $g(x)=3x$ is a linear function with a range of $y\in R$.

6. A

Step 1

Determine the change a vertical stretch of $\frac{1}{4}$ has on the function $y=5^x$.

To perform a vertical stretch by a factor of $\frac{1}{4}$, the function of the form $y=af(k(x-d))+c$ should have an a-value of $\frac{1}{4}$.

Step 2
Determine the change a reflection in the y-axis has on the function $y=5^x$.
For a reflection in the y-axis, the function of the form $y=af(k(x-d))+c$ should have a k-value of -1.

Step 3
Determine the new equation of the function.
$y = 5^x$
$y = f(x)$
$y = \frac{1}{4}f(-1x)$
$y = \frac{1}{4}(5)^{-x}$

7. **OR**

Step 1
Identify the transformations.
The transformations are a reflection in the x-axis, a vertical stretch about the x-axis by a factor of $\frac{1}{2}$, and a horizontal translation 1 unit to the right.

Step 2
State the domain and range.
The domain and range of $g(x)$ are $x \in R$ and $y < 0$.

Step 3
Draw the graph of $g(x)$ by graphing $f(x)$ with all the transformations.
Label each transformation with its equation.

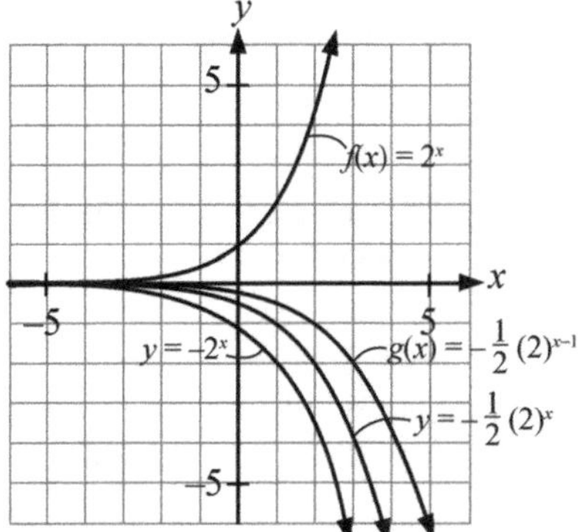

8. **B**

Step 1
Rewrite 16 as a power with a base of 4.
$16^x = (4^2)^x$
$= 4^{2x}$
$f(x) = 16^x$ is equivalent to $f(x) = 4^{2x}$.

Step 2
Rewrite the expression 4^{2x} with a negative exponent. Remember $x^{-1} = \left(\frac{1}{x}\right)$.
$4^{2x} = \left(\frac{1}{4}\right)^{-2x}$
$f(x) = 16^x$ is equivalent to $f(x) = \left(\frac{1}{4}\right)^{-2x}$.

Step 3
Rewrite the expression 4^{2x} as a power with a base of 2.
$4^{2x} = (2^2)^{2x}$
$= 2^{4x}$
$f(x) = 16^x$ is equivalent to $f(x) = 2^{4x}$.

Step 4
Rewrite the expression $\left(\frac{1}{2}\right)^{-8x}$ with a positive exponent.
$\left(\frac{1}{2}\right)^{-8x} = 2^{8x}$
$= 256^x$
Therefore, $f(x) = \left(\frac{1}{2}\right)^{-8x}$ is not equivalent to $f(x) = 16^x$.

9. **B**

The graph of the function $y = \left(\frac{1}{2}\right)^x$ decreases as x increases. The graph of $y = \left(\frac{1}{2}\right)^x$ lies above its horizontal asymptote of $y = 0$ and has a y-intercept of 1.

The transformed function described can be expressed in the form $y = a\left(\frac{1}{2}\right)^x + c$.

Since the range of the transformed function is $y < 5$, the function must have been reflected in the x-axis and translated vertically up 5 units. There is no vertical stretch since the y-intercept is still 1 unit from the horizontal asymptote of $y = 5$, so $a = -1$ and $c = 5$.

The equation for an exponential function that has a base of $\frac{1}{2}$, a y-intercept at 4, and a range of $y < 5$ is $f(x) = -\left(\frac{1}{2}\right)^x + 5$.

10. **a) B**

The data shows exponential decay, since the rebound heights decrease after each successive bounce.

An exponential decay curve should be steep at first and then flatten out as you move from left to right (remember the graph of $f(x) = a^x$, where $0 < a < 1$). Also, the graph should not touch the x-axis, which makes choice D incorrect.
The correct graph depicting the decay of rebound heights, h, over the bounce number, n, is shown in choice B.

b) C

A tennis ball is softer (squishier) than a golf ball, so it will not rebound as high after each bounce compared to the golf ball. The data values of rebound heights, h, would be *smaller* for each value of n. Therefore, the rebound heights would decline more quickly than those represented by the graph of the golf ball.

11. C

Step 1
Define the variables given with respect to the general formula $N_t = N_0 \times R^{\frac{t}{p}}$.

- At time 0, the mass is 300 g.
  $N_0 = 300$
- The substance is reduced to $\frac{1}{2}$ its mass during each period.
  $R = \frac{1}{2}$
- It takes 7 years for the substance to reduce to $\frac{1}{2}$ its mass, so the period is 7.
  $p = 7$

Step 2
Substitute the values $N_0 = 300$, $R = \frac{1}{2}$, and $p = 7$ into the general formula $N_t = N_0 \times R^{\frac{t}{p}}$.

$$\begin{aligned} N_t &= N_0 \times R^{\frac{t}{p}} \\ &= 300 \times \left(\frac{1}{2}\right)^{\frac{t}{7}} \\ &= 300\left(\frac{1}{2}\right)^{\frac{t}{7}} \end{aligned}$$

12. C

The formula for the decay of iodine-131 is given as:

$$N_t = 12\ 600\left(\frac{1}{2}\right)^{\frac{t}{8.04}}$$

where t is the time in days and N_t is the amount of iodine remaining after t days.

To find the amount of iodine remaining after 30 days, substitute $t = 30$ in the formula, and then evaluate.

$$\begin{aligned} N_{30} &= 12\ 600\left(\frac{1}{2}\right)^{\frac{30}{8.04}} \\ &\approx 12\ 600(0.075\ 292\ 8519) \\ &\approx 948.689\ 9342 \text{ kg} \end{aligned}$$

Therefore, the approximate mass remaining after 30 days, to the nearest whole kilogram, is 949 kg.

13. a) OR

The value of 1.065 in the equation describes the growth factor of 1.065 of their stock value. When the growth factor is converted to a percentage, it is $1.065 \times 100\% = 106.5\%$.

Since 100% means no growth (stays the same at 100% of its original amount), the annual average rate of return is $106.5 - 100 = 6.5\%$.

b) OR

The value of t is the number of years since 1989. Therefore, in 2000, $t = 2\ 000 - 1\ 989 = 11$.

Substitute $t = 11$ into the equation, and solve for $V(t)$, the value of the stock.

$$\begin{aligned} V(11) &= 20\ 000(1.065)^{11} \\ &= 39\ 983.028\ 01 \end{aligned}$$

To the nearest cent, the value of the stock in the year 2000 is \$39 983.03.

c) OR

An appropriate WINDOW setting could be x:[0, 20, 1], y:[0, 70 000, 10 000].

Then, enter the function as $Y_1 = 20\ 000(1.065)^\wedge x$ into your graphing calculator, and press GRAPH.

Then, use your TRACE feature to locate the point that is as close to a y-value = 60 000 (triple the value of 20 000). This value is highlighted in the calculator screen shown below.

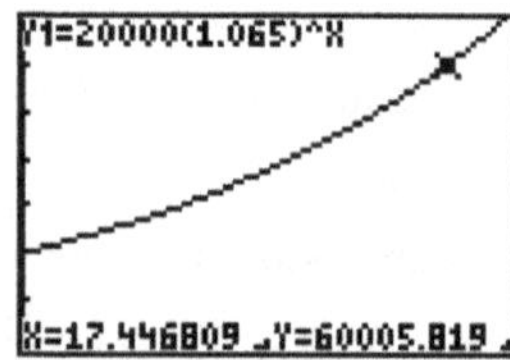

According to this point, the x-value, or time, t, is 17.446 809 years. This means the stock triples 17.446 809 years after Jan. 1, 1989, which is $1\ 989 + 17.446\ 809 = 2\ 006.446\ 809$.

Therefore, the stock triples about half-way through the year 2006.

Discrete Functions

DISCRETE FUNCTIONS

Table of Correlations

	Specific Expectation	Practice Questions	Unit Test Questions	Practice Test 1	Practice Test 2
DF1.0	Representing Sequences				
DF1.1	*make connections between sequences and discrete functions, represent sequences using function notation, and distinguish between a discrete function and a continuous function*	1	1	23	
DF1.2	*determine and describe a recursive procedure for generating a sequence, given the initial terms, and represent sequences as discrete functions in a variety of ways*	2, 3	2		
DF1.3	*connect the formula for the nth term of a sequence to the representation in function notation, and write terms of a sequence given one of these representations or a recursion formula*	4, 5	3	24	
DF1.4	*represent a sequence algebraically using a recursion formula, function notation, or the formula for the nth term and describe the information that can be obtained by inspecting each representation*	6, 7	4	25	
DF1.5	*determine, through investigation, recursive patterns in the Fibonacci sequence, in related sequences, and in Pascal's triangle, and represent the patterns in a variety of ways*	8, 9	5	26	
DF1.6	*determine, through investigation, and describe the relationship between Pascal's triangle and the expansion of binomials, and apply the relationship to expand binomials raised to whole-number exponents*	10, 11	6		
DF2.0	Investigating Arithmetic and Geometric Sequences and Series				
DF2.1	*identify sequences as arithmetic, geometric, or neither, given a numeric or algebraic representation*	12, 13	7	27	
DF2.2	*determine the formula for the general term of an arithmetic sequence [i.e., $t_n=a+(n-1)d$] or geometric sequence (i.e., $t_n=ar^{n-1}$), through investigation using a variety of tools and strategies, and apply the formula to calculate any term in a sequence*	14, 15	8	28	
DF2.3	*determine the formula for the sum of an arithmetic or geometric series, through investigation using a variety of tools and strategies, and apply the formula to calculate the sum of a given number of consecutive terms*	16, 17	9, 10a, 10b, 10c	29a, 29b, 29c	
DF2.4	*solve problems involving arithmetic and geometric sequences and series, including those arising from real-world applications*	18, 19a, 19b, 19c	11	30	
DF3.0	Solving Problems Involving Financial Applications				
DF3.1	*make and describe connections between simple interest, arithmetic sequences, and linear growth, through investigation with technology*	20, 21	12		
DF3.2	*make and describe connections between compound interest, geometric sequences, and exponential growth, through investigation with technology*	22, 23	13	31	
DF3.3	*solve problems, using a scientific calculator, that involve the calculation of the amount, A (also referred to as future value, FV), the principal, P (also referred to as present value, PV), or the interest rate per compounding period, i, using the compound interest formula in the form $A = P(1 + i)^n$ [or $FV = PV(1 + i)^n$]*	24, 25	14	32	

DF3.4	*determine, through investigation using technology, the number of compounding periods, n, using the compound interest formula in the form $A = P(1 + i)^n$ [or $FV = PV(1 + i)^n$]; describe strategies for calculating this number; and solve related problems*	26, 27	15		
DF3.5	*explain the meaning of the term annuity, and determine the relationships between ordinary simple annuities (i.e., annuities in which payments are made at the end of each period, and compounding and payment periods are the same), geometric series, and exponential growth, through investigation with technology*	28, 29a, 29b, 29c, 29d	16a, 16b, 16c		
DF3.6	*determine, through investigation using technology, the effects of changing the conditions (i.e., the payments, the frequency of the payments, the interest rate, the compounding period) of ordinary simple annuities*	30, 31	17, 18	33	
DF3.7	*solve problems, using technology that involve the amount, the present value, and the regular payment of an ordinary simple annuity*	32, 33	19		

DF1.1 make connections between sequences and discrete functions, represent sequences using function notation, and distinguish between a discrete function and a continuous function

Continuous and Discrete Functions

A function is continuous if its domain is the set or a subset of real numbers. The graph of a continuous function is a line or curve with no holes, breaks, or gaps.

A discrete function has a domain that is made up of natural numbers, whole numbers, integers, or a subset of these number sets. The graph of a discrete function will include points that are separate from each other and not connected by a continuous line or curve.

Example

Consider the function $f(x) = x + 2$. The graph is a line with a slope of 1 and a y-intercept of 2. The function has a domain of $x \in R$.

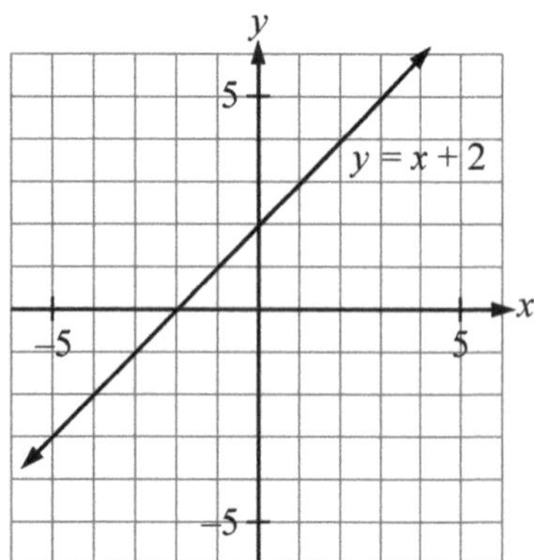

If the restriction $x \in N$ were placed on the domain of $f(x) = x + 2$, what would the range of the function be?

Solution

Step 1

Determine the range.

If the restriction $x \in N$ were placed on the domain of $f(x) = x + 2$, the range would become 3, 4, 5, 6, …

Step 2

Graph the function.

The set of points (1, 3), (2, 4), (3, 5), (4, 6), … make up the graph.

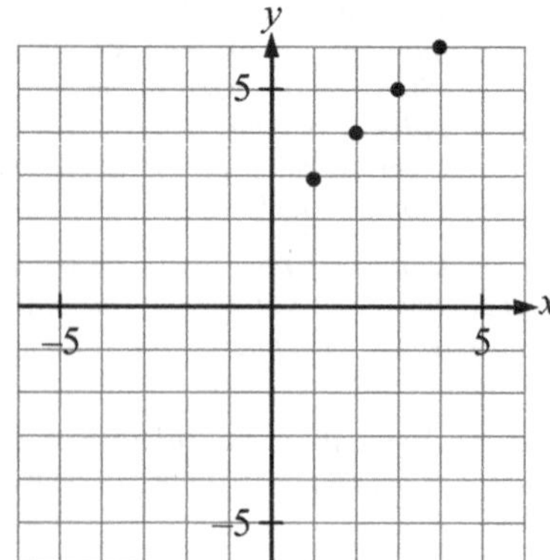

Without the restriction the function is continuous, and with the restriction the function becomes discrete.

A sequence is the range of a function whose domain is the set of natural numbers, whole numbers, or a subset of these integers. A sequence must have a first term, so the domain of a sequence could be {−5, −4, −3, …} but not the entire set of integers. Since these conditions exist on the domain of a sequence, it must be a discrete function.

Example

Determine the sequence generated by the function $f(x) = 2^{x+2}$ for the domain {−2, −1, 0, …}.

Solution

Step 1

Solve the function for the given values.

$f(-2) = 2^{-2+2} = 2^0 = 1$

$f(-1) = 2^{-1+2} = 2^1 = 2$

$f(0) = 2^{0+2} = 2^2 = 4$

$f(1) = 2^{1+2} = 2^3 = 8$

Step 2

Determine the sequence.

The sequence is 1, 2, 4, 8, ….

Use the following information to answer the next question.

A list of functions is given.

I. $f(x) = \frac{x+1}{x-5}, 1 \leq x \leq 10$

II. $f(x) = 3x + 2, x \in W$

III. $f(x) = 4^x, x \in N$

IV. $f(x) = 2x^2, x \in R$

1. Which of the given functions are continuous?

A. I, II, and III **B.** II and III

C. I and IV **D.** IV only

DF1.2 determine and describe a recursive procedure for generating a sequence, given the initial terms, and represent sequences as discrete functions in a variety of ways

Determining Sequences Using a Recursive Procedure

To generate a sequence using a recursive procedure, the first term (or first few terms) must be given. An operation is then performed to the first term to obtain the next term. Each successive term is formed by performing the given operation on the previous terms. For example, in order to determine the tenth term, you need to know the ninth term.

A recursive procedure can also be used to either form or describe a given sequence.

Example

A sequence has a first term of 5.
Each subsequent term is formed by adding 6 to the previous term.

List the first six terms of the sequence.

Solution

The second term is $5 + 6 = 11$. The third term is $11 + 6 = 17$. Continue adding 6 to the previous terms to obtain the next term in the sequence.
$17 + 6 = 23$
$23 + 6 = 29$
$29 + 6 = 35$

Therefore, the first six terms are 5, 11, 17, 23, 29, and 35.

---

2. Which of the following sequences with a first term of 2 is formed recursively by multiplying each preceding term by 4 and adding 3 to obtain the next term?

A. 2, 25, 53, 109,...

B. 2, 11, 47, 191,...

C. 2, 11, 14, 17,...

D. 2, 8, 11, 44,...

Use the following information to answer the next question.

A sequence with a first term of 3 is formed by multiplying each preceding number by 2 to obtain the next term.

Numerical Response

3. The sixth term in the sequence is _______.

DF1.3 connect the formula for the nth term of a sequence to the representation in function notation, and write terms of a sequence given one of these representations or a recursion formula

Representing Sequences in Function Notation

Consider the sequence generated by $f(x) = 2^x$, $x \in N$. The first few terms are as follows:
$2^1, 2^2, 2^3, 2^4, \ldots$
$2, 4, 8, 16, \ldots$
Without the condition $x \in N$, the domain would be all real numbers, and $f(x)$ would be a continuous function instead of a sequence.

For sequences, the notation t_n, which represents the nth (or general) term of a sequence, is used instead of $f(x)$. The given sequence is defined by the equation $t_n = 2^n$, and it is understood that $n \in N$.

Example

Determine the first four terms of the sequence $t_n = 2n + 4$.

Solution

Given the notation, it is understood that the given function's domain is the set of natural numbers.

Since the domain is the set of natural numbers $(1, 2, 3, \ldots)$, calculate the first four terms of the sequence as follows:

$t_1 = 2(1) + 4 = 6$
$t_2 = 2(2) + 4 = 8$
$t_3 = 2(3) + 4 = 10$
$t_4 = 2(4) + 4 = 12$

The first four terms of the given sequence are 6, 8, 10, and 12.

---

4. The formula $t_1 = 5,\ t_n = 2t_{n-1},\ n > 1$ represents which of the following sequences?
   A. $5, 25, 125, 625, \ldots$
   B. $5, 10, 20, 40, \ldots$
   C. $5, 10, 15, 20, \ldots$
   D. $5, 7, 9, 11, \ldots$

5. Which of the following sequences is equivalent to the function $f(x) = 3x,\ x \in N$?
   A. $t_1 = 0,\ t_n = 3t_{n-1},\ n > 1$
   B. $t_1 = 3,\ t_n = 3t_{n-1},\ n > 1$
   C. $t_1 = 0,\ t_n = 3 + t_{n-1},\ n > 1$
   D. $t_1 = 3,\ t_n = 3 + t_{n-1},\ n > 1$

DF1.4 represent a sequence algebraically using a recursion formula, function notation, or the formula for the nth term and describe the information that can be obtained by inspecting each representation

Representing Sequences Algebraically

Sequences can be represented algebraically using several methods: a recursion formula, function notation, or a general-term formula. Each of these methods may describe information regarding the type of relationship that exists between the terms.

A sequence is a discrete quadratic function if the second differences between the terms are constant. The general term will have the form $f(n) = an^2 + bn + c$ or $t_n = an^2 + bn + c$, in which $a \neq 0$ and $a, b, c \in \mathbb{R}$.

Example

Determine the equation for the general term and a recursive formula for the sequence 0, 6, 16, 30, 48....

Solution

Subtracting the consecutive terms gives first differences of 6, 10, 14, and 18. Subtracting the consecutive first differences gives the second differences, which are a constant 4, 4, and 4, so this sequence is a quadratic function of the form $t_n = an^2 + bn + c$.

Using the first three terms of the sequence, $t_1 = 0$, $t_2 = 6$, and $t_3 = 16$, substitute the terms into $t_n = an^2 + bn + c$ as follows:
$0 = a(1)^2 + b(1) + c$, $6 = a(2)^2 + b(2) + c$, and $16 = a(3)^2 + b(3) + c$. The simplified equations are $0 = a + b + c$, $6 = 4a + 2b + c$, and $16 = 9a + 3b + c$.

The system of equations can be solved by subtracting the first equation from both the second and the third to eliminate the unknown c and leave two equations in two unknowns.

② $6 = 4a + 2b + c$
① $\underline{0 = a + b + c}$
④ $6 = 3a + b$

③ $16 = 9a + 3b + c$
① $\underline{0 = a + b + c + 0}$
⑤ $16 = 8a + 2b$

Multiply equation 4 by two and subtract this from equation 5 to get the solution for parameter a.

$$\begin{aligned} ⑤ \quad 16 &= 8a + 2b \\ 2 \times ④ \quad \underline{-12} &\underline{= 6a + 2b} \\ 4 &= 2a \\ 2 &= a \end{aligned}$$

Substituting this value into equation 4 gives $6 = 3(2) + b$, so $b = 0$. Substituting these two values into the first equation gives $0 = 2 + 0 + c$, so $c = -2$, and the general term of the sequence is $t_n = (2)n^2 + (0)n + (-2)$ or $t_n = 2n^2 - 2$. This solution can be verified, since $t_1 = 2(1)^2 - 2 = 0$, $t_2 = 2(2)^2 - 2 = 6$, $t_3 = 2(3)^2 - 2 = 16$, and so on.

The recursive formula must have the form $t_1 = 0$, $t_n = t_{n-1} + an + b$, with $a = 4$, since the second differences are a constant value of 4. Substituting into $t_2 = t_1 + an + b$ gives $6 = 0 + 4(2) + b$, so $b = -2$. The recursive formula is $t_1 = 0$, $t_{n-1} + 4n - 2$, $n > 1$.

In general, if the recursive formula has the form $t_1 = 0$, $t_n = t_{n-1} + an + b$, then the sequence will be a discrete quadratic function.

6. Which of the following recursive definitions would form a sequence that is a discrete quadratic function?

A. $t_1 = 1$, $t_n = t_{n-1} + 3$, $n > 1$

B. $t_1 = 5$, $t_n = 3t_{n-1} + 2$, $n > 1$

C. $t_1 = 2$, $t_n = t_{n-1} + n^2 + 3$, $n > 1$

D. $t_1 = 4$, $t_n = t_{n-1} + 3n + 1$, $n > 1$

Open Response

7. Determine the equation of the general term for the sequence 5, 14, 25, 38, 53, ...

DF1.5 determine, through investigation, recursive patterns in the Fibonacci sequence, in related sequences, and in Pascal's triangle, and represent the patterns in a variety of ways

The Fibonacci Sequence and Pascal's Triangle

There are several common recursive patterns in nature that are important to understand. These patterns are used in many areas of mathematics.

The Fibonacci Sequence

This pattern was discovered by Leonardo Fibonacci. The Fibonacci sequence (1, 1, 2, 3, 5, 8, 13, 21, …) is defined by the following recursive formula:

$t_1 = 1, t_2 = 1$

$t_n = t_{n-1} + t_{n-2}, n \in \mathbb{N}$ and $n > 2$

Example

The seeds in a sunflower are in tightly packed spirals, beginning in the centre. The number of seeds in each spiral follows Fibonacci's sequence. How many seeds will be in the 12th spiral?

Solution

The recursive formula of a Fibonacci sequence is as follows:

$t_1 = 1, t_2 = 1$

$t_n = t_{n-1} + t_{n-2}, n \in N$ and $n > 2$

After the first two terms, all terms are formed by adding the two preceding terms. Term three is formed as follows:

$$\begin{aligned} t_3 &= t_{3-1} + t_{3-2} \\ &= t_2 + t_1 \\ &= 1 + 1 \\ &= 2 \end{aligned}$$

Likewise,

$$\begin{aligned} t_4 &= t_{4-1} + t_{4-2} \\ &= t_3 + t_2 \\ &= 2 + 1 \\ &= 3 \end{aligned}$$

The first twelve terms of the Fibonacci sequence are 1, 1, 2, 3, 5, 8, 13, 21, 34, 55,89, 144.

Therefore, there will be 144 seeds in the 12th spiral.

Pascal's Triangle

The following pattern of numbers is called Pascal's Triangle. It is named after the French mathematician Blaise Pascal.

```
        1
      1   1
    1   2   1
  1   3   3   1
 1  4   6   4  1
1  5  10  10  5  1
```

Notice that any number in the pattern can be obtained by adding the two numbers diagonally above it. For example, $10 = 4 + 6$. Continuing this pattern, the next row of the triangle will be 1, 6, 15, 20, 15, 6, 1.

8. Which of the following sequences has a recursive pattern similar to the Fibonacci sequence?

A. 5, 10, 15, 20, …

B. 5, 10, 20, 35, …

C. 5, 10, 15, 25, …

D. 5, 10, 20, 40, …

Numerical Response

9. The 10th term of a Fibonacci sequence, defined recursively by $t_1 = 1, t_2 = 1$, $t_n = t_{n-1} + t_{n-2}, n > 2$, is ________.

DF1.6 determine, through investigation, and describe the relationship between Pascal's triangle and the expansion of binomials, and apply the relationship to expand binomials raised to whole-number exponents

Pascal's Triangle and the Binomial Expansion

One approach to developing a method for expanding binomials is to look for a pattern in the expansions. Begin by examining powers of $x + y$.

$$\begin{aligned} (x+y)^0 &= 1 \\ (x+y)^1 &= 1x + 1y \\ (x+y)^2 &= 1x^2 + 2xy + 1y^2 \\ (x+y)^3 &= 1x^3 + 3x^2y + 3xy^2 + 1y^3 \\ (x+y)^4 &= 1x^4 + 4x^3y + 6x^2y^2 + 4xy^3 + 1y^4 \\ (x+y)^5 &= 1x^5 + 5x^4y + 10x^3y^2 + 10x^2y^3 + 5xy^4 + 1y^5 \end{aligned}$$

From the expansions, the following can be observed:

1. The number of terms is one more than the power. For example, $(x + y)^4$ has 5 terms.
2. The degree (sum of the exponents) of every term is equal to the power of the binomial.
   For example, the term $10x^2y^3$ is of degree 5, and it is part of the expansion of $(x + y)^5$.
3. The coefficients form a pattern that relates to the rows in Pascal's triangle.
   1st 1
   2nd 1 1
   3rd 1 2 1
   4th 1 3 3 1
   5th 1 4 6 4 1
   6th 1 5 10 10 5 1
   The coefficients of the terms in the expansion of binomials of the form $(a + b)^n$, $n \in W$ can be taken from the $n + 1$ row of Pascal's triangle.

Example

Write the coefficients of the terms of the expansion of $(a + b)^3$.

Solution

Since the binomial is raised to the third power, the coefficients come from the 4th row of Pascal's triangle.

1
1 1
1 2 1
1 3 3 1
1 4 6 4 1
1 5 10 10 5 1

Therefore, the coefficients are 1, 3, 3, and 1.

Example

Give the expanded form of $(x - 2)^5$.

Solution

Using the pattern from Pascal's triangle, expand $(x - 2)^5$ as $(x + (-2))^5$. The coefficients are from the 6th row of the triangle.

$$\begin{aligned}
&(x-2)^5 \\
&= (x + (-2))^5 \\
&= \begin{pmatrix} 1x^5 + 5(x)^4(-2) + 10(x)^3(-2)^2 \\ +10(x)^2(-2)^3 + 5(x)(-2)^4 + 1(-2)^5 \end{pmatrix} \\
&= \begin{pmatrix} x^5 + 5(x^4)(-2) + 10(x^3)(4) \\ +10(x^2)(-8) + 5(x)(16) + (-32) \end{pmatrix} \\
&= x^5 - 10x^4 + 40x^3 - 80x^2 + 80x - 32
\end{aligned}$$

---

10. When expanded, which of the following expressions would have the coefficients 1, 4, 6, 4, and 1?

A. $(a + b)^2$ **B.** $(a + b)^3$

C. $(a + b)^4$ **D.** $(a + b)^5$

11. The simplified expansion of the binomial $(2x + y)^3$ is

A. $8x^3 + y^3$

B. $2x^3 + 6x^2y + 6xy^2 + y^3$

C. $8x^3 + 4x^2y + 2xy^2 + y^3$

D. $8x^3 + 12x^2y + 6xy^2 + y^3$

DF2.1 identify sequences as arithmetic, geometric, or neither, given a numeric or algebraic representation

Identifying Arithmetic and Geometric Sequences

A sequence is **arithmetic** if the difference between consecutive terms is constant. This number is called the **common difference**.

A sequence is **geometric** if the quotient or ratio of consecutive terms is constant. This number is called the **common ratio**.

Example

Classify the sequence 1, 4, 9, 16,...
as arithmetic, geometric, or neither.

Solution

Step 1

Determine the first differences of the sequence.

$4 - 1 = 3$
$9 - 4 = 5$
$16 - 9 = 7$

These are not constant. The sequence is not arithmetic.

Step 2

Determine the ratio of consecutive terms.

$\frac{4}{1} = 4$

$\frac{9}{4} = 2.25$

$\frac{16}{9} \cong 1.78$

These are not constant. The sequence is not geometric.

Therefore, this sequence is neither arithmetic nor geometric.

Example

Classify the sequence 16, 8, 4, 2,...
as arithmetic, geometric, or neither.

Solution

Step 1

Determine the first differences of the sequence.

$8 - 16 = -8$
$4 - 8 = -4$
$2 - 4 = -2$

These are not constant. The sequence is not arithmetic.

Step 2

Determine the ratio of consecutive terms.

$\frac{8}{16} = \frac{1}{2}$

$\frac{4}{8} = \frac{1}{2}$

$\frac{2}{4} = \frac{1}{2}$

These are constant.

Therefore, this sequence is geometric.

Example

Classify the sequence 1, 4, 7, 10,...
as arithmetic, geometric, or neither.

Solution

Step 1

Determine the first differences of the sequence.

$4 - 1 = 3$
$7 - 4 = 3$
$10 - 7 = 3$

These are constant.

Step 2

Determine the ratio of consecutive terms.

$\frac{4}{1} = 4$

$\frac{7}{4} = 1.75$

$\frac{10}{7} \cong 1.43$

These are not constant. The sequence is not geometric.

This sequence is arithmetic.

---

12. Which of the following sequences is arithmetic?

A. 5, 25, 125, 625, ...

B. 5, 10, 15, 20, ...

C. 5, 10, 20, 40, ...

D. 5, 7, 11, 17, ...

Open Response

13. Classify the sequence $t_n = 13 - 3n$ as arithmetic, geometric, or neither.

DF2.2 determine the formula for the general term of an arithmetic sequence [i.e., $t_n=a+(n-1)d$] or geometric sequence (i.e., $t_n=ar^{n-1}$), through investigation using a variety of tools and strategies, and apply the formula to calculate any term in a sequence

The General Term of an Arithmetic or Geometric Sequence

The general term of either an arithmetic or a geometric sequence can be determined and utilized to solve a number of related problems.

If a represents the first term of an arithmetic sequence and d represents the common difference, the sequence will be $a, a+d, a+2d, a+3d, \ldots$. The coefficient of d is always one less than the term number. Therefore, the general term for an arithmetic sequence is $t_n = a+(n-1)d$.

If a represents the first term of a geometric sequence and r represents the common ratio, the sequence will be $a, ar, ar^2, ar^3, \ldots$. The exponent on r is always one less than the term number. Therefore, the general term for a geometric sequence is $t_n = ar^{n-1}$.

Example

The 20th term of the sequence 5, 12, 19, 26, … is _________.

Solution

Step 1

Determine the first differences of the sequence.

$12-5=7$
$19-12=7$
$26-19=7$

The first differences are constant, so this sequence is arithmetic.

Step 2

Determine the 20th term of the sequence.

The sequence is arithmetic. The first term is $a = 5$, and the common difference is $d = 7$. Substitute these numbers into the formula for the general term $t_n = a+(n-1)d$.

$$t_n = a+(n-1)d$$
$$t_{20} = 5+(20-1)(7)$$
$$t_{20} = 5+133$$
$$t_{20} = 138$$

Numerical Response

14. The eighth term of the sequence $\frac{1}{2}$, 2, 8, 32, … is _________.

Open Response

15. In simplified form, determine the equation for the general term of the sequence −5, −1,,3, 7, …, and find which term in the sequence has a value of 203.

DF2.3 determine the formula for the sum of an arithmetic or geometric series, through investigation using a variety of tools and strategies, and apply the formula to calculate the sum of a given number of consecutive terms

DF2.4 solve problems involving arithmetic and geometric sequences and series, including those arising from real-world applications

Applications of Arithmetic and Geometric Sequences and Series

There are many real-life problems that can be solved using the formulas for the sum of a series.

The general term of an arithmetic sequence is given by $t_n = a + (n - 1)d$, where t_n is the value of the nth term, a is the value of the first term in the sequence, and d is the common difference.

There are two formulas that can be used to find the sum, S_n, of an arithmetic series:

- When a, n, and d are known, use $S_n = \frac{n}{2}[2a + (n - 1)d]$.
- When a, n, and t_n are known, use $S_n = \frac{n}{2}(a + t_n)$.

The general term of a geometric sequence is given by $t_n = ar^{n-1}$, where t_n is the value of the nth term, a is the value of the first term in the sequence, and r is the common ratio.

There are two formulas that can be used to find the sum, S_n, of a geometric series:

- When a, n, and r are known, use $S_n = \frac{a(r^n - 1)}{r - 1}, r \neq 1$.
- When a, r, and t_n are known, use $S_n = \frac{rt_n - a}{r - 1}, r \neq 1$.

Example

For eight weeks over the summer, Lexi had a job mowing lawns. She had 5 customers in her first week. Each week after that, she had 2 more lawns to mow than she had during the previous week.

How many lawns did she mow in her 8th week?

Solution

The sequence representing the number of lawns mowed each week by Lexi is 5, 7, 9, ... This sequence is an arithmetic sequence with a common difference of 2.

The question asks for the number of lawns mowed during the 8th week only and not the total during all 8 weeks. Use the general term formula of an arithmetic sequence to find the 8th term.

Substitute 5 for a, 2 for d, and 8 for n into the formula $t_n = a + (n - 1)d$.

$$t_n = a + (n - 1)d$$
$$t_8 = 5 + (8 - 1)2$$
$$t_8 = 19$$

Lexi mowed 19 lawns in her 8th week.

How many lawns did she mow in total during the summer?

Solution

Since the question asks for the total number of lawns mowed over the 8 weeks, determine the sum of the first eight terms of the arithmetic series.

Use the sum formula $S_n = \frac{n}{2}[2a + (n - 1)d]$, where $n = 8$, $a = 5$, and $d = 2$.

$$S_n = \frac{n}{2}[2a + (n - 1)d]$$
$$S_n = \frac{8}{2}[2(5) + (8 - 1)2]$$
$$S_n = 96$$

Lexi mowed 96 lawns over the 8 weeks.

If Lexi charged \$6 per lawn, how much money did she make during the first 6 weeks?

Solution

Step 1
Find the number of lawns Lexi mowed in 6 weeks.
Use the sum formula for an arithmetic series $S_n = \frac{n}{2}[2a+(n-1)d]$, where $a = 5$, $d = 2$, and $n = 6$.

$S_n = \frac{n}{2}[2a+(n-1)d]$

$S_6 = \frac{6}{2}[2(5)+(6-1)2]$

$S_6 = 60$

Lexi mowed 60 lawns in the first 6 weeks.

Step 2
Calculate the total amount of money she earned.
Multiply the number of lawns mowed by the amount she charged per lawn.
$60 \times 6 = 360$
Lexi earned \$360.00 mowing lawns in the first 6 weeks.

Example

Each year, Farmer Brown buys some land to increase the overall size of his farm. In the first year, he bought 4 ha. Each year after, he buys 15% more land than he bought the previous year.

To the nearest hundredth, how much land will he have purchased after 10 years?

Solution

Step 1
Determine the series that represents the given information.
The amounts of land he purchased represent a geometric series. In the first year, he bought 4 ha.
$t_1 = 4$ ha
In the second year, he bought 15% more.
$4 \times 1.15 = 4.6$ ha
In the third year, he bought 15% more.
$4.6 \times 1.15 = 5.29$ ha
Write the first three terms of the geometric series.
$4 + 4.6 + 5.29 + \ldots$

Step 2
Find the total area Farmer Brown purchased over the ten-year period.
Since you are finding the sum of the first 10 terms in the series, $n = 10$. Since the first term is 4, $a = 4$. The common ratio (r) is 1.15 because each term after the first one is obtained by multiplying the previous term by 1.15.
To determine the sum, substitute $a = 4$, $r = 1.15$, and $n = 10$ into the formula $S_n = \frac{a(r^n - 1)}{r-1}$.

$S_n = \frac{a(r^n - 1)}{r-1}$

$S_{10} = \frac{4(1.15^{10} - 1)}{1.15-1}$

$S_{10} \approx 81.21$

In 10 years, Farmer Brown will have purchased approximately 81.21 ha of land.

---

16. The sum of the first 10 terms of the series $40 + 20 + 10 + 5 + \ldots$ is

A. $79\frac{59}{64}$ **B.** $422\frac{1}{2}$

C. 1 990 **D.** 81 840

Open Response

17. In the series $6 + 9 + 12 + 15 + \ldots$, determine the number of terms required to reach a sum of 972.

Use the following information to answer the next question.

In order to save money to buy a car, Renee decides to start an annuity. She deposits $500 the first month and increases the amount of each monthly deposit by $50 for a period of 15 months.

18. The value of the last deposit Renee makes is

A. $1 200 **B.** $1 900

C. $12 750 **D.** $13 125

Use the following information to answer the next multipart question.

19. An oil well produced 320 000 barrels of oil in its first month of production. Statistics show that production usually decreases by 3% for every month the well produces oil. The well will be shut down when production gets below 10 000 barrels per month as the costs of keeping the well operating will be greater than the profits from the sale of the oil.

Open Response

a) To the nearest barrel, determine the expected number of barrels that will be produced during the first year of operation.

b) To the nearest barrel, determine the number of barrels produced in the 24th month of operation.

c) Determine the number of months the oil well will operate.

DF3.1 make and describe connections between simple interest, arithmetic sequences, and linear growth, through investigation with technology

Simple Interest, Arithmetic Sequences, and Linear Growth

Simple interest is interest based only on the original amount invested, the principal.

The formula for calculating simple interest is $I = Prt$, where I is the interest earned, P is the principal, r is the annual interest rate expressed as a decimal, and t is the length of time in years.

Example

Determine both the interest earned and the value of the investment for the first 5 years if $1 000 earns simple interest at 4%/*a*.

Solution

The interest can be determined from the simple interest formula.

$I = Prt$
$= (1\ 000)(0.04)t$
$= 40t$

The information is summarized in the given table.

Year	Total Interest ($)	Value ($)
1	40	1 040
2	80	1 080
3	120	1 120
4	160	1 160
5	200	1 200

Therefore, the interest earned after 5 years is $200, and the value of the investment is $1 200.

A relationship can be developed between simple interest and arithmetic sequences.

Example

An investment of $1 000 earns simple interest at a rate of 4%/*a* for 5 years.

Generate the arithmetic sequence that represents the values of the investment from the time the $1 000 is invested until the end of the 5 years, and then determine the relationship between the term number and the length of the investment in years.

Solution

Step 1
Generate the sequence.

- Initially, the investment is $1 000, so the first term in the arithmetic sequence is $1 000.
- After 1 year of earning simple interest at a rate of 4 %/*a*, the value of the investment is $1\ 000 + 1\ 000(0.04)(1) = \$1\ 040$, representing the second term in the sequence.
- After 2 years, the value of the investment is $1\ 000 + 1\ 000(0.04)(2) = \$1\ 080$, representing the third term in the sequence.

The sequence can be written as
1 000, 1 040, 1 080, ….
The common difference is $40, so the sequence can be extended until the end of the 5-year term.
1 000, 1 040, 1 080, 1 120, 1 160, 1 200

Step 2
Relate the term number to the length of the investment.
$t_1 = 1\ 000$ (principal)
$t_2 = 1\ 040$ (value at the end of year 1)
$t_3 = 1\ 080$ (value at the end of year 2)
$t_4 = 1\ 120$ (value at the end of year 3)
$t_5 = 1\ 160$ (value at the end of year 4)
$t_6 = 1\ 200$ (value at the end of year 5)

It can be seen that the term number is one more than the length of the investment (in years). For example, $t_4 = 1\ 120$ represents the value of the investment at the end of year 3.

In the general term formula for an arithmetic sequence $t_n = a + (n - 1)d$, a is the first term (or the principal value of the investment) and d is the common difference (or interest earned on the investment each year).

To find the value of the investment after n years, it is necessary to find the value of t_{n+1}. In other words, to find the value of the investment after 5 years, it is necessary to find the value of $t_{n+1} = t_{5+1} = t_6$.

Since the graphs of all arithmetic sequences are linear, an investment using simple interest will grow linearly.

20. Which of the following equations represents the value of a \$500 investment with a simple interest rate of 6%/a over several years?

A. $t_n = 30n$

B. $t_n = 3\ 000n$

C. $t_n = 500(1 + 6n)$

D. $t_n = 500(1 + 0.06n)$

Open Response

21. Describe an investment that could be represented by the function $f(x) = 800(1 + 0.03x)$.

DF3.2 make and describe connections between compound interest, geometric sequences, and exponential growth, through investigation with technology

Compound Interest, Geometric Sequences, and Exponential Growth

The formula for compound interest is $A = P(1 + i)^n$, where A is the value of the investment, P is the principal, i is the interest rate for the compounding period, and n is the number of times the interest is compounded.

Example

An investment of \$1 000 earns interest at a rate of 4%/a, compounded annually, for 5 years.

Determine the value of the investment for the first 5 years, and determine the total amount of interest earned over the life of the investment.

Solution

Method 1
Determine the yearly interest using the simple interest formula.

Since the principal changes after each year, the interest is calculated recursively.

$$\begin{aligned} I_1 &= Prt \\ &= (1\ 000)(0.04)(1) \\ &= 40 \end{aligned}$$

$$\begin{aligned} I_2 &= (1\ 000 + 40)(0.04)(1) \\ &= 41.6 \end{aligned}$$

$$\begin{aligned} I_3 &= (1\ 040 + 41.60)(0.04)(1) \\ &= 43.26 \end{aligned}$$

$$\begin{aligned} I_4 &= (1\ 081.6 + 43.26)(0.04)(1) \\ &= 44.99 \end{aligned}$$

$$\begin{aligned} I_5 &= (1\ 124.86 + 44.99)(0.04)(1) \\ &= 46.79 \end{aligned}$$

Determine the value of the investment at the end of each year.

The information is summarized in the given table.

	Interest ($)	Value ($)
Year 1	40	1 040.00
Year 2	41.60	1 081.60
Year 3	43.26	1 124.86
Year 4	44.99	1 169.85
Year 5	46.79	1 216.64

Therefore, the interest earned over the life of the investment is 1 216.64 – 1 000 = $216.64.

Method 2
Determine the value of the investment at the end of each year, using the compound interest formula.

$$\begin{aligned} A_1 &= 1\ 000(1+0.04)^1 \\ &= 1\ 040 \end{aligned}$$

$$\begin{aligned} A_2 &= 1\ 000(1+0.04)^2 \\ &= 1\ 081.60 \end{aligned}$$

$$\begin{aligned} A_3 &= 1\ 000(1+0.04)^3 \\ &= 1\ 124.86 \end{aligned}$$

$$\begin{aligned} A_4 &= 1\ 000(1+0.04)^4 \\ &= 1\ 169.86 \end{aligned}$$

$$\begin{aligned} A_5 &= 1\ 000(1+0.04)^5 \\ &= 1\ 216.65 \end{aligned}$$

Therefore, the interest earned over the life of the investment is 1 216.65 – 1 000 = $216.65.

In method 1, the interest values are rounded to the nearest cent at each step, which causes the one cent variation in the solution values.

Example

An investment of $1 000 earns compound interest at a rate of 4%/*a* compounded annually for 5 years.

Generate the geometric sequence that represents the values of the investment from the time the $1 000 is invested until the end of the 5 years, and then determine the relationship between the term number and the length of the investment in years.

Solution

Step 1
Generate the sequence.
Initially, the investment is $1 000, so the first term in the geometric sequence is $1 000.
After 1 year of earning compound interest at a rate of 4 %/*a* compounded annually, the value of the investment is
$1\ 000(1+0.04)^1 = \$1\ 040$, representing the second term in the sequence.
After 2 years, the value of the investment is
$1\ 000(1+0.04)^2 = \$1\ 081.60$, representing the third term in the sequence.
The sequence can be written as
1 000, 1 040, 1 081.60, ….
The common ratio is 1.04, so the sequence can be extended until the end of the five-year term.
1 000, 1 040, 1 081.60,
1 124.86, 1 169.86, 1 216.65

Step 2
Relate the term number to the length of the investment.
$t_1 = 1\ 000$ (principal)
$t_2 = 1\ 040$ (value at the end of year 1)
$t_3 = 1\ 081.60$ (value at the end of year 2)
$t_4 = 1\ 124.86$ (value at the end of year 3)
$t_5 = 1\ 169.86$ (value at the end of year 4)
$t_6 = 1\ 216.65$ (value at the end of year 5)

It can be seen that the term number is one more than the length of the investment (in years). For example, $t_4 = 1\ 124.86$ represents the value of the investment at the end of year 3.
In the general term formula for a geometric sequence $t_n = ar^{n-1}$, a is the first term (or the principal value of the investment) and r is the common ratio.
To find the value of the investment after n years, it is necessary to find the value of t_{n+1}. In other words, to find the value of the investment after 5 years, it is necessary to find the value of $t_{n+1} = t_{5+1} = t_6$.

Since the graphs of all geometric sequences are exponential, an investment in compound interest will grow exponentially.

Use the following information to answer the next question.

Jorge invested \$2 000 in a mutual fund that promised a return of 6%/*a* compounded semi-annually.

22. If x is the number of years that the money is invested, which of the following functions represents Jorge's investment?

A. $f(x) = 2\ 000(1 + 0.03x)$

B. $f(x) = 2\ 000(1 + 0.06x)$

C. $f(x) = 2\ 000(1.03)^{2x}$

D. $f(x) = 2\ 000(1.06)^{x}$

23. Which of the following graphs could represent the growth of a principal of \$4 000 invested at 5%/*a* compounded annually?

A. 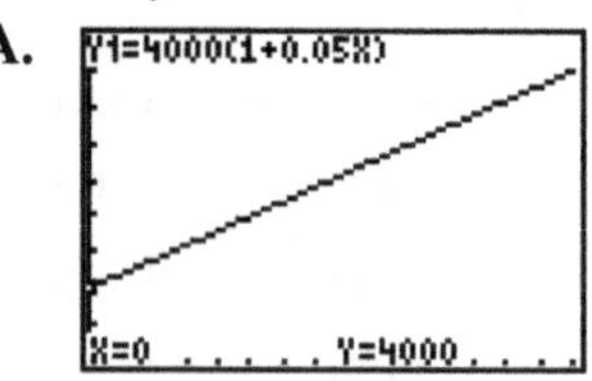

B. 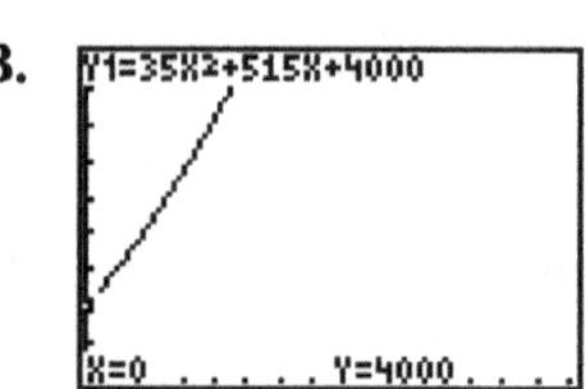

C. 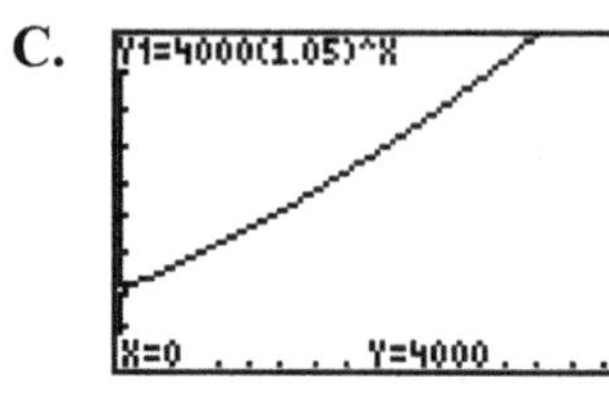

D. 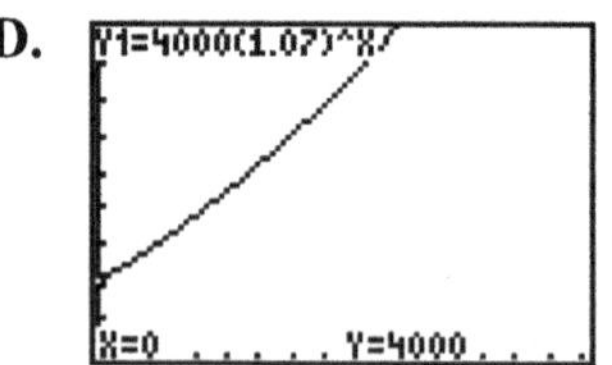

DF3.3 solve problems, using a scientific calculator, that involve the calculation of the amount, A (also referred to as future value, FV), the principal, P (also referred to as present value, PV), or the interest rate per compounding period, i, using the compound interest formula in the form $A = P(1 + i)^n$ [or $FV = PV(1 + i)^n$]

Solving Compound Interest Problems

Many everyday situations involve investments and the calculation of interest. For compound interest problems, the resulting amount (A) or final value (FV) can be found using the compound interest formula $A = P(1+i)^n$ or $FV = PV(1+i)^n$. In this formula, A or FV is the accumulated amount, P or PV is the principal or original investment, i is the interest rate (as a decimal) per compounding period, and n is the number of compounding periods over the total time of the investment. The formula can be used to solve for any one of the variables when the others are known.

Example

Natasha wants to place \$60 000 into an investment account. She has these two options:

1. The option of 10%/a compounded semi-annually for 4 years
2. The option of 10%/a compounded daily for 4 years

Determine which option is the best choice for Natasha.

Solution

Step 1

Use the formula $A = P(1+i)^n$ to calculate the total amount for option 1.

Option 1 is compounding semi-annually.

$$\begin{aligned} i &= 0.10 \div 2 \\ &= 0.05 \\ n &= 4 \times 2 \\ &= 8 \\ A &= P(1+i)^n \\ &= 60\ 000(1+0.05)^8 \\ &= 60\ 000(1.05)^8 \\ &= \$88\ 647.33 \end{aligned}$$

Step 2

Use the formula $A = P(1+i)^n$ to calculate the total amount for option 2.

Option 2 is compounding daily.

$$\begin{aligned} i &= 0.10 \div 365 \\ &= \frac{0.10}{365} \\ n &= 4 \times 365 \\ &= 1\ 460 \\ A &= P(1+i)^n \\ &= 60\ 000\left(1+\left(\frac{0.10}{365}\right)\right)^{1\ 460} \\ &= \$89\ 504.58 \end{aligned}$$

The best choice for Natasha is to put her \$60 000 investment into the option that is compounded daily (option 2) since more money accumulates over the 4 years than in the option that is compounded semi-annually (option 1).

Example

An investment earning 8%/a compounded annually has a future value (FV) of \$40 000 after 15 years.

Determine the present value (PV) of the investment.

Solution

Since the interest is compounded annually, there are 15 compounding periods.

Use the compound interest formula $FV = PV(1+i)^n$, and substitute the given values into the formula.

$$\begin{aligned} i &= 0.08 \\ n &= 15 \\ FV &= PV(1+i)^n \\ 40\ 000 &= PV(1+0.08)^{15} \\ 40\ 000 &\approx PV(3.172\ 169\ 114) \\ \frac{40\ 000}{3.172\ 169\ 114} &\approx PV \\ 12\ 609.67 &\approx PV \end{aligned}$$

The present value of the investment is \$12 609.67.

24. A principal of \$2 000 is deposited into an account that earns interest and is compounded quarterly. If the investment has earned \$2 416 in interest after 10 years, the yearly interest rate is

A. 1.9% **B.** 4.1%

C. 8.0% **D.** 8.2%

Use the following information to answer the next question.

An investment of \$10 000 has an interest rate of 12%/*a*.

Numerical Response

25. Rounded to the nearest dollar, what is the difference in the amount of interest earned when this investment is compounded yearly compared to when it is compounded monthly for a period of 5 years? \$__________

DF3.4 determine, through investigation using technology, the number of compounding periods, n, using the compound interest formula in the form $A = P(1+i)^n$ [or $FV = PV(1+i)^n$]; describe strategies for calculating this number; and solve related problems

Solving Compound Interest Problems Using the TVM Solver

Compound interest problems can be solved using graphing calculator technology. The TVM Solver is an application program in the TI-83 graphing calculator that can be used to solve a variety of money-related problems, including those involving compound interest. The program is found by pressing APPS 1: Finance… 1: TVM Solver…. The resulting screen will be displayed as shown.

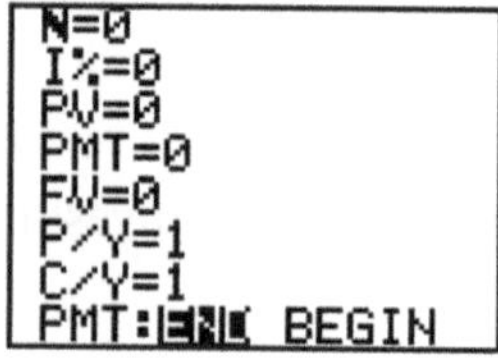

These variables have the following meanings:

- N = total number of payment periods (for compound interest problems, payments are not made, so *N* represents the duration of the investment in years)
- I% = annual interest rate
- PV = present value (for compound interest problems, the present value is often referred to as the principal *P*)
- PMT = regular payment amount (for compound interest problems, payments are not made, so PMT = 0)
- FV = future value (for compound interest problems, the future value is often referred to as the amount *A*)
- P/Y = total number of payments per year (for problems with no payments, P/Y must be set to 1)
- C/Y = total number of compounding periods per year
  Note that if P/Y does not equal C/Y, then the value of P/Y must be input first, followed by the value for C/Y. (The default is for the value of C/Y to be the same as what was input for the value of P/Y.)
- PMT: END BEGIN = timing of each payment (either at the end or at the beginning of the payment period)
  Choose END for compound interest problems.

When you are entering amounts into the TVM Solver, also remember these points:

- Cash inflow (money received) must be entered into the application as a positive number.
- Cash outflow (money paid) must be entered into the application as a negative number.

For the sake of simplicity, enter 0 for whichever variable is being solved. Once all the known information has been input into the application, return to the unknown variable and press ALPHA ENTER to solve. Any one variable can be solved for when the others are known.

Example

Solution

Example

How long will it take for a $5 000 investment to triple in value if interest is 9% per year compounded quarterly?

Solution

Use the TVM Solver application in a TI-83 or similar graphing calculator to solve.

Enter the given values for I%, PV, FV, and C/Y. The value of N is unknown. The value of FV = 15 000 because triple means 3 × PV = 3 × 5 000. The value of PMT is 0 and the value of P/Y is 1 because this is a compound interest problem.

```
N=0
I%=9.00
PV=-5000
PMT=0
FV=15000
P/Y=1
C/Y=4
PMT:END BEGIN
```

Move your cursor to the N variable, and press ALPHA ENTER.

```
N=12.34362048
I%=9
PV=-5000
PMT=0
FV=15000
P/Y=1
C/Y=4
PMT:END BEGIN
```

According to the TVM Solver result, it takes a little more than 12 years for the money to triple in value. Since the interest is compounded quarterly, you need to round up to the nearest quarter year, i.e., 0.25, 0.50, 0.75, or 1.

It would take 12.5 years for the invested amount of $5 000 to triple in value.

Use the following information to answer the next question.

A principal of $25 000 is deposited into an account that earns interest at 6%/*a*, compounded semi-annually.

26. Expressed to the nearest tenth, the number of years for the investment to reach a value of at least $35 000 is

A. 5.7 **B.** 5.8

C. 11.4 **D.** 11.6

Use the following information to answer the next question.

A principal amount of $10 000 is invested at 5%/*a*, compounded monthly.

Numerical Response

27. Rounded to the nearest month, how many months will it take for the investment to be worth at least $20 000?

DF3.5 explain the meaning of the term annuity, and determine the relationships between ordinary simple annuities (i.e., annuities in which payments are made at the end of each period, and compounding and payment periods are the same), geometric series, and exponential growth, through investigation with technology

Determining the Value of an Ordinary Simple Annuity Using the Compound Interest Formula

An **annuity** is a series of equal value deposits made at regular time intervals into an account earning compound interest at a fixed rate. An **ordinary simple annuity** is a special type of annuity in which the deposits (payments) are made at the end of each regular time interval and the number of deposits (payments) made in a year equal the number of compounding periods in a year. For example, a monthly investment of $100 made at the end of each month that earns interest at a rate of 7%/*a* compounded monthly is an ordinary simple annuity.

To determine the value of an annuity, apply the compound interest formula as follows:

1. Use the formula $A = P(1 + i)^n$ to calculate the value of each deposit over its investment term.
2. Add the end value of each deposit together.

Another method of determining the value of an annuity is to generate a geometric series and calculate its sum using the sum of the terms of a geometric series formula $S_n = \dfrac{a(r^n - 1)}{r - 1}$.

Example

For 6 months, Sarah makes monthly deposits of \$400 at the end of each month into an account earning interest at a rate of 12%/*a* compounded monthly.

Determine the total value of the annuity at the end of the 6 months.

Solution

Method 1

Determine the total value of the annuity by using the formula $A = P(1 + i)^n$.

Each \$400 deposit is earning monthly interest of $\dfrac{12\%}{12 \text{ months}} = 1\%/\text{month}$.

$$A = P(1 + i)^n$$
$$= 400(1.01)^n$$

The first deposit has been in the account for 5 months (from the end of the first month to the end of the sixth month). Therefore, $n = 5$, and its present value is $400(1.01)^5$.

The second deposit has been in the account for 4 months (from the end of the second month to the end of the sixth month). Therefore, $n = 4$, and its present value is $400(1.01)^4$.

This continues until $n = 0$, which occurs at the end of the sixth month when \$400 is deposited, but has not earned any interest. The present value of the \$400 deposited at the end of 6 months is $400(1.01)^0 = 400$.

Calculate the total value of the annuity using the given geometric series.

$$\begin{pmatrix} 400(1.01)^5 + 400(1.01)^4 \\ +400(1.01)^3 + 400(1.01)^2 \\ +400(1.01)^1 + 400(1.01)^0 \end{pmatrix}$$
$$\approx \$2\ 460.81$$

Method 2

Use the formula for the sum of the terms of a geometric series $S_n = \dfrac{a(r^n - 1)}{r - 1}$ to find the total value of the annuity.

The series $400 + 400(1.01)^1 + 400(1.01)^2 + \ldots$ is geometric. It has a common ratio of 1.01 and a first term of 400.

Calculate the sum of the six terms, S_6.

$$S_n = \frac{a(r^n - 1)}{r - 1}$$
$$S_6 = \frac{400((1.01)^6 - 1)}{(1.01) - 1}$$
$$S_6 \approx \$2\ 460.81$$

The total value of the annuity at the end of the 6 months is \$2 460.81.

Because a geometric series with a common ratio value of $r > 1$ represents exponential growth, it can be seen that ordinary simple annuities also represent exponential growth.

Use the following information to answer the next question.

Jane deposits \$500 at the beginning of each month into an account earning interest at 6%/*a*, compounded monthly.

28. The total value of her investment after one year is

A. \$6 016.27 **B.** \$6 030.00

C. \$6 167.78 **D.** \$6 198.62

Use the following information to answer the next multipart question.

29. Bill starts an annuity by making yearly deposits of $800 at the beginning of each year into an account earning interest at 8%/*a* compounded quarterly. He makes the deposits for 10 consecutive years.

Open Response

a) Write the expression that gives the value of the very first deposit at the beginning of the tenth year, and calculate the value of this deposit.

b) Write and explain the series that represents the total value of the annuity at the beginning of the tenth year, and calculate the total value of the annuity at the beginning of the tenth year.

c) Write the series that represents the total value of the annuity at the end of the 10th year, and find the total value of the investment.

d) If Bill needs the investment to have a total value of $15 000 at the end of 10 years, what amount should he deposit each year?

DF3.6 determine, through investigation using technology, the effects of changing the conditions (i.e., the payments, the frequency of the payments, the interest rate, the compounding period) of ordinary simple annuities

Effects of Changing the Conditions of Ordinary Simple Annuities

The future values of an ordinary simple annuity can vary greatly when the annuity's conditions (or variables) are changed. For example, a change in the interest rate or the frequency of payment can significantly change the future value of an ordinary simple annuity.

The TVM Solver is an application program in the TI-83 graphing calculator that can be used to solve a variety of money-related problems, including those involving annuities. The program is found by pressing APPS 1:Finance…1:TVM Solver…. The resulting screen will be displayed as shown.

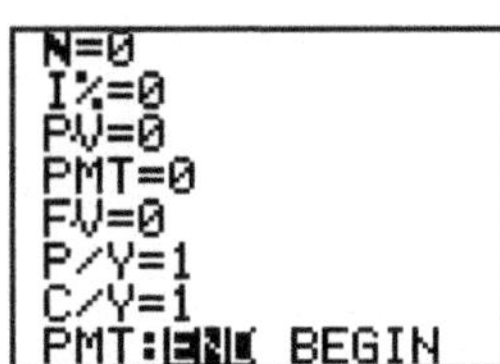

These variables have the following meanings:

- N = total number of payment periods
- I% = annual interest rate
- PV = present value
- PMT = regular payment amount
- FV = future value
- P/Y = total number of payments per year
- C/Y = total number of compounding periods per year
  Note that the default is for the value of C/Y to be the same as what was input for the value of P/Y. This is convenient because P/Y = C/Y for ordinary simple annuities.
- PMT: END BEGIN = timing of each payment (for ordinary simple annuities, payments are made at the end of each payment period).

When you are entering amounts into the TVM Solver, also remember these points:

- Cash inflow (money received) must be entered into the application as a positive number.
- Cash outflow (money paid) must be entered into the application as a negative number.

For the sake of simplicity, enter 0 for whichever variable is being solved. Once all the known information has been inputted into the application, return to the unknown variable and press ALPHA ENTER to solve. Any one variable can be solved for when the others are known, and comparisons can be made when any variable is altered.

Example

An investor is planning to set up a 10-year annuity and is considering his contribution options. He is beginning his investment with a present value of 0, and he will contribute \$3 600 to the investment every year for the life of the investment.

Using the TVM Solver on a TI-83 calculator, compare the future values of the investment if the annual contribution is invested annually, quarterly, or monthly.

Solution

As the number of payments in the year increase, the amount of each payment will decrease.

Step 1
Create a table showing each payment amount for an annual investment of \$3 600 where payments are made on an annual, quarterly, and monthly basis.
Let N represent the number of compounding periods made over the 10-year life of the investment.

N	P/Y and C/Y	PMT
10	Annually: 1	$=\frac{\$3\ 600}{1}$ $=\$3\ 600$
40	Quarterly: 4	$=\frac{\$3\ 600}{4}$ $=\$900$
120	Monthly: 12	$=\frac{\$3\ 600}{12}$ $=\$300$

Step 2

Use the TVM Solver to create a table showing the future value of the investment at annual interest rates of 6%, 8%, and 10% where the payments are made annually, quarterly, and monthly.

The TVM Solver can be accessed by selecting APPS 1:Finance 1:TVM Solver.

An example of how to complete the TVM Solver calculation for an annual interest rate of 10% where payments are made monthly is as follows:

N = 10 × 12 = 120
I% = 10
PV = 0
PMT = –300
FV=
P/Y = 12
C/Y = 12
PMT = END

Payments	6%	8%	10%
Annually ($)	47 450.86	52 151.62	57 374.73
Quarterly ($)	48 841.10	54 361.78	60 662.30
Monthly ($)	49 163.80	54 883.81	61 453.49

Step 3

Discuss the findings in the table.

According to the table of values, changing the number of payments per year does not drastically change the future value of the investment. An example for an annual interest rate of 6% is as follows:

- Annual to quarterly change at 6%: \$48 841.10 – \$47 450.86 = \$1 390.24 over the life of the investment or \$139.02 per year.
- Annual to monthly change at 6%: \$49 163.80 – \$47 450.86 = \$1 712.94 over the life of the investment or \$171.29 per year.

However, the future values do change dramatically when the annual interest rates change.

- 6% → 8% change: From \$54 151.62 – \$47 450.86 = \$4 700.76 (compounded annually) to \$54 883.81 – \$49 163.80 = \$5 720.01 (compounded monthly) or about \$470 per year to \$572 per year.
- 6% → 10% change: From \$57 374.73 – \$47 450.86 = \$9 923.86 (compounded annually) to \$61 453.59 – \$49 163.80 = \$12 289.69 (compounded monthly) or about \$992 per year to \$1 229 per year.

Use the following information to answer the next question.

At age 25, John and Jill both start annuities to plan for their retirement. John decides to deposit \$100 at the end of each month into an account earning interest at 6%/*a*, compounded monthly.
Jill deposits \$1 200 at the end of each year into an account earning interest at 6%/*a*, compounded annually.

30. Rounded to the nearest dollar, how much more will John's investment be worth when they both are 65 years old?

A. \$2 292 **B.** \$3 288

C. \$13 435 **D.** \$14 430

Use the following information to answer the next question.

Zack starts an annuity by depositing $200 at the end of each month into an account earning interest at 4%/*a*, compounded monthly. James deposits $2 400 at the end of each year into an account earning interest at 4%/*a*, compounded yearly.

Numerical Response

31. To the nearest dollar, the difference in the amount of interest earned between the two investments over a three-year period is $_________.

DF3.7 solve problems, using technology that involve the amount, the present value, and the regular payment of an ordinary simple annuity

Solving Simple Annuity Problems

To solve problems involving annuities, make sure that you distinguish between the values and terms of a loan and those of a savings or retirement plan.

Example

Ethan is 24. He wants to put aside $250 at the end of every month into a retirement fund earning 9%/a interest compounded monthly until he is 55. At 55, he wants to withdraw regular monthly amounts until the fund is depleted over the next 20 years (at age 75).

How much will his regular monthly withdrawals be when he retires at age 55?

Solution

This problem is a retirement investment.
The first step to the problem is to determine the final accumulated amount, *FV*, of the retirement savings plan from age 24 to 55.

Step 1
The total number of years that the monthly deposits are made is 55 – 24 = 31years.
Since the deposits are made monthly, the total number of compounds over the 31 years is N = 31 × 12 = 372. This value and the other values in the problem can be entered into the TVM Solver of your graphing calculator to enable you to find the final accumulated amount, FV, as shown below.

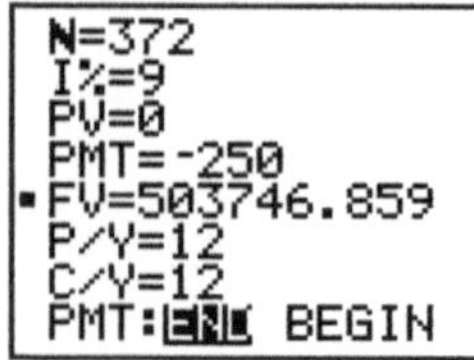

According to the resulting value, FV, on the screen, the total accumulated amount in the retirement fund after 31 years, when Ethan is 55 years old, is $503 746.86.

Step 2

The second step of this problem is to see how the present value or principal of $503 746.86 will deplete to a future value of FV = 0 after the next 20 years. The total number of compounds is N = 20 × 12 = 240.

Now, enter PV = −503 746.86, and determine the monthly withdrawals, PMT, that can be made over the next 240 months. Enter these values into the TVM Solver as shown below to solve for PMT.

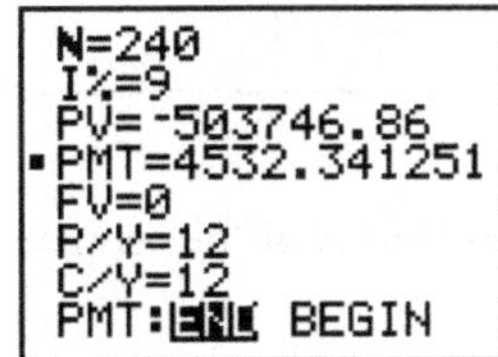

According to the resulting value, PMT, on the screen, the regular amount of $4 532.34 can be withdrawn monthly from the account over the 20 years until it is completely depleted (at age 75).

Use the following information to answer the next question.

> Sue has $5 000 in an account earning interest at 7%/*a*, compounded monthly. She wants to save money to buy a $25 000 car in 5 years. She starts an annuity by making regular deposits into the account at the end of each month.

32. Rounded to the nearest dollar, what is the minimum that Sue would have to deposit each month in order to have at least $25 000 at the end of 5 years?

A. $249 **B.** $250

C. $251 **D.** $252

Use the following information to answer the next question.

> Karen starts an annuity by depositing $300 at the end of each month into an account earning interest at 5%/*a*, compounded monthly. At the end of 3 years, she has a total of $14 471.61 in the account.

Numerical Response

33. To the nearest dollar, the amount of money she had in the account before she started the annuity would be $_________.

ANSWERS AND SOLUTIONS
DISCRETE FUNCTIONS

1. D	**9. 55**	**17. OR**	**23. C**	**c) OR**
2. B	**10. C**	**18. A**	**24. C**	**d) OR**
3. 96	**11. D**	**19. a) OR**	**25. 544**	**30. C**
4. B	**12. B**	**b) OR**	**26. A**	**31. 144**
5. D	**13. OR**	**c) OR**	**27. 167**	**32. C**
6. D	**14. 8192**	**20. D**	**28. D**	**33. 2450**
7. OR	**15. OR**	**21. OR**	**29. a) OR**	
8. C	**16. A**	**22. C**	**b) OR**	

1. D

Since a continuous function must have a domain that is the set of, or a subset of, the real number system, functions I and IV could be continuous (and functions II and III can be immediately eliminated).

Since function I is undefined at $x = 5$ (because $\frac{6}{0}$ is undefined), there will be a break in the graph. Therefore, function I is not continuous after all. The domain of function II is the set of whole numbers (0, 1, 2, 3, 4,...), so function II is discrete. Function III has a domain that is the set of natural numbers (1, 2, 3, 4,...) and is also a discrete function. Function IV is the only function whose domain is the unrestricted set of real numbers and is therefore the only continuous function.

2. B

Step 1
Calculate the second term
To get the second term, multiply 2 by 4, and then add 3
$2(4) + 3 = 11$

Step 2
Calculate the third term
To get the third term, multiply 11 by 4, and then add 3
$11(4) + 3 = 47$

Step 3
Calculate the fourth term
To get the third term, multiply 47 by 4, and then add 3
$47(4) + 3 = 191$
The sequence is 2, 11, 47, 191,...

3. 96

Generate the terms of the sequence using the given procedure.
$t_1 = 3$
$t_2 = 3(2) = 6$
$t_3 = 6(2) = 12$
$t_4 = 12(2) = 24$
$t_5 = 24(2) = 48$
$t_6 = 48(2) = 96$

The terms are 3, 6, 12, 24, 48, and 96.

The sixth term is 96.

4. B

Use the given recursion formula. The first term is 5. Find the second term.

$$\begin{aligned} t_2 &= 2t_1 \\ &= 2(5) \\ &= 10 \end{aligned}$$

Find the third term.

$$\begin{aligned} t_3 &= 2t_2 \\ &= 2(10) \\ &= 20 \end{aligned}$$

Find the fourth term.

$$\begin{aligned} t_4 &= 2t_3 \\ &= 2(20) \\ &= 40 \end{aligned}$$

Therefore, the sequence is 5, 10, 20, 40,...

5. D

Generate the sequence using the given function, $f(x) = 3x,\ x \in N$. The first term is $f(1) = 3(1) = 3$, the second term is $f(2) = 3(2) = 6$, and the third term is $f(3) = 3(3) = 9$. The sequence 3, 6, 9, ... is formed by adding 3 to the previous term to determine the next term, which is defined recursively by $t_1 = 3$, $t_n = 3 + t_{n-1},\ n > 1$.

6. D

Since $t_1 = 4$, $t_n = t_{n-1} + 3n + 1$ has the form $t_1 = 0$, $t_n = t_{n-1} + an + b$, it will be a discrete quadratic function.

The terms are 4, 11, 21, 34, 50…, which gives first differences of 7, 10, 13, and 16 and a constant second difference of 3.

7. OR

Step 1
Determine the first differences.
Subtracting consecutive terms gives first differences of 9, 11, 13, and 15.
The first differences are not constant.

Step 2
Determine the second differences.
The second differences are a constant 2, so this sequence is a quadratic function of the form $t_n = an^2 + bn + c$.

Step 3
Substitute the first three terms of the sequence and the corresponding term numbers into the quadratic function $t_n = an^2 + bn + c$ to generate a system of three equations.
Given $t_1 = 5$, $t_2 = 14$, and $t_3 = 25$, substitute these values into $t_n = an^2 + bn + c$.

$5 = a(1)^2 + b(1) + c$, which simplifies to $5 = a + b + c$ ①.

$14 = a(2)^2 + b(2) + c$, which simplifies to $14 = 4a + 2b + c$ ②.

$25 = a(3)^2 + b(3) + c$, which simplifies to $25 = 9a + 3b + c$ ③.

Step 4
Solve the system.
Subtract equation 1 from equations 2 and 3 to eliminate the unknown c and leave two equations in two unknowns.

② $14 = 4a + 2b + c$
① $\underline{5 = a + b + c}$
④ $9 = 3a + b$

③ $25 = 9a + 3b + c$
① $\underline{5 = a + b + c}$
⑤ $20 = 8a + 2b$

Multiplying equation 4 by 2 and subtracting 2 × ④ from equation 5 gives the solution for parameter a.

⑤ $20 = 8a + 2b$
2 × ④ $\underline{18 = 6a + 2b}$
$2 = 2a$
$1 = a$

Substituting $a = 1$ into equation 4 gives the solution for parameter b.

$9 = 3(1) + b$
$9 = 3 + b$
$6 = b$

Substituting $a = 1$ and $b = 6$ into equation 1 gives the solution for parameter c.

$5 = a + b + c$
$5 = 1 + 6 + c$
$5 = 7 + c$
$-2 = c$

Step 5
State the general term of the sequence.

The general term is given by $t_n = an^2 + bn + c$, where $a = 1$, $b = 6$, and $c = -2$.

$t_n = (1)n^2 + (6)n + (-2)$
$= n^2 + 6n - 2$

Step 6
Verify the general term formula.

$t_1 = (1)^2 + 6(1) - 2 = 5$

$t_2 = (2)^2 + 6(2) - 2 = 14$

$t_3 = (3)^2 + 6(3) - 2 = 25$

The equation of the general term for the sequence 5, 14, 25, 38, 53, … is $t_n = n^2 + 6n - 2$.

8. C

The Fibonacci sequence is formed by adding the first two terms of a sequence to form the third term, adding the second and third terms to form the fourth term, and so on.

Step 1
Identify the sequence type for 5, 10, 15, 20, ….
The sequence 5, 10, 15, 20, … is an arithmetic sequence with a common difference of 5.

Step 2
Identify the sequence type for 5, 10, 20, 35, ...
The sequence 5, 10, 20, 35, ... is neither arithmetic nor geometric. The first differences of this sequence are 5, 10, 15, respectively.

Step 3
Identify the sequence type for 5, 10, 20, 40, ...
The sequence 5, 10, 20, 40, ... is a geometric sequence with a common ratio of 2.

Step 4
Identify the sequence type for 5, 10, 15, 25, ...
The sequence 5, 10, 15, 25, ... is formed in a manner similar to the Fibonacci sequence.
Given the first and second terms, the third and fourth terms can be determined as follows:

$$\begin{aligned} t_3 &= 5 + 10 \\ &= 15 \\ t_4 &= 10 + 15 \\ &= 25 \end{aligned}$$

9. 55

Step 1
Deduce the sequence represented by $t_1 = 1, t_2 = 1,$ $t_n = t_{n-1} + t_{n-2}$, and $n > 2$.
The recursive formula shows that, after the first two terms, all the terms are formed by adding the two preceding terms.

Step 2
Use the recursive formula and the defined values to calculate the third term in the sequence.

$$\begin{aligned} t_3 &= t_{3-1} + t_{3-2} \\ &= t_2 + t_1 \\ &= 1 + 1 \\ &= 2 \end{aligned}$$

Step 3
Use the recursive formula and the defined values to calculate the remaining terms in the sequence.

$$\begin{aligned} t_4 &= t_{4-1} + t_{4-2} \\ &= t_3 + t_2 \\ &= 2 + 1 \\ &= 3 \end{aligned}$$

This calculation can be repeated to identify the terms in the sequence until the 10th term is reached. The first 10 terms of the Fibonacci sequence are 1, 1, 2, 3, 5, 8, 13, 21, 34, and 55. Therefore, the 10th term of the sequence is 55.

10. C

Look at Pascal's triangle.

1
1 1
1 2 1
1 3 3 1
1 4 6 4 1
1 5 10 10 5 1

Note that the coefficients for the terms of the expansion $(x + y)^n$ come from the $(n + 1)^{\text{th}}$ row.

The coefficients 1, 4, 6, 4, and 1 are in the fifth row. Therefore, the binomial is raised to the power of $5 - 1 = 4$.

Also, since the second term in each row is equal to the power of the binomial expression, and the second term in the fifth row is 4, the power of the binomial expression is 4.

11. D

Since the binomial $(2x + y)^3$ has an exponent of 3, the expanded form corresponds to the fourth row of Pascal's triangle.

1
1 1
1 2 1
1 3 3 1
1 4 6 4 1
1 5 10 10 5 1

Note that the coefficients for the terms of the expansion $(x + y)^n$ come from the $(n + 1)^{\text{th}}$ row.

The coefficients of the fourth row are 1, 3, 3, and 1. Therefore, the entire expansion is as follows:

$$\begin{aligned} &(2x + y)^3 \\ &= 1(2x)^3 + 3(2x)^2y + 3(2x)y^2 + y^3 \\ &= 1(8x^3) + 3(4x^2)y + 6xy^2 + y^3 \\ &= 8x^3 + 12x^2y + 6xy^2 + y^3 \end{aligned}$$

12. B

Step 1
Determine the first differences of the sequence 5, 25, 125, 625, ...

$$\begin{aligned} 25 - 5 &= 20 \\ 125 - 25 &= 100 \\ 625 - 125 &= 500 \end{aligned}$$

The differences are not constant; therefore, the sequence is not arithmetic.

Step 2
Determine the first differences of the sequence 5, 10, 20, 40, ….

$10 - 5 = 5$
$20 - 10 = 10$
$40 - 20 = 20$

The differences are not constant; therefore, the sequence is not arithmetic.

Step 3
Determine the first differences of the sequence 5, 7, 11, 17, ….

$7 - 5 = 2$
$11 - 7 = 4$
$17 - 11 = 6$

The differences are not constant; therefore, the sequence is not arithmetic.

Step 4
Determine the first differences of the sequence 5, 10, 15, 20, ….

$10 - 5 = 5$
$15 - 10 = 5$
$20 - 15 = 5$

The differences are constant; therefore, the sequence is arithmetic.

13. OR

Step 1
Determine the terms of the sequence.

$t_n = 13 - 3n$
$t_1 = 13 - 3(1)$
$= 10$
$t_2 = 13 - 3(2)$
$= 7$
$t_3 = 13 - 3(3)$
$= 4$
$t_4 = 13 - 3(4)$
$= 1$

Therefore, the sequence is 10, 7, 4, 1, …

Step 2
Determine the first differences of the sequence.

$7 - 10 = -3$
$4 - 7 = -3$
$1 - 4 = -3$

These are constant.

Step 3
Determine the ratio of consecutive terms.

$\frac{7}{10} = 0.7$

$\frac{4}{7} \approx 0.57$

$\frac{1}{4} = 0.25$

These are not constant.

Therefore, this sequence is arithmetic.

14. 8192

Step 1
Determine the first differences of the sequence.

$2 - \frac{1}{2} = 1.5$
$8 - 2 = 6$
$32 - 8 = 24$

The differences are not constant, so this sequence is not arithmetic.

Step 2
Determine the ratio of consecutive terms of the sequence.

$\frac{2}{\frac{1}{2}} = 4$

$\frac{8}{2} = 4$

$\frac{32}{8} = 4$

The ratios are constant, a common ratio, so this sequence is geometric.

Step 3
Determine the general term formula for the given sequence using $t_n = ar^{n-1}$.

The sequence is geometric with a first term of $a = \frac{1}{2}$ and a common ratio of $r = 4$. Substitute into the formula $t_n = ar^{n-1}$.

$t_n = ar^{n-1}$
$= \frac{1}{2}(4)^{n-1}$

Step 4
Substitute 8 for n, and solve.

$$t_n = \frac{1}{2}(4)^{n-1}$$
$$t_8 = \frac{1}{2}(4)^{8-1}$$
$$t_8 = \frac{1}{2}(4)^7$$
$$t_8 = \frac{1}{2}(16\ 384)$$
$$t_8 = 8\ 192$$

15. OR

Step 1
Determine the first differences of the sequence.

$$-1-(-5)=4$$
$$3-(-1)=4$$
$$7-3=4$$

Since these differences are constant, this sequence is arithmetic.

Step 2
Determine the formula for the general term, $t_n = a+(n-1)d$, of the given sequence.

The sequence is arithmetic with a first term of $a=-5$ and a common difference of $d=4$. Substitute these values into the formula for the general term.

$$\begin{aligned} t_n &= a+(n-1)d \\ &= -5+(n-1)(4) \\ &= -5+4n-4 \\ &= 4n-9 \end{aligned}$$

Step 3
Substitute 203 for t_n, and solve.

$$\begin{aligned} t_n &= 4n-9 \\ 203 &= 4n-9 \\ 212 &= 4n \\ 53 &= n \end{aligned}$$

The number 203 is the 53rd term of the given sequence.

16. A

The series is geometric with a first term of $a=40$ and a common ratio of $r=\frac{20}{40}=\frac{1}{2}$. Substitute these values into the formula $S_n=\frac{a(r^n-1)}{r-1}$.

$$\begin{aligned} S_n &= \frac{a(r^n-1)}{r-1} \\ S_{10} &= \frac{40\left(\left(\frac{1}{2}\right)^{10}-1\right)}{\frac{1}{2}-1} \\ &= \frac{40\left(\frac{1}{1\ 024}-1\right)}{-\frac{1}{2}} \\ &= -80\left(-\frac{1\ 023}{1\ 024}\right) \\ &= 5\left(\frac{1\ 023}{64}\right) \\ &= \frac{5\ 115}{64} \\ &= 79\frac{59}{64} \end{aligned}$$

17. OR

This is an arithmetic series with a first term of $a=6$, a common difference of $d=3$, and a sum of $S_n=972$.

Step 1
Substitute these values into the formula $S_n=\frac{n}{2}(2a+(n-1)d)$, and simplify.

$$\begin{aligned} S_n &= \frac{n}{2}(2a+(n-1)d) \\ 972 &= \frac{n}{2}(2(6)+(n-1)(3)) \\ 972 &= \frac{n}{2}(12+3n-3) \\ 1\ 944 &= n(9+3n) \\ 1\ 944 &= 9n+3n^2 \\ 0 &= 3n^2+9n-1\ 944 \end{aligned}$$

Step 2
Since the result is a quadratic equation, determine the values of n by factoring the quadratic.

$$0 = 3n^2+9n-1\ 944$$
$$0 = n^2+3n-648$$
$$0=(n-24)(n+27)$$
$$n=24 \text{ or } n=-27$$

The values of n are 24 or -27.

Since n must be a natural number, 24 terms are required to reach a sum of 972.

18. A

The 15 deposits form an arithmetic sequence with a first term of $a = \$500$ and a common difference of $d = \$50$.

The last deposit is the 15th term, so substitute $n = 15$ into the formula $t_n = a + (n - 1)d$.

$$t_n = a + (n - 1)d$$
$$t_{15} = 500 + (15 - 1)50$$
$$= \$1\ 200$$

19. a) OR

The monthly barrel production will form a geometric series with a first term of $a = 320\ 000$ and a common ratio of $r = 1 - 3\% = 1 - 0.03 = 0.97$.

Since the sum of the first 12 terms equals the number of barrels produced in the first year, substitute the given values into the formula for the sum of a geometric series $S_n = \dfrac{a(r^n - 1)}{r - 1}$.

$$S_n = \frac{a(r^n - 1)}{r - 1}$$
$$S_{12} = \frac{320\ 000((0.97)^{12} - 1)}{0.97 - 1}$$
$$S_{12} = 3\ 265\ 681 \text{ barrels}$$

The expected production in the first year will be 3 265 681 barrels.

b) OR

The monthly barrel production will form a geometric series with a first term of $a = 320\ 000$ and a common ratio of $r = 1 - 3\% = 1 - 0.03 = 0.97$.

Since the number of barrels produced in the 24th month is term 24 in the series, substitute the given values into the general term formula $t_n = ar^{n-1}$.

$$t_n = ar^{n-1}$$
$$t_{24} = (320\ 000)(0.97)^{24-1}$$
$$t_{24} \approx 158\ 818$$

The number of barrels produced in the 24th month of operation is 158 818 barrels.

c) OR

The monthly barrel production will form a geometric series with a first term of $a = 320\ 000$ and a common ratio of $r = 1 - 3\% = 1 - 0.03 = 0.97$.

Step 1

To find how long the well will operate, determine which term in the series is 10 000.

Substitute 320 000 for a, 0.97 for r, and 10 000 for t_n into the general term formula $t_n = ar^{n-1}$, and then simplify.

$$t_n = ar^{n-1}$$
$$10\ 000 = 320\ 000(0.97)^{n-1}$$
$$0.031\ 25 = (0.97)^{n-1}$$

Step 2

Rearrange the equation such that the left side is equal to zero, and replace the zero with y.

$$0.031\ 25 = (0.97)^{n-1}$$
$$0 = (0.97)^{n-1} - 0.031\ 25$$
$$y = (0.97)^{n-1} - 0.031\ 25$$

Step 3

Using your TI-83 or similar graphing calculator, graph the equation $y = (0.97)^{n-1} - 0.031\ 25$, using a window setting of X:[0, 250, 20], Y:[−1, 1, 0.25], and determine the x-intercept.

This will yield the solution to the equation $0 = (0.97)^{n-1} - 0.031\ 25$.

The x-intercept is at $n = 114.782\ 87$.

Since the term number corresponds with the number of months the well is in operation, the well will operate for approximately 114.8 months.

In full months, the oil well will only be able to operate for 114 months because by 115 months, the well would be producing less than 10 000 barrels/month and would already have been shut down.

20. D

Step 1

Calculate the interest earned each year.

$$I = Prt$$
$$= (500)(0.06)(1)$$
$$= \$30$$

Step 2

Determine the sequence.

The value of the investment at the end of each year would form the arithmetic sequence \$530, \$560, \$590,… with a common difference of \$30.

Step 3
Determine the general term equation using the formula $t_n = a + (n - 1)d$.

Substitute 530 for a and 30 for d.

$$\begin{aligned} t_n &= a + (n-1)d \\ &= 530 + (n-1)(30) \\ &= 500 + 30n \\ &= 500(1 + 0.06n) \end{aligned}$$

21. OR

The function $f(x) = 800(1 + 0.03x)$ has the following values:

$$\begin{aligned} f(1) &= 800(1 + 0.03(1)) \\ &= 824 \\ f(2) &= 800(1 + 0.03(2)) \\ &= 848 \\ f(3) &= 800(1 + 0.03(3)) \\ &= 872 \end{aligned}$$

Since these values can continue according to the given function, these amounts represent the values of an investment with a principal amount of \$800 invested at a simple interest rate of 3%/a, where $f(1)$ is the value of the investment at the end of the first year, $f(2)$ is the value of the investment at the end of the second year, and so on.

22. C

Determine the interest rate used for each compounded period.

Since the interest is compounded semi-annually, the yearly interest rate needs to be divided by 2.

Therefore, the interest rate is $\frac{6\%}{2} = 3\%$ for each compounded period.

Determine the number of compounding intervals.

The number of compounding intervals is $2x$ since the interest is compounded twice per year.

Substitute the interest rate and the compounding intervals into the formula $A = P(1 + i)^n$.

$$\begin{aligned} A &= P(1+i)^n \\ f(x) &= 2\ 000(1 + 0.03)^{2x} \\ f(x) &= 2\ 000(1.03)^{2x} \end{aligned}$$

The function that represents Jorge's investment is $f(x) = 2\ 000(1.03)^{2x}$.

23. C

Substituting the given interest of 5%/a compounded annually and the principal of \$4 000 into the compound interest formula $A = P(1 + i)^n$ gives $A = 4\ 000(1 + 0.05)^n$. Thus, the growth can be represented by the exponential function $f(x) = 4\ 000(1.05)^x$. The graphs in A and B are not exponential so cannot represent the growth of an investment at compound interest.

24. C

Step 1
Calculate the total value of the investment after ten years.
\$2 000 + \$2 416 = \$4 416

Step 2
Determine the term of the investment.
Since the interest is compounded quarterly for 10 years, each the term n is calculated as follows:
$n = 10 \times 4 = 40$

Step 3
Substitute the total value of the investment and the term length into the formula $A = P(1 + i)^n$.

$$\begin{aligned} A &= P(1+i)^n \\ 4\ 416 &= 2\ 000(1+i)^{40} \\ 2.208 &= (1+i)^{40} \\ (2.208)^{\frac{1}{40}} &= \left((1+i)^{40}\right)^{\frac{1}{40}} \\ 1.019\ 9995 &= 1 + i \\ 0.019\ 9995 &= i \end{aligned}$$

Step 4
This is the quarterly interest rate. To find the yearly interest rate, multiply the quarterly interest rate by 4.

$$\begin{aligned} 0.019\ 9995 \times 4 &= 0.079\ 998 \\ &= 8.0\% \end{aligned}$$

25. 544

Step 1
Determine the value of the investment after 5 years when interest is compounded monthly.

The monthly rate is $\frac{12\%}{12} = 1\%$, and interest is compounded $12 \times 5 = 60$ times. Therefore, $i = 0.01$ and $n = 60$. Substitute these values into the formula $A = P(1 + i)^n$.

$$\begin{aligned} A &= P(1+i)^n \\ &= 10\ 000(1 + 0.01)^{60} \\ &= \$18\ 166.97 \end{aligned}$$

Step 2
Determine the value of the investment after 5 years when interest is compounded yearly.

Substitute the given values into the formula $A = P(1 + i)^n$.

$$\begin{aligned} A &= P(1 + i)^n \\ &= 10\ 000(1 + 0.12)^5 \\ &= \$17\ 623.42 \end{aligned}$$

The investment compounded monthly will earn more interest than the investment compounded yearly.

Step 3
Determine the difference in interest earned when interest is compounded monthly and when interest is compounded yearly.
$18 166.97 – $17 623.42 = $543.55

Rounded to the nearest dollar, the difference in interest earned is $544.

26. A

Use a graphing calculator to calculate the number of years it will take for the investment to reach $35 000.

Use the TVM Solver to input the values shown.

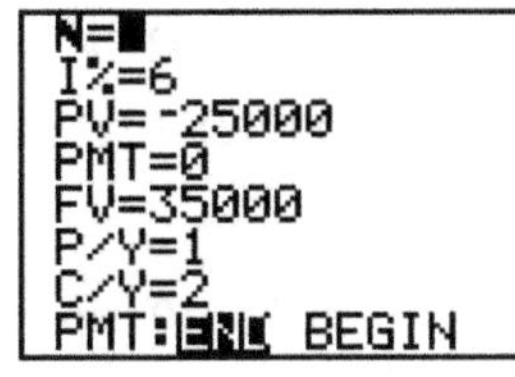

Highlighting N and pressing SOLVE, or ALPHA ENTER, gives 5.691 574 271.

Therefore it will take 5.7 years for the investment to reach a value of $35 000.

27. 167

Use the TVM Solver in a TI-83 or similar graphing calculator to input the given values.

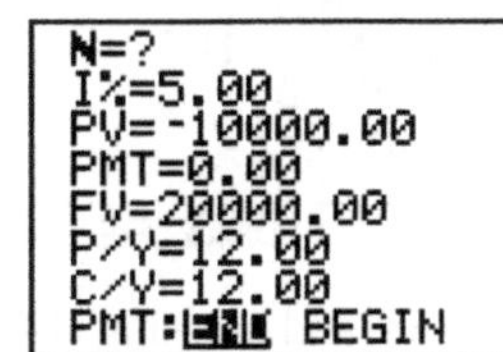

Highlighting *N* and pressing ALPHA ENTER gives 166.701 6567.

In order for the investment to be worth at least $20 000, it will have to be invested for at least 167 months, when rounded to the nearest month.

28. D

Step 1
Determine the monthly interest rate.
The monthly interest rate is 6% ÷ 12 = 0.5%.

Step 2
Calculate the ratio between consecutive terms.

$$\begin{aligned} r &= 1 + 0.005 \\ &= 1.005 \end{aligned}$$

Step 3
Determine the geometric series.
The last deposit has interest that gets compounded once, and the second last deposit has interest that gets compounded twice, and so on.
The total value of the investment is the geometric series $500(1.005)^1 + 500(1.005)^2 + 500(1.005)^3 + \ldots + 500(1.005)^{12}$.

Step 4

Use the formula $S_n = \frac{a(r^n - 1)}{r - 1}$ to find the sum of the 12 terms.

$$S_n = \frac{a(r^n - 1)}{r - 1}$$

$$S_{12} = \frac{500(1.005)^1((1.005)^{12} - 1)}{(1.005) - 1}$$

$$S_{12} = \$6\ 198.62$$

29. a) OR

Use the compound interest formula $A = P(1 + i)^n$.

The quarterly interest rate is 8% ÷ 4 = 2%, so $1 + i = 1.02$. The principal deposited is $800, so $P = 800$. Since the first deposit has been in the bank for 9 full years, it has been compounded 9 × 4 = 36 times, so $n = 36$.

Substitute these values into $A = P(1 + i)^n$ to get the value of the first deposit at the beginning of the tenth year.

$$\begin{aligned} A &= P(1 + i)^n \\ &= 800(1.02)^{36} \\ &= \$1\ 631.91 \end{aligned}$$

The value of the first deposit at the beginning of the tenth year is $1 631.91.

b) OR

Step 1

Determine the series.

All of the terms will be of the form $800(1.02)^x$, where:
$x = 0$ for the last deposit (at the beginning of the tenth year, \$800 will have been deposited into the account, but no interest will have accrued),
$x = 4$ for the second last deposit (at the beginning of the ninth year, \$800 will have been deposited and interest will be compounded 4 times over the course of that 9th year),
$x = 8$ for the third last deposit, and so on up to
$x = 36$ for the first deposit.

Written with the last deposit first, the series is
$800(1.02)^0 + 800(1.02)^4 + 800(1.02)^8 + \ldots + 800(1.02)^{36}$
. This is a geometric series with a common ratio of $r = (1.02)^4$.

Step 2

Determine the total value of the annuity.
Use the formula for the sum of the terms of a geometric series $S_n = \dfrac{a(r^n - 1)}{r - 1}$.

Calculate the sum of the 10 terms.

$$S_n = \frac{a(r^n - 1)}{r - 1}$$

$$S_{10} = \frac{800(1.02)^0((1.02)^4)^{10} - 1)}{(1.02)^4 - 1}$$
$$= \$11\ \ 723.96$$

The total value of the investment is \$11 723.96.

c) OR

Step 1

Write the series that represents the total value of the annuity at the end of the 10th year.
Since Bill makes his deposit at the beginning of each year and the question asks for the total value of the investment at the end of the 10th year, each deposit will have had the interest compounded four more times.

The series of terms is $800(1.02)^4 + 800(1.02)^8$ $+800(1.02)^{12} + \ldots + 800(1.02)^{40}$.

Step 2

Use the formula $S_n = \dfrac{a(r^n - 1)}{r - 1}$ to find the total value of the annuity.

$$S_n = \frac{a(r^n - 1)}{r - 1}$$

$$S_{10} = \frac{800(1.02)^4((1.02)4)^{10} - 1)}{(1.02)^4 - 1}$$
$$= \$12\ \ 690.40$$

d) OR

Step 1

Determine the series.

The terms all have the form $P(1.02)^x$, where $x = 4, 8, 12, \ldots, 40$ and $S_n = 15\ \ 000$.

The series is $P(1.02)^4 + P(1.02)^8$ $+P(1.02)^{12} + \ldots + P(1.02)^{40}$.

Step 2

Substitute the variables into the formula $S_n = \dfrac{a(r^n - 1)}{r - 1}$.

$$S_n = \frac{a(r^n - 1)}{r - 1}$$

$$15\ \ 000 = \frac{P(1.02)^4((1.02)^4)^{10} - 1)}{(1.02)^4 - 1}$$

$15\ \ 000 \approx 15.863P$
$\$945.60 \approx P$

Therefore, if Bill makes 10 deposits of \$945.60 under the stated conditions, the annuity will be worth \$15 000 at the end of 10 years.

30. C

Step 1

Determine the future value of John's investment.
Use the TVM Solver feature of a TI-83 or similar graphing calculator to input the values given for John's investment.

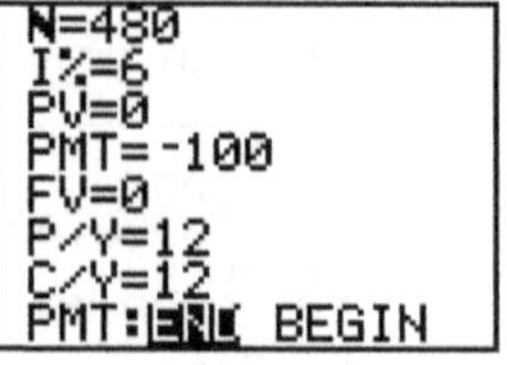

Highlighting FV and pressing SOLVE, or ALPHA ENTER, gives 199 149.07.

Step 2
Determine the future value of Jill's investment.

Use the TVM Solver feature of a TI-83 or similar graphing calculator to input the values given for Jill's investment.

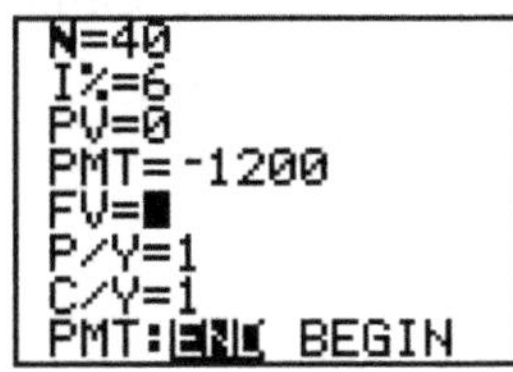

Highlighting FV and pressing SOLVE, or ALPHA ENTER, gives 185 714.36.

Step 3
Subtract the value of Jill's investment from the value of John's investment.
$199 149.07 – $185 714.36 = $13 434.71

Rounded to the nearest dollar, John's investment will be worth $13 435 more than Jill's investment by the time they are 65.

31. 144

Step 1
Use the TVM Solver to determine the future value of Zack's investment.

Enter the values as shown.

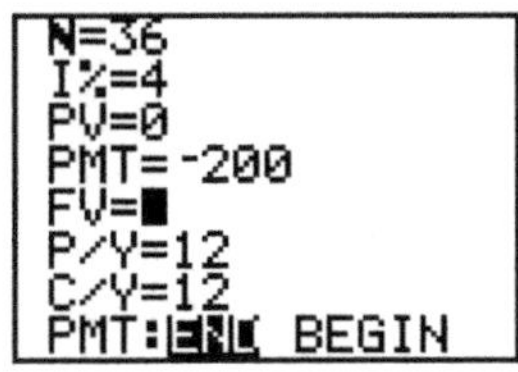

Highlighting FV and pressing SOLVE, or ALPHA ENTER, gives 7 636.31.

The principal invested is 36 × $200 = $7 200, so the interest earned is $7 636.31 – $7 200 = $436.31.

Step 2
Use the TVM Solver to determine the future value of James' investment.

Enter the values as shown.

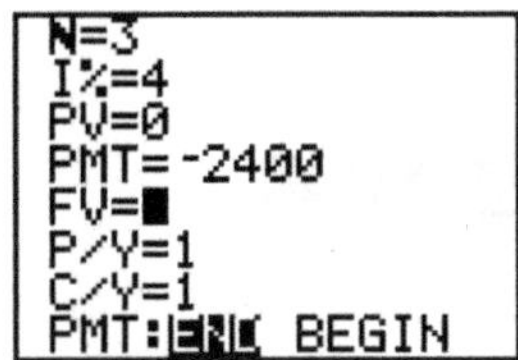

Highlighting FV and pressing SOLVE, or ALPHA ENTER, gives 7 491.84.

The principal invested is 3 × $2 400 = $7 200, so the interest earned is
$7 491.84 – $7 200 = $291.84.

Calculate the difference in interest.
$436.31 – $291.84 = $144.47

Rounded to the nearest dollar, the difference in the amount of interest is $144.

32. C

Use the TVM Solver to input the values shown.

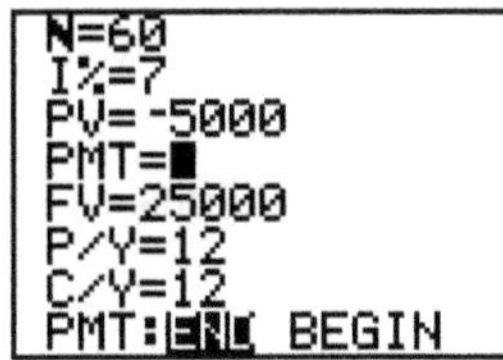

Highlighting PMT and pressing SOLVE, or ALPHA ENTER, gives –250.190 63.

In order to have at least $25 000, Sue would have to make regular deposits of $251 each month (she would need to round up in order to ensure a $25 000 value).

33. 2450

Use the TVM Solver to input the given values as shown.

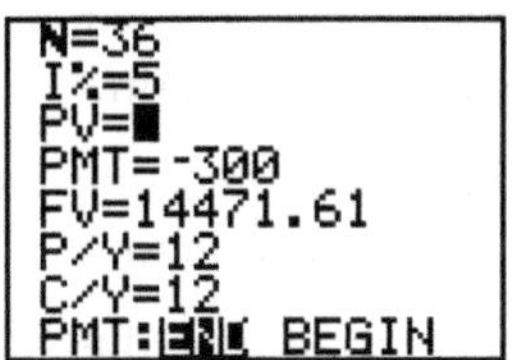

Highlighting PV and pressing SOLVE, or ALPHA ENTER, gives –2 450.002 047.

The present value is the amount of money in the account before the annuity started; therefore, Karen had $2 450 in the account originally.

UNIT TEST — DISCRETE FUNCTIONS

Use the following information to answer the next question.

Peter made a list of functions.

I. $f(x) = x^4 + 42x^3 - 5$, $-8 \leq x \leq -2$

II. $f(x) = \dfrac{2x - 1}{5 - x}$, $x \in I$

III. $f(x) = \dfrac{3x}{2^{x+4}}$, $x \in W$

IV. $f(x) = 5^{3x} + 8x^2$, $x \in R$

1. Which of the functions on Peter's list are discrete?

A. I, II, and III

B. I and II only

C. II and III only

D. I, II, III, and IV

2. Which of the following recursive procedures would generate the sequence 1, 5, 25, 125, …?

A. Subtract the two preceding terms to get the next term.

B. Multiply each preceding term by 5 to obtain the next term.

C. Add the two preceding terms together to get the next term.

D. Square each preceding term, and add 4 to obtain the next term.

Open Response

3. Determine the first four terms of a sequence with a recursive formula of $t_n = 1 + n + t_{n-1}$, where $t_1 = 2$ and $n > 1$.

Open Response

4. Determine a recursive formula to represent the sequence $\frac{1}{2}, \frac{7}{6}, \frac{23}{12}, \frac{163}{60}, \ldots$.

Use the following information to answer the next question.

The first half of the 10th row of Pascal's triangle is the sequence 1, 9, 36, 84, 126.

Numerical Response

5. The eighth term in the 11th row is _______.

6. The first three terms of the expansion of $(x^2 - 3y)^6$ are

A. $x^5 - 15x^6y + 90x^5y^2$

B. $x^{12} - 6x^{10}y + 15x^8y^2$

C. $x^8 - 18x^7y + 135x^6y^2$

D. $x^{12} - 18x^{10}y + 135x^8y^2$

7. Which of the following sequences is neither arithmetic nor geometric?

A. $\frac{1}{2}, 1, \frac{3}{2}, 2, \ldots$

B. $\frac{1}{2}, 1, \frac{3}{2}, \frac{5}{2}, \ldots$

C. $\frac{1}{2}, -1, 2, -4, \ldots$

D. $\frac{1}{2}, -1, -\frac{5}{2}, -4, \ldots$

Numerical Response

8. The 30th term of the sequence 4, 8, 12, 16, … is __________.

9. The sum of the first 15 terms of the series 40, 35, 30, 25, … is
   A. 75 **B.** 115
   C. 825 **D.** 1 125

Use the following information to answer the next multipart question.

10. The sum of the geometric series $3 + t_2 + t_3 + \ldots + 3\ 072$ is 6 141.

Open Response

a) Determine the common ratio.

b) Using a common ratio of 2, determine the 15th term of the given geometric series.

c) Using a common ratio of 2, determine the sum of the first 15 terms of the given geometric series.

Use the following information to answer the next question.

A city plans a monthly lottery where the first prize is $20 000, and the prize money will increase by 10% each month for one year.

11. To the nearest dollar, the amount of prize money that will be awarded is
   A. $62 769 **B.** $240 073
   C. $427 686 **D.** $627 676

12. An arithmetic sequence with a general term that simplifies to $t_n = 400(2 + 0.06n)$ could represent a principal investment of
   A. $400 invested at a simple interest rate of 3%/*a*
   B. $400 invested at a simple interest rate of 6%/*a*
   C. $800 invested at a simple interest rate of 3%/*a*
   D. $800 invested at a simple interest rate of 6%/*a*

13. Which of the following investments could be represented by the function $f(x) = 3\ 000(1.02)^{4x}$ if x represents the number of years the money is invested?
   A. $3 000 invested at 2%/*a*, compounded quarterly
   B. $3 000 invested at 8%/*a*, compounded quarterly
   C. $3 000 invested at 2%/*a*, compounded yearly
   D. $3 000 invested at 8%/*a*, compounded yearly

Use the following information to answer the next question.

The future value of an investment is \$4 500 after 8 years invested at a rate of 6%/*a*, compounded quarterly.

Numerical Response

14. To the nearest dollar, the present value of the investment is \$_________.

Use the following information to answer the next question.

A principal of \$1 500 is invested in an account earning 8%/*a*, compounded annually. When the value of the investment is at least \$25 000, the money will be withdrawn.

Numerical Response

15. To the nearest tenth of a year, the number of years that the money will be in the account is _________.

Use the following information to answer the next multipart question.

16. Jill is 20 years old. To plan for retirement, Jill starts an annuity by making yearly deposits of \$1 000 into an account earning interest at 6%/*a* compounded monthly. She makes the deposits at the beginning of each year for five consecutive years.

Open Response

a) Write the series that represents the total value of the annuity at the end of the fifth year, and then find the total value.

b) Write the series that represents the total value of the annuity when Jill turns 65, and find the total value of the investment.

c) If Jill needs the investment to have a total value of \$100 000 when she reaches age 65, calculate the amount she should have deposited each year.

Use the following information to answer the next question.

At age 15, Keysha starts an annuity to save for her retirement at age 65. She deposits \$50 at the end of each month into an account earning interest at 5%/*a*, compounded monthly. Julie waits until she is 40 to start saving and deposits \$200 at the end of each month into an account earning interest at 5%/*a*, compounded monthly.

17. At age 65, the difference in value between the two investments is

A. \$13 834.40 **B.** \$14 330.66

C. \$14 390.37 **D.** \$14 886.63

Use the following information to answer the next question.

Bob has two options to choose from in order to save money for a new car he plans to purchase in 5 years. With the first option, he would deposit $400 at the end of each month into an account that earns interest at 5%/*a*, compounded monthly. With the second option, Bob would deposit $4 000 at the end of each year into an account that earns interest at 4%/*a*, compounded annually.

18. At the end of 5 years, how much more money will Bob have saved by investing in the first option instead of the second option?

A. $4 704.11 **B.** $5 505.01

C. $5 537.14 **D.** $5 538.59

Use the following information to answer the next question.

Don has $3 000 in an account earning interest at 8%/a, compounded quarterly. He starts an annuity by making regular deposits of $150 into the account at the end of every quarter.

19. How much interest will Don have earned after 6 years?

A. $2 692.11 **B.** $2 780.14

C. $2 788.59 **D.** $2 879.86

ANSWERS AND SOLUTIONS — UNIT TEST

1. C	6. D	b) OR	14. 2794	17. B
2. B	7. B	c) OR	15. 36.6	18. C
3. OR	8. 120	11. C	16. a) OR	19. C
4. OR	9. A	12. C	b) OR	
5. 120	10. a) OR	13. B	c) OR	

1. C

Since a discrete function must have a domain of natural numbers, whole numbers, or integers, both functions II and III are discrete.

Function I is continuous over the given interval and is therefore not discrete.

Function IV is continuous over the set of real numbers and is therefore not discrete.

2. B

Step 1
Build a sequence that has $t_1 = 1$ by squaring each preceding term and adding 4 to obtain the next term.

$$\begin{aligned} t_2 &= (t_1)^2 + 4 \\ &= 1^2 + 4 \\ &= 5 \end{aligned}$$

$$\begin{aligned} t_3 &= (t_2)^2 + 4 \\ &= 5^2 + 4 \\ &= 29 \end{aligned}$$

$$\begin{aligned} t_4 &= (t_3)^2 + 4 \\ &= 29^2 + 4 \\ &= 845 \end{aligned}$$

The sequence is 1, 5, 29, 845, ..., which is not the given sequence.

Step 2
Build a sequence that has $t_1 = 1$ and $t_2 = 5$ by adding the two previous terms together to get the next term.

$$\begin{aligned} t_3 &= t_2 + t_1 \\ &= 5 + 1 \\ &= 6 \end{aligned}$$

$$\begin{aligned} t_4 &= t_3 + t_2 \\ &= 6 + 5 \\ &= 11 \end{aligned}$$

The sequence is 1, 5, 6, 11, ..., which is not the given sequence.

Step 3
Build a sequence that has $t_1 = 1$ and $t_2 = 5$ by subtracting the two previous terms to get the next term.

$$\begin{aligned} t_3 &= t_2 - t_1 \\ &= 5 - 1 \\ &= 4 \end{aligned}$$

$$\begin{aligned} t_4 &= t_3 - t_2 \\ &= 4 - 5 \\ &= -1 \end{aligned}$$

The sequence is 1, 5, 4, −1, ..., which is not the given sequence.

Step 4
Build a sequence that has $t_1 = 1$ by multiplying each preceding term by 5 to obtain the next term.

$$\begin{aligned} t_2 &= 5(t_1) \\ &= 5(1) \\ &= 5 \end{aligned}$$

$$\begin{aligned} t_3 &= 5(t_2) \\ &= 5(5) \\ &= 25 \end{aligned}$$

$$\begin{aligned} t_4 &= 5(t_3) \\ &= 5(25) \\ &= 125 \end{aligned}$$

The sequence is 1, 5, 25, 125, ..., which matches the given sequence.

3. OR

The first term is given in the recursive formula as $t_1 = 2$. Determine the other terms.

$$\begin{aligned} t_2 &= 1 + 2 + t_1 \\ &= 1 + 2 + 2 \\ &= 5 \end{aligned}$$

$$\begin{aligned} t_3 &= 1 + 3 + t_2 \\ &= 1 + 3 + 5 \\ &= 9 \end{aligned}$$

$$\begin{aligned} t_4 &= 1 + 4 + t_3 \\ &= 1 + 4 + 9 \\ &= 14 \end{aligned}$$

Therefore, the first four terms of the sequence are 2, 5, 9, and 14.

4. OR

Step 1
Subtract consecutive terms.

$$t_2 - t_1 = \frac{7}{6} - \frac{1}{2} = \frac{2}{3}$$

$$t_3 - t_2 = \frac{23}{12} - \frac{7}{6} = \frac{3}{4}$$

$$t_4 - t_3 = \frac{163}{60} - \frac{23}{12} = \frac{4}{5}$$

Therefore, $\frac{2}{3}$ is added for term 2, $\frac{3}{4}$ is added for term 3, and $\frac{4}{5}$ is added for term 4.

Step 2
Determine the recursive formula.
A fraction is added where the numerator equals the term number and the denominator is one larger than the term number.

Therefore, the recursive formula is $t_1 = \frac{1}{2}$,

$$t_n = t_{n-1} + \frac{n}{n+1}, n > 1.$$

5. 120

Because of symmetry, the entire 10th row is 1, 9, 36, 84, 126, 126, 84, 36, 9, 1.

Start with 1 as the first and last terms of the 11th row, and add consecutive terms from the 10th row to form the remaining terms in the 11th row. This creates the sequence 1, 10, 45, 120, 210, 252, 210, 120, 45, 10, 1.

Therefore, the eighth term in the eleventh row is 120.

6. D

Step 1
Determine the first three terms of the seventh row of Pascal's triangle.
Write the first six rows.

```
          1
        1   1
      1   2   1
    1   3   3   1
  1   4   6   4   1
1   5  10  10   5   1
```

Continue the pattern of adding numbers in the previous row to generate numbers in the next row.

```
  1+  5+  10+  10+  5+  1
    ↓   ↓    ↓    ↓   ↓
1   6   15   20   15  6   1
```

The first three terms of the seventh row are 1, 6, and 15.

Step 2
Use these values to determine the first three terms of the expansion.

In general, $(x + y)^6$
$= x^6 + 6x^5y + 15x^4y^2 + 20x^3y^3 + 15x^2y^4 + 6xy^5 + y^6$.

$$(x^2 - 3y)^6$$
$$= 1(x^2)^6 + 6(x^2)^5(-3y) + 15(x^2)^4(-3y)^2$$
$$= 1(x^{12}) + 6(x^{10})(-3y) + 15(x^8)(9y^2)$$
$$= x^{12} - 18x^{10}y + 135x^8y^2$$

The first three terms are $x^{12} - 18x^{10}y + 135x^8y^2$.

7. B

Step 1

Determine the first differences of the sequences.

- $\frac{1}{2}, 1, \frac{3}{2}, 2, \ldots 1 - \frac{1}{2} = \frac{1}{2}$

  $\frac{3}{2} - 1 = \frac{1}{2}$

  $2 - \frac{3}{2} = \frac{1}{2}$

  The sequence has a common difference of $\frac{1}{2}$; therefore, it is arithmetic.

- $\frac{1}{2}, -1, 2, -4, \ldots -1 - \frac{1}{2} = -1.5$

  $2 - (-1) = 3$

  $-4 - 2 = -6$

  The sequence has no common difference; therefore, it is not arithmetic.

- $\frac{1}{2}, 1, \frac{3}{2}, \frac{5}{2}, \ldots 1 - \frac{1}{2} = \frac{1}{2}$

  $\frac{3}{2} - 1 = \frac{1}{2}$

  $\frac{5}{2} - \frac{3}{2} = 1$

  The sequence has no common difference; therefore, it is not arithmetic.

- $\frac{1}{2}, -1, -\frac{5}{2}, -4, \ldots -1 - \frac{1}{2} = -1.5$

  $-\frac{5}{2} - (-1) = -1.5$

  $-4 - \left(-\frac{5}{2}\right) = -1.5$

  The sequence has a common difference of -1.5; therefore, it is arithmetic.

Step 2

Determine the ratio of consecutive terms of only the sequences $\frac{1}{2}, -1, 2, -4, \ldots$ and $\frac{1}{2}, 1, \frac{3}{2}, \frac{5}{2}, \ldots$ since the other two sequences have been determined to be arithmetic.

- $\frac{1}{2}, -1, 2, -4, \ldots$

  $\frac{-1}{\frac{1}{2}} = -2$

  $\frac{2}{-1} = -2$

  $\frac{-4}{2} = -2$

  There is a common ratio between consecutive terms of -2; therefore, it is geometric.

- $\frac{1}{2}, 1, \frac{3}{2}, \frac{5}{2}, \ldots$

  $\frac{1}{\frac{1}{2}} = 2$

  $\frac{\frac{3}{2}}{1} = \frac{3}{2}$

  $\frac{\frac{5}{2}}{\frac{3}{2}} = \frac{5}{3}$

  There is no common ratio between consecutive terms; therefore, it is not geometric.

The sequence $\frac{1}{2}, 1, \frac{3}{2}, \frac{5}{2}, \ldots$ is neither arithmetic nor geometric.

8. 120

The sequence is arithmetic with a first term of $a = 4$ and a common difference of $d = 4$. Substitute these values into the formula $t_n = a + (n - 1)d$.

$t_n = a + (n - 1)d$

$t_{30} = 4 + (30 - 1)(4)$

$t_{30} = 4 + 116$

$t_{30} = 120$

9. A

This is an arithmetic series with a first term of $a = 40$ and a common difference of $d = -5$. Substitute these values into the formula $S_n = \frac{n}{2}(2a + (n - 1)d)$ to find the sum of the first 15 terms of the series.

$$S_n = \frac{n}{2}(2a + (n - 1)d)$$
$$S_{15} = \frac{15}{2}(2(40) + (15 - 1)(-5))$$
$$S_{15} = 7.5(80 - 70)$$
$$S_{15} = 75$$

10. a) OR

The series is geometric. The first term is $a = 3$, the last term is $t_n = 3\ 072$, and the sum of n terms is $S_n = 6\ 141$.

Substitute the variables into the equation $S_n = \frac{rt_n - a}{r - 1}$, and solve for r.

$$\begin{aligned} S_n &= \frac{rt_n - a}{r - 1} \\ 6\ 141 &= \frac{r(3\ 072) - 3}{r - 1} \\ 6\ 141r - 6\ 141 &= 3\ 072r - 3 \\ 3\ 069r &= 6\ 138 \\ r &= 2 \end{aligned}$$

Therefore, the common ratio is 2.

b) OR

In the formula $t_n = ar^{n-1}$, substitute 3 for a, 2 for r, and 15 for n.

$$t_n = ar^{n-1}$$
$$t_{15} = 3(2)^{15-1}$$
$$= 49\ 152$$

The 15th term in the given geometric series is 49 152.

c) OR

In the formula $S_n = \frac{a(r^n - 1)}{r - 1}$, substitute 3 for a, 2 for r, and 15 for n.

$$S_n = \frac{a(r^n - 1)}{r - 1}$$
$$S_{15} = \frac{3(2^{15} - 1)}{(2) - 1}$$
$$S_{15} = 98\ 301$$

The sum of the first 15 terms of the given geometric series is 98 301.

11. C

The 12 prizes will form a geometric series with a first term of $a = \$20\ 000$.

Step 1
Find the common ratio.

$$r = 1 + 10\%$$
$$r = 1 + 0.1$$
$$r = 1.1$$

Step 2
Substitute the variables into the formula $S_n = \frac{a(r^n - 1)}{r - 1}$.

$$S_n = \frac{a(r^n - 1)}{r - 1}$$
$$S_{12} = \frac{20\ 000(1.1^{12} - 1)}{1.1 - 1}$$
$$S_{12} = \$427\ 686$$

12. C

Step 1
Expand the equation $t_n = 400(2 + 0.06n)$, and write it in the form $t_n = a + (n - 1)d$.

$$\begin{aligned} t_n &= 400(2 + 0.06n) \\ &= 800 + 24n \\ &= 800 + 24n + 24 - 24 \\ &= 824 + 24n - 24 \\ &= 824 + 24(n - 1) \end{aligned}$$

Step 2
Interpret the general term equation given by $t_n = 824 + 24(n - 1)$.

Since $a = 824$ and $d = 24$, the value of the investment at the end of the first year is \$824 and the common difference is 24. Therefore, \$24 of interest is earned each year.
If the value of the investment after one year is \$824 and \$24 of interest is earned that year, the principal amount invested would be \$824 – \$24 = \$800.

Step 3
Calculate the annual interest rate, r.
For an initial investment of \$800, \$24 of interest is earned in one year.

$$\begin{aligned} r &= \frac{24}{800} \\ &= 0.03 \\ &= 3\% \end{aligned}$$

A sequence with the general term $t_n = 400(2 + 0.06n)$ could represent a principal investment of \$800 invested at a simple interest rate of 3%/a.

13. B

Compare the equation $f(x) = 3\ 000(1.02)^{4x}$ with the formula $A = P(1+i)^n$ to find that $n = 4x$, $1 + i = 1.02$, and $P = 3\ 000$.

Since the compounding period is $4x$, the money is compounded quarterly. The quarterly interest rate is 2%, so the yearly interest rate is $2\% \times 4 = 8\%$. P is the initial investment, so the initial investment is \$3 000.

The equation $f(x) = 3\ 000(1.02)^{4x}$ represents \$3 000 invested at 8%/a, compounded quarterly.

14. 2794

The quarterly interest rate is $6\% \div 4 = 1.5\%$, and the number of compounding periods is $8 \times 4 = 32$. Therefore, $i = 0.015$ and $n = 32$. Substitute these values into the formula $FV = PV(1+i)^n$, and solve for PV.

$$\begin{aligned} FV &= PV(1+i)^n \\ 4\ 500 &= PV(1+0.015)^{32} \\ 4\ 500 &\approx PV(1.610\ 32\ldots) \\ \$2\ 794 &\approx PV \end{aligned}$$

15. 36.6

Use the TVM Solver to input the values as shown.

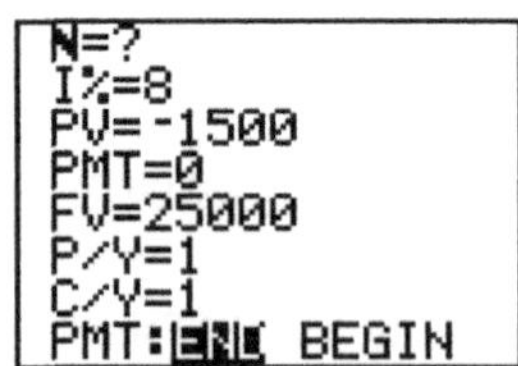

Highlighting N and pressing SOLVE, or ALPHA ENTER, gives 36.556 297 51.

It will take 36.6 years for the investment to reach a value of \$25 000.

16. a) OR

Step 1
Determine the series.

The monthly interest rate is $6\% \div 12 = 0.5\%$, so $1 + r = 1.005$.

Since there are 12 compounding periods in a year, the terms will have the form $1\ 000(1.005)^n$, where the following conditions apply:

- $n = 12$ for the last deposit—at the beginning of the fifth year when only 12 compounding periods (or 1 year) remain.
- $n = 24$ for the second last deposit—at the beginning of the fourth year when only 24 compounding periods (or 2 years) remain.
- $n = 36$ for the third last deposit, and so on up to $n = 12 \times 5 = 60$ for the first deposit.

Written with the last deposit first, the series is

$$1\ 000(1.005)^{12} + 1\ 000(1.005)^{24} + 1\ 000(1.005)^{36} + 1\ 000(1.005)^{48} + 1\ 000(1.005)^{60}.$$

This is a geometric series with a common ratio of $r = (1.005)^{12}$.

Step 2
Find the total value of the investment.

Use the formula for the sum of the terms of a geometric series $S_n = \dfrac{a(r^n - 1)}{r - 1}$.

$$\begin{aligned} S_n &= \frac{a(r^n - 1)}{r - 1} \\ S_5 &= \frac{1\ 000(1.005)^{12}\left(\left((1.005)^{12}\right)^5 - 1\right)}{(1.005)^{12} - 1} \\ &= \$6\ 004.86 \end{aligned}$$

The total value of the investment is \$6 004.86.

b) OR

Step 1
Calculate the number of compounding periods.

When Jill is 65, the first deposit will have been in the account for 45 years.

The number of compounding periods for the first deposit is $n = 12 \times 45 = 540$.

Step 2
Determine the series.

For the other deposits in the series, the value of n will decrease by multiples of 12.

$$1\ 000(1.005)^{492} + 1\ 000(1.005)^{504} + 1\ 000(1.005)^{516} + 1\ 000(1.005)^{528} + 1\ 000(1.005)^{540}$$

Step 3
Determine the total value of the annuity.
Substitute the known values into the formula
$S_n = \frac{a(r^n - 1)}{r - 1}$, and solve.

$$S_n = \frac{a(r^n - 1)}{r - 1}$$

$$S_5 = \frac{1\ 000(1.005)^{492}\left(\left((1.005)^{12}\right)^5 - 1\right)}{(1.005)^{12} - 1}$$

$S_5 = \$65\ \ 797.95$

Therefore, the total value of the investment is \$65 797.95.

c) OR

Step 1
Determine the series.
In this situation, the terms all have the form $P(1.005)^x$, where $x = 492, 504, 516, 528, 540$ and $S_n = 100\ \ 000$.
The series is
$P(1.005)^{492} + P(1.005)^{504} + P(1.005)^{516}$
$+P(1.005)^{528} + P(1.005)^{540}$.

Step 2
Substitute into the sum formula.

$$S_n = \frac{a(r^n - 1)}{r - 1}$$

$$100\ \ 000 = \frac{P(1.005)^{492}\left(\left((1.005)^{12}\right)^5 - 1\right)}{(1.005)^{12} - 1}$$

$100\ \ 000 = 65.797\ 95P$
$1\ \ 519.80 = P$

Jill should have made five deposits of \$1 519.80 under the stated conditions for her annuity to be worth \$100 000 when she reaches age 65.

17. B

Step 1
Determine the value of the investment Keysha starts at age 15.
Use the TVM Solver to input the values as shown.

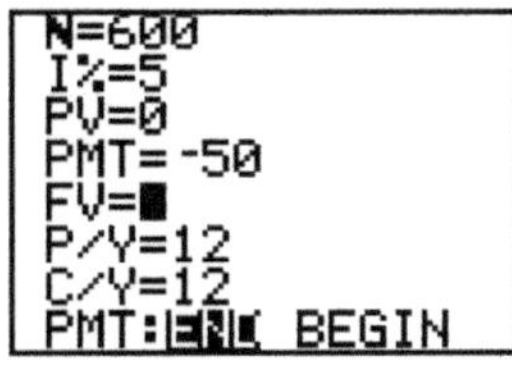

Highlighting FV and pressing SOLVE, or ALPHA ENTER, gives 133 432.60.

Step 2
Determine the value of the investment Julie starts at age 40.
Use the TVM Solver to input the values as shown.

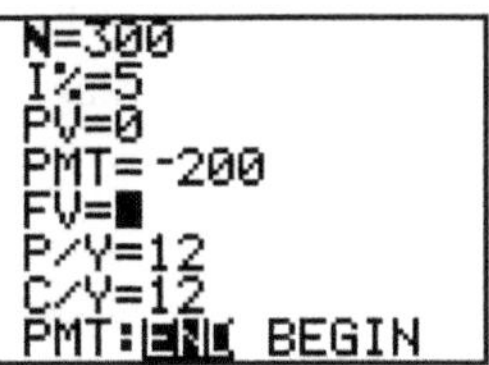

Highlighting FV and pressing SOLVE, or ALPHA ENTER, gives 119 101.94.

Step 3
Determine the difference between the two investments.
Subtracting the two values gives a result of \$133 432.60 – \$119 101.94 = \$14 330.66.

18. C

Step 1
Determine the final value of the investment with the first option.
Use the TVM Solver to input the values shown for the first option.

Highlighting FV and pressing SOLVE, or ALPHA ENTER, gives 27 202.43.

Step 2
Determine the final value of the investment with the second option.
Use the TVM Solver to input the values shown for the second option.

Highlighting FV and pressing SOLVE, or ALPHA ENTER, gives 21 665.29.

Step 3
Determine the difference between the two investment options.

Subtracting the two values gives a result of $27 202.43 – $21 665.29 = $5 537.14. Bob will save an extra $5 537.14 by investing using the first option.

19. C

Step 1
Determine the future value of the investment.

Use the TVM Solver to input the given values as shown.

Highlighting FV and pressing SOLVE, or ALPHA ENTER, gives 9 388.59.

Step 2
Calculate the total amount deposited into the account over 6 years (24 quarters).
$3 000 + 24($150) = $6 600

Step 3
Calculate the total interest earned by subtracting Don's total investment amount from the future value of the investment.
$9 388.598 – $6 600 = $2 788.59
Therefore, the total interest earned is $2 788.59.

Trigonometry

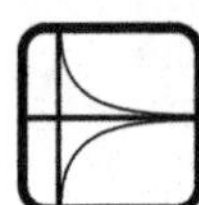

TRIGONOMETRIC FUNCTIONS

Table of Correlations

	Specific Expectation	Practice Questions	Unit Test Questions	Practice Test 1	Practice Test 2
TR1.0	Determining and Applying Trigonometric Ratios				
TR1.1	*determine the exact values of the sine, cosine, and tangent of the special angles: 0°, 30°, 45°, 60°, and 90°*	1, 2	1	34	
TR1.2	*determine the values of the sine, cosine, and tangent of angles from 0° to 360°, through investigation using a variety of tools and strategies*	3, 4	2		15
TR1.3	*determine the measures of two angles from 0° to 360° for which the value of a given trigonometric ratio is the same*	5, 6	3	35	16
TR1.4	*define the secant, cosecant, and cotangent ratios for angles in a right triangle in terms of the sides of the triangle and relate these ratios to the cosine, sine, and tangent ratios*	7, 8	4	36	17
TR1.5	*prove simple trigonometric identities, using the Pythagorean identity* $sin^2x + cos^2x = 1$*; the quotient identity tanx = sinxcosx; and the reciprocal identities secx = 1cosx, cscx = 1sinx, and cotx = 1tanx*	9, 10	5	37	18
TR1.6	*pose problems involving right triangles and oblique triangles in two-dimensional settings, and solve these and other such problems using the primary trigonometric ratios, the cosine law, and the sine law (including the ambiguous case)*	11, 12	6, 7a, 7b	38	19
TR1.7	*pose problems involving right triangles and oblique triangles in three-dimensional settings, and solve these and other such problems using the primary trigonometric ratios, the cosine law, and the sine law*	13, 14	8	39	20
TR2.0	Connecting Graphs and Equations of Sinusoidal Functions				
TR2.1	*describe key properties of periodic functions arising from real-world applications, given a numeric or graphical representation*	15, 16a, 16b, 16c	9		21
TR2.2	*predict, by extrapolating, the future behaviour of a relationship modelled using a numeric or graphical representation of a periodic function*	17, 18	10	40	
TR2.3	*make connections between the sine ratio and the sine function and between the cosine ratio and the cosine function by graphing the relationship between angles from 0° to 360° and the corresponding sine ratios or cosine ratios, with or without technology defining this relationship as the function f(x) = sinx or f(x) = cosx, and explaining why the relationship is a function*	19, 20	11		22
TR2.4	*sketch the graphs of f(x) = sinx and f(x) = cosx for angle measures expressed in degrees, and determine and describe their key properties (i.e., cycle, domain, range, intercepts, amplitude, period, maximum and minimum values, increasing/decreasing intervals)*	21, 22	12	41	
TR2.5	*determine, through investigation using technology, the roles of the parameters a, k, d, and c in functions of the form y = af(k(x-d)) + c, where f(x) = sinx or f(x) = cosx with angles expressed in degrees, and describe these roles in terms of transformations on the graphs of f(x) = sinx and f(x) = cosx (i.e., translations; reflections in the axes; vertical and horizontal stretches and compressions to and from the x- and y-axes)*	23, 24	13	42	23

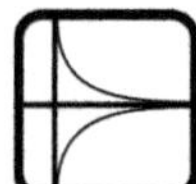

TR2.6	*determine the amplitude, period, phase shift, domain, and range of sinusoidal functions whose equations are given in the form $f(x) = a\sin(k(x-d)) + c$ or $f(x) = a\cos(k(x-d)) + c$*	25, 26	14, 15		
TR2.7	*sketch graphs of $y = af(k(x - d)) + c$ by applying one or more transformations to the graphs of $f(x) = \sin x$ and $f(x) = \cos x$, and state the domain and range of the transformed functions*	27, 28	16		24
TR2.8	*represent a sinusoidal function with an equation, given its graph or its properties*	29, 30	17	43	
TR3.0	Solving Problems Involving Sinusoidal Functions				
TR3.1	*collect data that can be modelled as a sinusoidal function through investigation with and without technology, from primary sources, using a variety of tools or from secondary sources and graph the data*	31, 32			
TR3.2	*identify periodic and sinusoidal functions, including those that arise from real-world applications involving periodic phenomena, given various representations (i.e., tables of values, graphs, equations), and explain any restrictions that the context places on the domain and range*	33, 34	18	44	25
TR3.3	*determine, through investigation, how sinusoidal functions can be used to model periodic phenomena that do not involve angles*	35, 36			26
TR3.4	*predict the effects on a mathematical model (i.e., graph, equation) of an application involving periodic phenomena when the conditions in the application are varied*	37, 38	19	45	27
TR3.5	*pose problems based on applications involving a sinusoidal function, and solve these and other such problems by using a given graph or a graph generated with technology from a table of values or from its equation*	39a, 39b, 39c, 39d, 40	20, 21	46a, 46b, 47	28

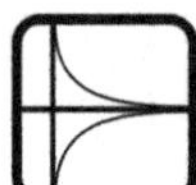

TR1.1 determine the exact values of the sine, cosine, and tangent of the special angles: 0°, 30°, 45°, 60°, and 90°

Exact Values for Primary Trigonometric Ratios

For most angles, the trigonometric ratios obtained using calculators are approximations. Using a calculator to determine the exact values of the primary trigonometric ratios (sine, cosine, and tangent) is only valid for the special angles of 0° and 90°.

Example

Determine the exact values for sin 90°, cos 0°, and tan 90°.

Solution

When using a scientific calculator, be sure it is set to degree mode. The exact values are given.

$\sin 90° = 1$
$\cos 0° = 1$
$\tan 90° = \text{undefined}$

For the remaining special angles (30°, 45°, and 60°), the exact trigonometric ratios can be determined by examining the primary trigonometric ratios in the two given special triangles.

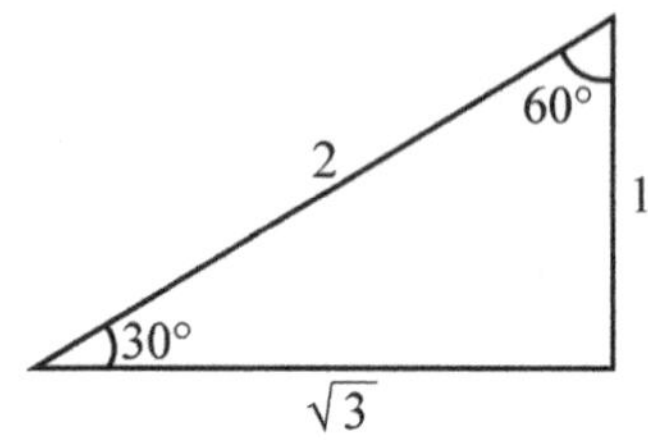

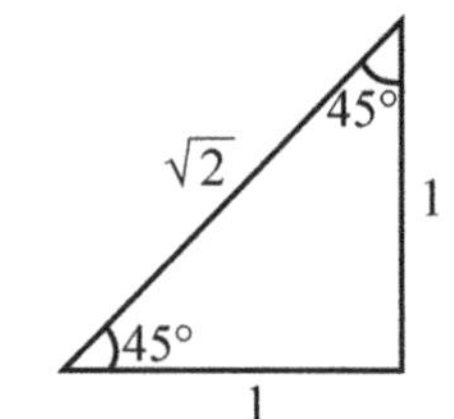

Example

Determine the exact values for sin 30°, cos 45°, and tan 60°.

Solution

Use the special triangles and the primary trigonometric ratios to evaluate the exact values.

$$\sin\theta = \frac{\text{opposite}}{\text{hypotenuse}}$$

$$\sin 30° = \frac{1}{2}$$

$$\cos\theta = \frac{\text{adjacent}}{\text{hypotenuse}}$$

$$\cos 45° = \frac{1}{\sqrt{2}}$$

$$\tan\theta = \frac{\text{opposite}}{\text{adjacent}}$$

$$\tan 60° = \frac{\sqrt{3}}{1}$$

---

1. What are the exact values of sin60°, cos 60°, and tan30°, respectively?

A. $\frac{1}{\sqrt{3}}, -\frac{\sqrt{3}}{2}, \frac{1}{\sqrt{2}}$

B. $\frac{\sqrt{3}}{2}, -\frac{1}{\sqrt{3}}, \frac{1}{2}$

C. $\frac{\sqrt{3}}{2}, -\frac{1}{2}, \frac{1}{\sqrt{2}}$

D. $\frac{\sqrt{3}}{2}, \frac{1}{2}, \frac{1}{\sqrt{3}}$

Numerical Response

2. If the exact value of $\cos 0° = a$ and $\tan 45° = c$, the value of $a + c$ is _______.

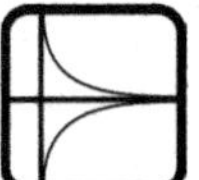

TR1.2 determine the values of the sine, cosine, and tangent of angles from 0° to 360°, through investigation using a variety of tools and strategies

Evaluating Primary Trigonometric Ratios from 0° to 360°

Angles from 0° to 360° can be drawn on a Cartesian plane. It is divided into four quadrants, which are labelled I, II, III, and IV.

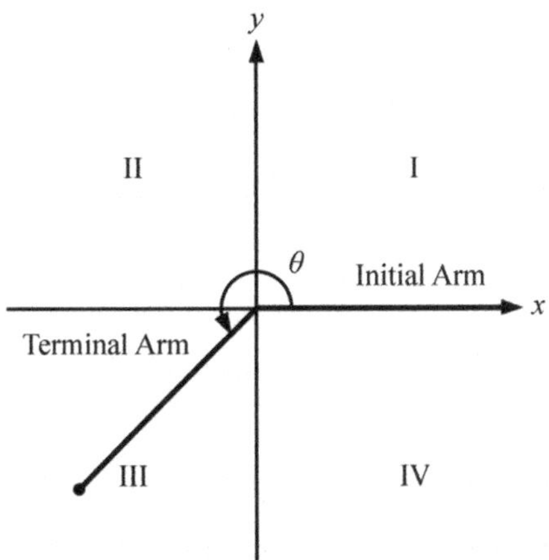

Angles on a Cartesian plane with their vertex at the origin and one arm along the positive x-axis are called angles in **standard position**.

The positive x-axis is called the **initial arm**, and all angles are measured between the initial arm and the rotating arm, called the **terminal arm**.

- When the terminal arm rotates in a counterclockwise direction, the angle is said to be a positive angle.
- When the terminal arm rotates in a clockwise direction, the angle is said to be a negative angle.
- When angles share the same terminal arm, they are called coterminal angles.

The **principal angle** is the smallest positive angle coterminal with the given angle.

For every angle in standard position, there is a reference angle. The **reference angle** is the angle between the terminal arm and the x-axis.
The reference angle is always positive and between 0° and 90°.

Starting from the bottom right (quadrant IV) and reading in a counterclockwise direction, the first letters of the trigonometric ratios that are positive are C-A-S-T. Those that are not positive are negative. This is known as the **CAST rule**.

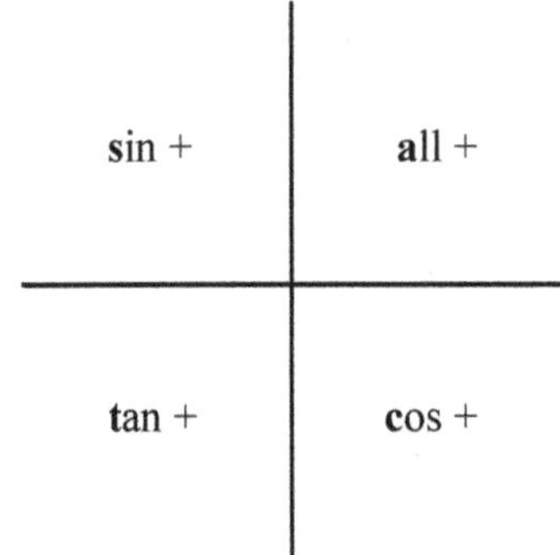

Exact Values

Special triangles can be used to determine exact values for the special angles 0°, 30°, 45°, 60°, and 90°. For values greater than 90° that are related to the special angles, the unit circle can be used.

The complete unit circle can be formed using the special triangles placed around the circle in addition to the positive and negative properties of each quadrant. The coordinates of the point $P(x, y)$ represent the location where the rotating arm intersects the circle.

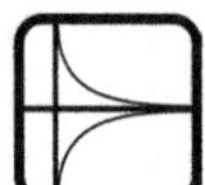

At this point, the x- and y-coordinates represent the horizontal and vertical dimensions of each special triangle.

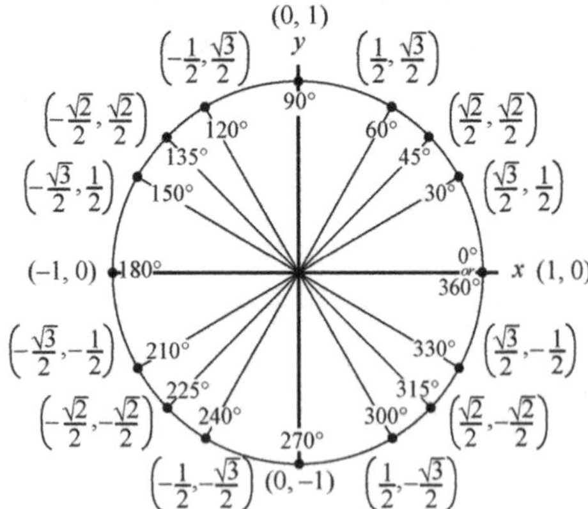

The full unit circle

When you are working with the unit circle and point $P(x, y)$ on the unit circle, recall the following relations:

$$\sin\theta = \frac{y}{r} = \frac{y}{1} = y \text{ (}y\text{-coordinate)}$$

$$\cos\theta = \frac{x}{r} = \frac{x}{1} = x \text{ (}x\text{-coordinate)}$$

$$\tan\theta = \frac{y}{r}$$

Example

Determine the exact value of sin 150°, cos 150°, and tan 150°.

Solution

Consider the special angle 150° on the unit circle. It is an angle in standard position, and it corresponds to a short triangle with a reference angle of 30° in quadrant II.

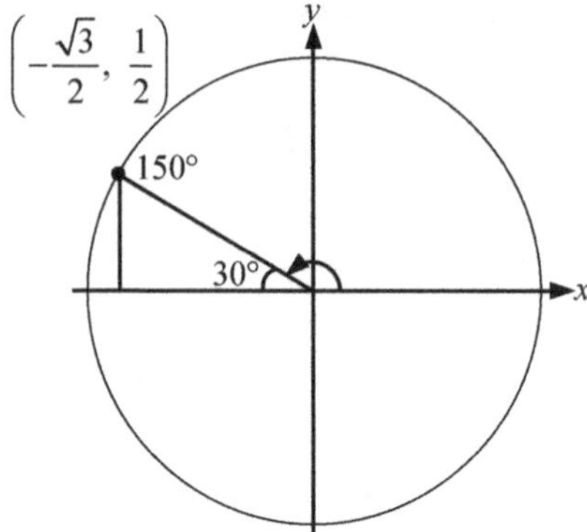

From the unit circle, point (x, y) at 150° has the coordinates $\left(-\frac{\sqrt{3}}{2}, \frac{1}{2}\right)$. Since $\sin\theta = y$ and at 150°, $y = \frac{1}{2}$, it follows that $\sin 150° = \frac{1}{2}$.

Similarly, since $\cos\theta = x$ and at 150°, $x = -\frac{\sqrt{3}}{2}$, it follows that $\cos 150° = -\frac{\sqrt{3}}{2}$.

For the calculation of tan 150°, recall that $\tan\theta = \frac{y}{x}$. Substitute the x- and y-coordinates of 150° to find the exact value.

$$\tan 150° = \frac{\frac{1}{2}}{-\frac{\sqrt{3}}{2}}$$

$$\tan 150° = \frac{1}{2} \times -\frac{2}{\sqrt{3}}$$

$$\tan 150° = -\frac{1}{\sqrt{3}}$$

The exact value of $\sin 150° = \frac{1}{2}$, of $\cos 150° = -\frac{\sqrt{3}}{2}$, and of $\tan 150° = -\frac{1}{\sqrt{3}}$.

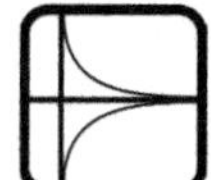

Approximate Values for Primary Trigonometric Ratios

For all angles, the primary trigonometric ratio values can be determined using a scientific calculator. A scientific calculator yields approximate values.
The use of a calculator is especially helpful for evaluating the primary trigonometric ratio values of non-special angles.

Example

Point P is on the unit circle and also on the terminal arm of an angle of 320° when it is drawn in standard position. To the nearest thousandth, determine the y-coordinate of point P.

Solution

The y-coordinate of point P is equal to the sine ratio for 320°. If you calculate sin 320° on your graphing calculator, you will get −0.642 787 6097.

Therefore, the y-coordinate of point P to the nearest thousandth is −0.643.

---

3. Point P is on both the unit circle and the terminal arm of a 314° angle, when it is drawn in standard position. To the nearest thousandth, what is the y-coordinate of point P?

A. −0.719 **B.** −0.159

C. 0.695 **D.** 0.987

Open Response

4. Find the value of cos 64° to three decimal places.

TR1.3 determine the measures of two angles from 0° to 360° for which the value of a given trigonometric ratio is the same

Evaluating Basic Trigonometric Equations

For any particular trigonometric ratio, there are often two solutions to a trigonometric equation within the potential angle values, $0° \leq \theta \leq 360°$.

To determine the measure of an angle for the given ratio value, use the inverse trigonometric function on a scientific calculator. On most scientific calculators, the inverse trigonometric functions are $\sin^{-1}$, $\cos^{-1}$, and $\tan^{-1}$.

The calculator will generate one solution, θ_1.
The second solution, θ_2, can be found by determining the quadrant in which the given trigonometric ratio has the same sign. There is a pattern to the solutions. Generally, for sine, $\theta_2 = 180° - \theta_1$, for cosine, $\theta_2 = 360° - \theta_1$, and for tangent, $\theta_2 = 180° + \theta_1$.

Example

Solve $\cos\theta = -0.364$, where $0° \leq \theta \leq 360°$, to the nearest tenth of a degree.

Solution

Method 1

To determine the measure of the unknown angle, enter $\cos^{-1}(-0.364)$ into a calculator. This gives a result of 111.3° (to the nearest tenth).
The second solution, θ_2, can be determined by observing that θ_2 must be in quadrant III (CAST rule, where cosine is negative in quadrants II and III), and by using $\theta_2 = 360° - \theta_1$.

$\theta_2 = 360° - 111.3°$
$\theta_2 = 248.7°$

To the nearest tenth, the complete solution to the equation $\cos\theta = -0.364$ is
$\theta = 111.3°$, or 248.7°.

Method 2
Using a sketching technique, the solutions can be obtained as follows:

1. Sketch the unit circle and axes.
2. Use a calculator to get the first solution, 111.3°, and sketch it.
3. Draw a vertical line from the endpoint of the angle (at approximately $x = -0.364$).
4. It is clear that the other angle is $360° - 111.3° = 248.7°$.

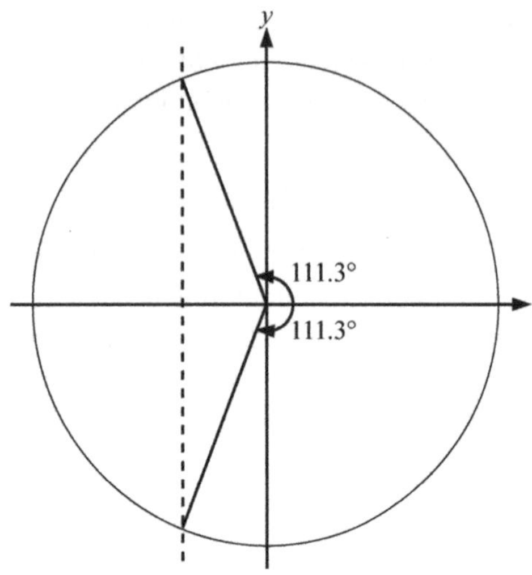

---

5. To the nearest tenth, what are the solutions for θ in the equation $\tan\theta = 4.474$, $0° \leq \theta < 360°$?

A. 102.6° and 282.6°

B. 77.4° and 282.6°

C. 77.4° and 257.4°

D. 1.4° and 181.4°

6. What is the other angle, θ, where $0° \leq \theta < 360°$, that has the same ratio as sin 210°?

A. 30° **B.** 150°

C. 240° **D.** 330°

TR1.4 define the secant, cosecant, and cotangent ratios for angles in a right triangle in terms of the sides of the triangle and relate these ratios to the cosine, sine, and tangent ratios

Reciprocal Trigonometric Ratios

A right-angled triangle can be labelled with respect to $\angle A$.

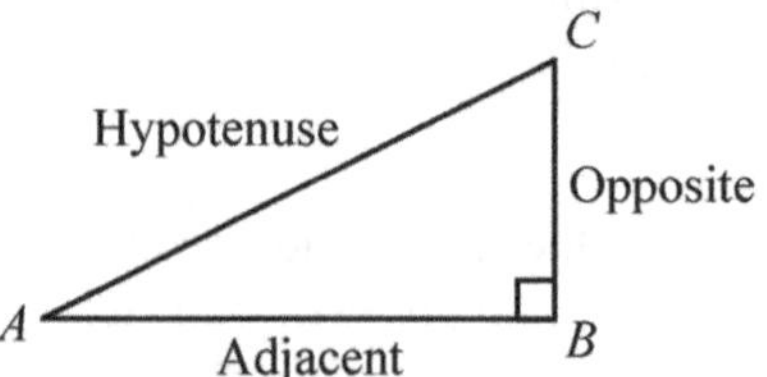

In addition to the primary trigonometric ratios, there are three other trigonometric ratios: cosecant, secant, and cotangent (with abbreviations csc, sec, and cot, respectively). They are the reciprocals of the primary trigonometric ratios.

$$\csc A = \frac{1}{\sin A} = \frac{\text{hypotenuse}}{\text{opposite}}$$

$$\sec A = \frac{1}{\cos A} = \frac{\text{hypotenuse}}{\text{adjacent}}$$

$$\cot A = \frac{1}{\tan A} = \frac{\text{adjacent}}{\text{opposite}}$$

Example

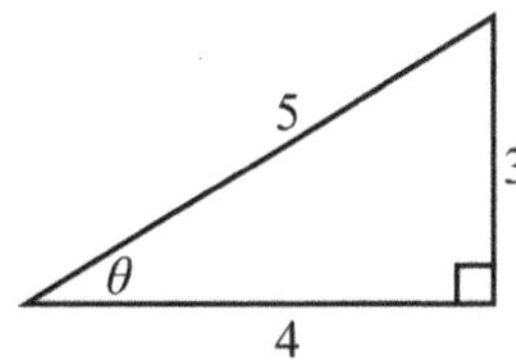

A diagram of a triangle is given.

Find csc θ, sec θ, and cot θ for the given triangle.

Solution

Step 1
Begin by labelling the triangle.

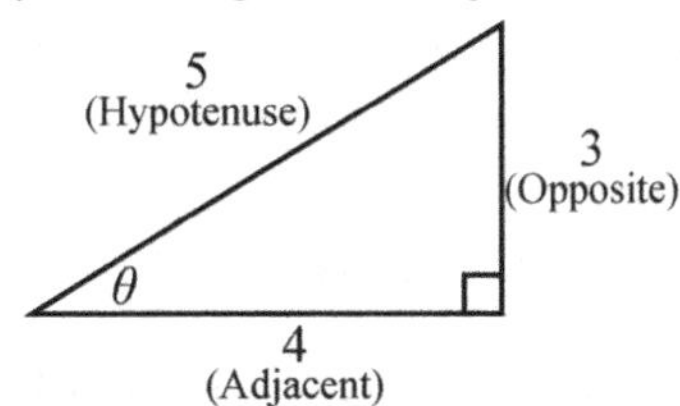

Step 2
Write the ratios for csc θ, sec θ, and cot θ.

$$\csc\theta = \frac{\text{hypotenuse}}{\text{opposite}} = \frac{5}{3}$$

$$\sec\theta = \frac{\text{hypotenuse}}{\text{adjacent}} = \frac{5}{4}$$

$$\cot\theta = \frac{\text{adjacent}}{\text{opposite}} = \frac{4}{3}$$

To find the secant, cosecant, or cotangent of a given angle using a calculator, apply the primary trigonometric function to the same angle, and take the reciprocal.

Example

Evaluate csc 57° to the nearest thousandth.

Solution

Cosecant is the reciprocal of sine. Using a scientific calculator, take the reciprocal of sin 57° to find csc 57°.

$$\csc 57^\circ = \frac{1}{\sin 57^\circ} \approx 1.192$$

---

7. In right-angled ΔABC, $AB = 12$ units, $\angle B = 90^\circ$, and $BC = 5$ units. What is the value of csc A?

A. $\frac{13}{5}$ **B.** $\frac{12}{5}$

C. $\frac{5}{12}$ **D.** $\frac{5}{13}$

8. To the nearest hundredth, what is the value of cot 240°?

A. 0.34 **B.** 0.58

C. 1.73 **D.** 2.90

TR1.5 prove simple trigonometric identities, using the Pythagorean identity $sin^2x + cos^2x = 1$; the quotient identity tanx = sinxcosx; and the reciprocal identities secx = 1cosx, cscx = 1sinx, and cotx = 1tanx

Simple Trigonometric Identities

An identity is an equality that is true for all permissible value replacements of the variables. Trigonometric identities are true for all permissible angle measure replacements of the variables. Some base trigonometric identities that can be used to simplify trigonometric expressions and also to create additional identities are the reciprocal identities, quotient identity, and the Pythagorean identity.

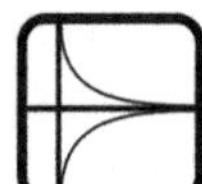

Reciprocal identities:

$\csc x = \dfrac{1}{\sin x}$

$\sec x = \dfrac{1}{\cos x}$

$\cot x = \dfrac{1}{\tan x}$

Quotient identity:

$\tan x = \dfrac{\sin x}{\cos x}$

Pythagorean identity:

$\sin^2 x + \cos^2 x = 1$

Proving Trigonometric Identities Algebraically

A helpful approach to proving identities algebraically is to use the basic identities (reciprocal, quotient, and Pythagorean) wherever possible. As with all proofs and verifications, each side of the equation is dealt with separately. The goal is to make legitimate substitutions and simplifications on each side to show that the two sides are the same.

The following steps are a general procedure to use in order to prove identities algebraically:

1. Split the equation into two parts: the left-hand side (LHS) and the right-hand side (RHS), without the equal sign.
2. Look for obvious substitutions using the basic identities—consider using a Pythagorean identity if squares of trigonometric expressions are involved.
3. Simplify the most complicated side with the goal of making it equal to the other side.
4. Write in terms of sines and cosines if necessary or possible.
5. Write expressions that include fractions as a single fraction.
6. Divide out common factors.
7. Multiply numerators and denominators by the same expression, possibly a conjugate, if necessary.

Example

Prove the identity $1 + \tan^2\theta = \sec^2\theta$.

Solution

Use a chart to help you work through the required steps of the proof.

	LHS	RHS	
	$1 + \tan^2\theta$	$\sec^2\theta$	
Write in terms of sine and cosine.	$1 + \dfrac{\sin^2\theta}{\cos^2\theta}$	$\dfrac{1}{\cos^2\theta}$	Write in terms of cosine.
Write the expression as a single fraction.	$\dfrac{\cos^2\theta + \sin^2\theta}{\cos^2\theta}$		
Use the Pythagorean identity.	$\dfrac{1}{\cos^2\theta}$		
	= RHS		

Since the RHS is equal to the LHS, the identity $1 + \tan^2\theta = \sec^2\theta$ is proven.

Example

Prove the identity $\dfrac{\sin^2 x}{1 + \cos x} = 1 - \cos x$.

Solution

Use a chart to work through the steps of the proof.

	LHS	RHS
Use the Pythagorean identity, and substitute $\sin^2 x = 1 - \cos^2 x$.	$\dfrac{\sin^2 x}{1 + \cos x}$ $\dfrac{1 - \cos^2 x}{1 + \cos x}$	$1 - \cos x$
Factor the numerator as a difference of squares.	$\dfrac{(1 - \cos x)(1 + \cos x)}{1 + \cos x}$	
Reduce the expanded fraction.	$\dfrac{(1 - \cos x)\cancel{(1 + \cos x)}}{\cancel{1 + \cos x}}$	
	$1 - \cos x$	
	= RHS	

Since the LHS equals the RHS, the identity $\dfrac{\sin^2 x}{1 + \cos x} = 1 - \cos x$ is proven.

---

9. To create an identity for the equation $\frac{\tan^2 x + 1}{\cot^2 x + 1} = B$, the value of B would need to be

A. $\sec^2 x$ **B.** $\cot^2 x$

C. $\tan^2 x$ **D.** $\cos^2 x$

Open Response

10. Prove the identity $\tan A + \cot A = \csc A \sec A$ algebraically.

TR1.6 pose problems involving right triangles and oblique triangles in two-dimensional settings, and solve these and other such problems using the primary trigonometric ratios, the cosine law, and the sine law (including the ambiguous case)

Solving Problems Using Trigonometric Laws and Ratios

Several strategies can be used when solving problems that involve the measures of sides and angles in both right and oblique triangles.

Primary trigonometric ratios can only be used for right triangles. The sine and cosine laws can be used to solve problems involving oblique triangles.

To solve problems involving different types of triangles, follow the given strategies:

1. Read the problem carefully. Determine the information you are being given and what you are being asked to solve for.
2. If a diagram is not given, draw a sketch to represent the situation presented in the problem.
3. Examine the triangles in the diagram in order to decide whether to use the primary trigonometric ratios, the sine law, or the cosine law. (Some problems may require more than one strategy.)
4. Make substitutions into the appropriate formulas, and use the correct algebraic steps to solve for the unknown values.
5. Check your calculations.
6. Write a concluding statement.

Example

A garden of red roses and a garden of yellow roses are planted in such a way that they form two triangles, as shown in the given diagram. The gardener would like to place landscaping fence around the yellow rose garden.

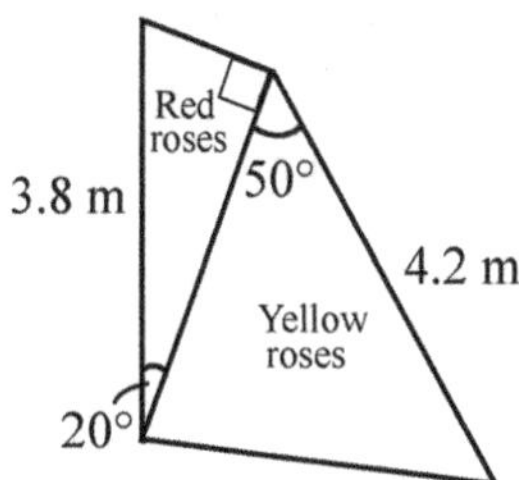

To the nearest tenth of a metre, how much fencing is needed to completely enclose the yellow rose garden?

Solution

Step 1

Label the given diagram.

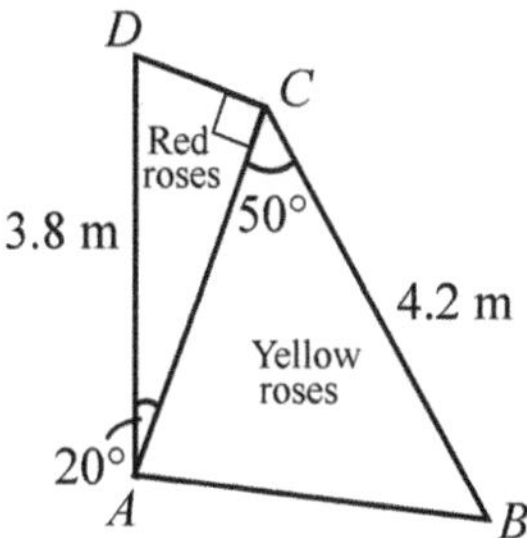

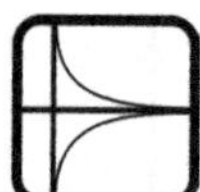

Step 2

In order to determine the perimeter of ΔABC, find the length of each side of the triangle. The length of side BC is given, but the lengths of sides AC and AB must be determined.

In ΔDAC, $\cos \angle DAC = \dfrac{AC}{AD}$.

Substitute 20° for $\angle DAC$ and 3.8 for AD.

$$\cos 20° = \frac{AC}{3.8}$$

$$AC = 3.8 \times \cos 20°$$

$$AC \approx 3.57$$

Step 3

In ΔABC, use the law of cosines to determine AB.

Substitute 3.57 for AC, 4.2 for BC, and 50° for $\angle ACB$ into the equation $(AB)^2 = (AC)^2 + (BC)^2 - 2(AC)(BC)\cos \angle ACB$.

$(AB)^2 = (3.57)^2 + (4.2)^2 - 2(3.57)(4.2)\cos 50°$

$(AB)^2 = 11.1089\ldots$

$AB \approx 3.33$

To the nearest tenth of a metre, the perimeter of ΔABC is 11.1 m$(4.2 + 3.57 + 3.33)$.

The gardener will require 11.1 m of fencing.

Example

In triangle QRS, $\angle R = 50°$, $r = 10$ cm, and $s = 12$ cm. Determine the measure(s) of $\angle Q$ to the nearest tenth of a degree.

Solution

Step 1

Sketch the triangles.

Triangle QRS has side lengths of r and s and a measure of $\angle R$, which is not between r and s. This is an ambiguous-case triangle, so there are two possible measures of $\angle Q$.

Case 1

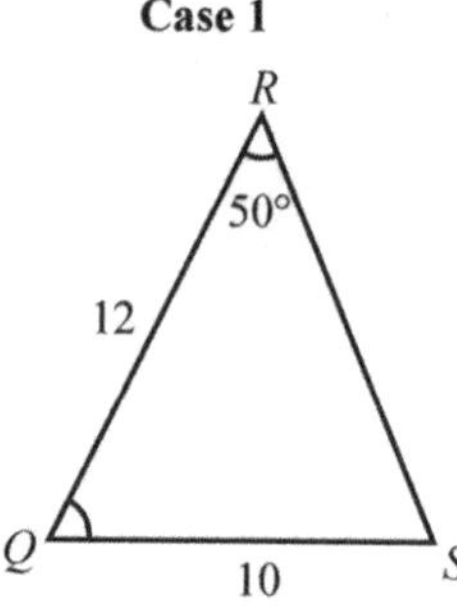

Case 2

R
12
50°
Q
10
S

Step 2

Use the sine law to determine the values of $\angle S$.

$$\frac{\sin S}{12} = \frac{\sin 50}{10}$$

$$\sin S = \frac{12\sin 50}{10}$$

$$\sin S = 1.2\sin 50$$

$$\sin S \approx 0.919$$

$$\angle S \approx 66.8°$$

or

$$\angle S \approx 180° - 66.8°$$

$$\approx 113.2°$$

Step 3

Determine the values of $\angle Q$.

The sum of the angles in any triangle is 180 °.

Therefore, $\angle Q + \angle R + \angle S = 180°$.

Since there are two possible measures for $\angle S$, there are also two possible meaures for $\angle Q$.

If $\angle S = 66.8°$, find the value of $\angle Q$.

$\angle Q = 180 - 50 - 66.8$

$\angle Q = 63.2°$

If $\angle S = 113.2°$, find the value of $\angle Q$.

$\angle Q = 180 - 50 - 113.2$

$\angle Q = 16.8°$

Therefore, to the nearest tenth of a degree, the measure of $\angle Q$ is either 63.2 ° or 16.8 °.

Use the following information to answer the next question.

Using its radar, ship A receives signals indicating that two other ships, B and C, are 4.8 km and 6.2 km away, respectively. The angle between the two radar signals is 74°, as shown in the given diagram.

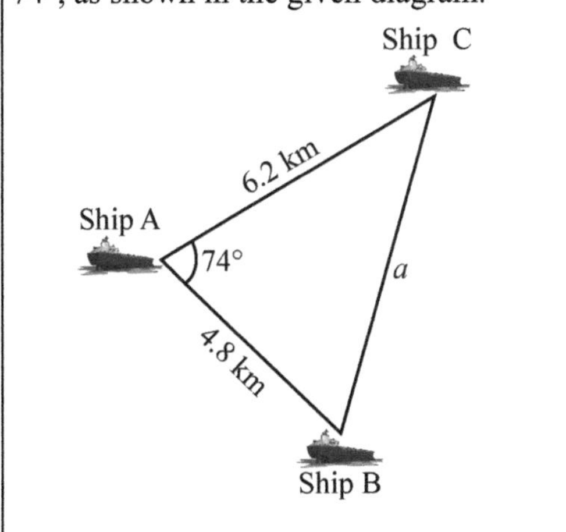

11. To the nearest tenth, what is the distance, *a*, between ships B and C?

A. 0.5 km **B.** 5.0 km

C. 6.7 km **D.** 7.1 km

Use the following information to answer the next question.

Olivia looks out the window of her apartment building and sees a sports car parked down the street at an angle of depression of 18°. A little farther down the street, she sees a police car parked at an angle of depression of 15°.
Her apartment window is 35 m above street level.

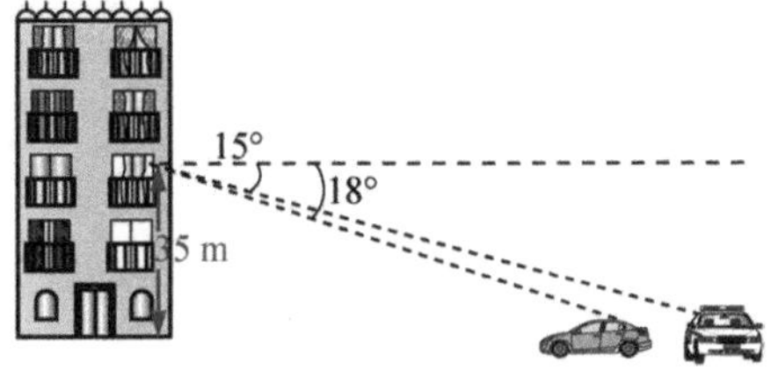

Numerical Response

12. To the nearest tenth of a metre, how far apart are the sports car and the police car? _________m

TR1.7 pose problems involving right triangles and oblique triangles in three-dimensional settings, and solve these and other such problems using the primary trigonometric ratios, the cosine law, and the sine law

Solving Triangle Problems in Three Dimensions

Trigonometric ratios and laws are useful for solving problems involving triangles in three-dimensional settings. Many three-dimensional problems can be broken down into multiple two-dimensional problems and solved using the following problem-solving strategies:

- Draw and label a sketch illustrating the problem.
- Determine the types of triangles found in the problem.
- Determine which strategies to use, such as trigonometric ratios, Pythagorean theorem, sine law, or cosine law.

Example

To determine the height of a spruce tree across a river, Alexa takes two measurements. Standing at point *A* directly across the river from the base of the tree, she determines that the angle of elevation to the top of the tree is 19.7°. For the second measurement, she walks 33 m parallel to the river to point *C* where she determines that the base of the tree and point *A* are 65.2° apart. From point *A*, the base of the tree and point *C* are 90.0° apart.

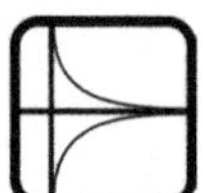

To the nearest tenth of a metre, calculate the height of the spruce tree.

Solution

Step 1
Sketch a labelled diagram that illustrates the problem and shows the given information.

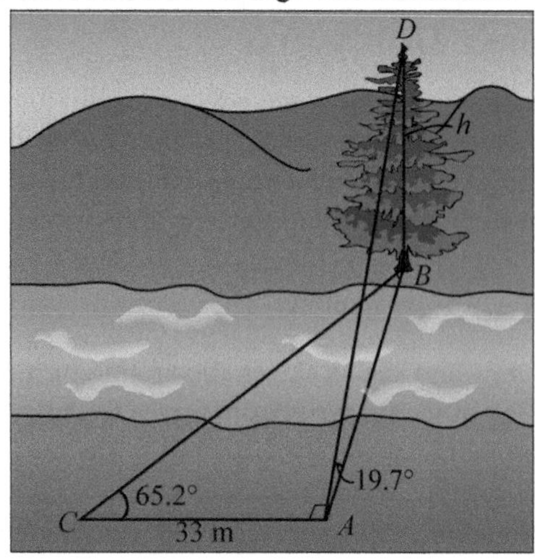

Step 2
Begin with triangle ABC, and determine the length AB using the tangent ratio

$\tan\theta = \frac{\text{opposite}}{\text{adjacent}}$.

$$\tan 65.2° = \frac{AB}{33}$$
$$33\tan 65.2° = AB$$
$$AB \approx 71.4 \text{ m}$$

Step 3
Use the tangent ratio in triangle ABD to determine the height of the tree BD.

$$\tan 19.7° = \frac{BD}{71.4}$$
$$71.4\tan 19.7° = BD$$
$$BD \approx 25.6 \text{ m}$$

To the nearest tenth of a metre, the height of the spruce tree is 25.6 m.

Example

From the top of a 100 m fire tower, a fire ranger at point R observes smoke coming from two separate fires. The angle of elevation from Fire A is 5° and from Fire B it is 3°. The angle that the two fires make with the base of the tower, T, is 87°.

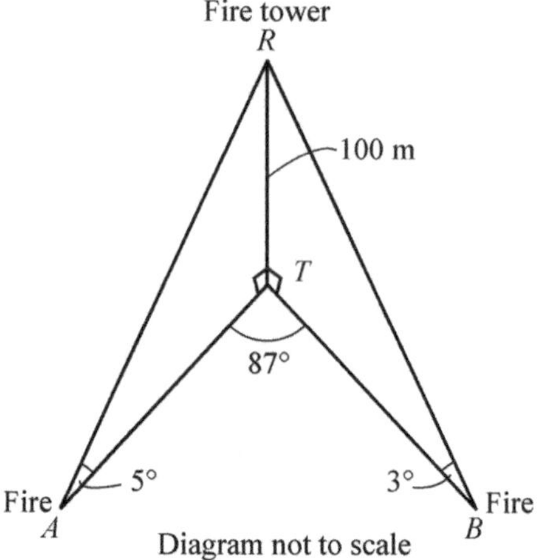

To the nearest metre, what is the distance from Fire A to Fire B?

Solution

Step 1
Draw a diagram, and label it as shown.

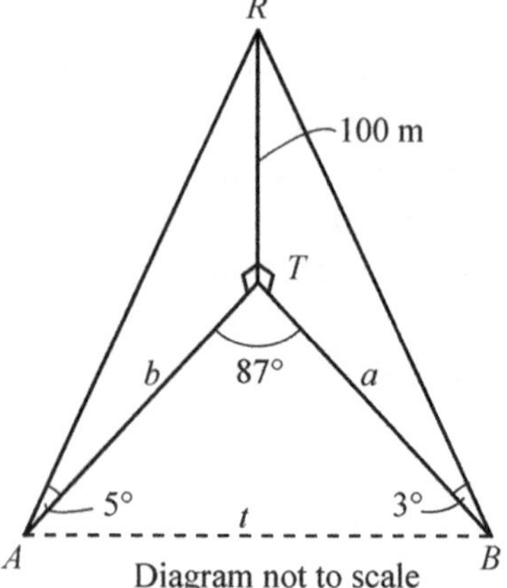

Step 2

Solve for sides a and b.

Since ΔART and ΔBRT are right triangles, use the primary trigonometric ratios to solve for a and b.

Solve for a using the tangent ratio.

$$\tan\theta = \frac{\text{opposite}}{\text{adjacent}}$$
$$\tan 3^\circ = \frac{100}{a}$$
$$a = \frac{100}{\tan 3^\circ}$$
$$a \approx 1\ 908\text{m}$$

Solve for b using the tangent ratio.

$$\tan\theta = \frac{\text{opposite}}{\text{adjacent}}$$
$$\tan 5^\circ = \frac{100}{b}$$
$$b = \frac{100}{\tan 5^\circ}$$
$$b \approx 1\ 143\text{ m}$$

Step 3

Since two sides and the angle between the two sides are known, solve for t in ΔATB using the cosine law $t^2 = a^2 + b^2 - 2ab(\cos T)$.

$$t^2 = a^2 + b^2 - 2ab(\cos T)$$
$$t^2 \approx 1\ 908^2 + 1\ 143^2 - 2(1\ 908)(1\ 143)\cos 87^\circ$$
$$t^2 \approx 4\ 946\ 913 - 228\ 273.1123$$
$$t^2 \approx 4\ 718\ 639.888$$
$$t \approx 2\ 172\text{ m}$$

The distance from Fire A to Fire B is 2 172 m.

Use the following information to answer the next question.

A weather balloon is flying in a field outside of a town. One end of a lightweight rope is attached to the base of the weather balloon, and the other end of the rope is anchored to the ground at point P. On a windy day, Rachel decides to determine the length of the rope, x, between P and the connection point, located at the base of the weather balloon. Since it is a windy day the rope has an angle of 85° with the ground at point P. She locates two points, A and B, which are 200 m apart and form a triangle with point P. She notices that the balloon is at an angle of elevation of 38° from point B and $\angle PAB = 60°$.

13. To the nearest metre, what is the distance from the weather balloon to point B?

A. 132 m **B.** 178 m

C. 180 m **D.** 214 m

Use the following information to answer the next question.

The given diagram shows a triangle in three dimensions.

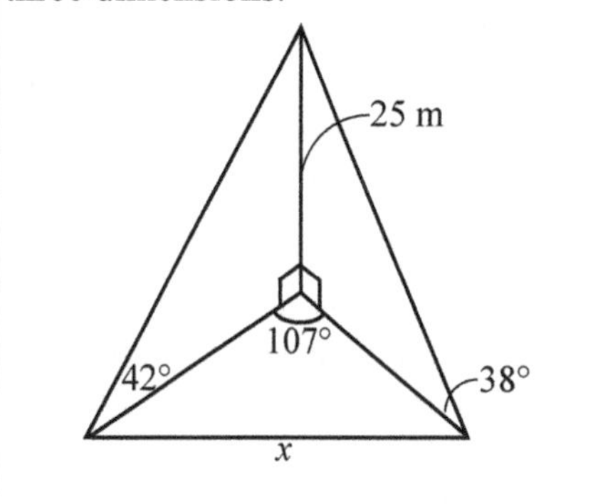

Numerical Response

14. To the nearest tenth of a metre, the length of x is __________m.

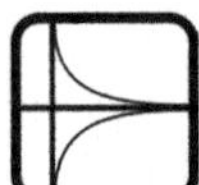

TR2.1 describe key properties of periodic functions arising from real-world applications, given a numeric or graphical representation

Characteristics of Periodic Functions

In everyday life, there are countless familiar phenomena that repeat over time. For example, the news is reported hourly on the radio, the leaves drop off the trees every fall, the height of a particular position on a ferris wheel repeats as the wheel turns, sound waves rise and fall, the sun comes up and goes down, and so on. When the repetition forms a consistent pattern and can be described by a function, that function is known as a **periodic function**.

Each repetitive set of y-values over a particular x-interval of the domain is called a **cycle**, and the length of this x-interval is called the **period** of the function.

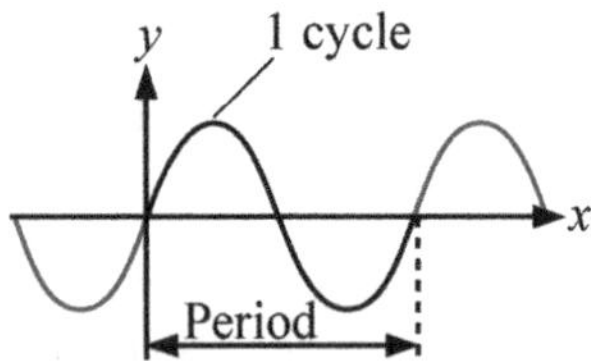

If the graph of the periodic function oscillates regularly between its maximum and minimum y-values, the equation of the axis, y, located halfway between the maximum and minimum points, is given as

$$y = \frac{\text{maximum} + \text{minimum}}{2}.$$

The **amplitude**, $|a|$, of the graph is the vertical distance from the function's horizontal midline axis to any maximum or minimum point. The amplitude can be calculated by

$$|a| = \frac{|\text{maximum} - \text{minimum}|}{2}.$$

The **range** of an oscillating periodic function is the set of all the y-values represented by the graph. The range of a periodic function is minimum $\leq y \leq$ maximum.

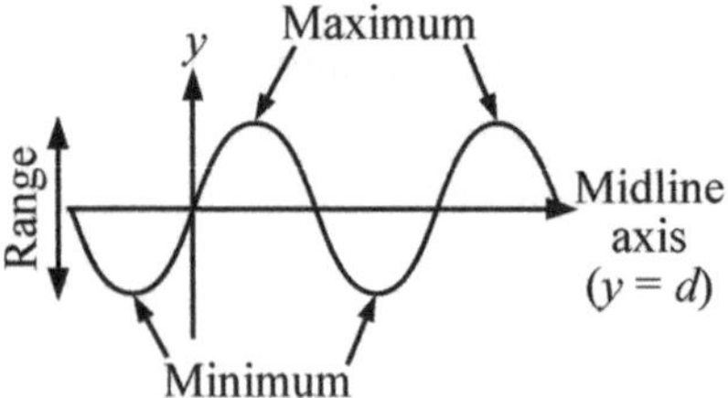

Example

The graph of a periodic function is given.

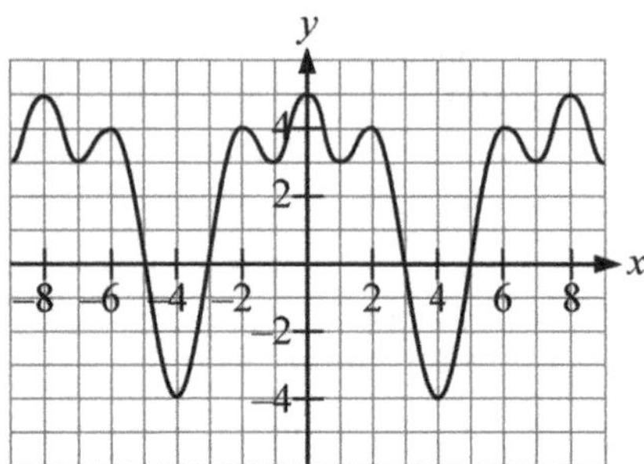

Determine the period, the equation of the horizontal midline axis, the amplitude, and the range of the graph of the given periodic function.

Solution

Step 1

Examine the repetitive nature of the graph of the function to determine the period.

Since the length of the x-interval of the cycle is its period, the distance from one maximum value ($y = 5$) to each of the next repeated maximum values is 8 units. Therefore, the period of the given function is 8 units.

$$-8 \xrightarrow{8} 0 \xrightarrow{8} 8$$

Step 2
Find the equation of the horizontal midline axis y, the amplitude $|a|$, and the range of the function shown in the given graph.
The equation of the horizontal midline axis is found by $y = \frac{\text{maximum} + \text{minimum}}{2}$.
The maximum y-value is 5, and the minimum y-value is -4.

$$y = \frac{5+(-4)}{2}$$

$$y = \frac{1}{2}$$

The amplitude is found by

$$|a| = \frac{|\text{maximum} - \text{minimum}|}{2}.$$

$$|a| = \frac{|5-(-4)|}{2}$$

$$|a| = \frac{9}{2}$$

The range (minimum $\le y \le$ maximum) is $-4 \le y \le 5$.

Example

The table gives the maximum and minimum heights of the tide at St. Andrews, station 40, in the Bay of Fundy on September 1, 2008.

Time	Height (m)
01:23	7.3
07:44	0.3
13:47	7.3
20:07	0.4

If the height of the tide defines a periodic function with respect to time, determine the approximate period of the function.

Solution

The first high tide occurs at 01:23, and the next occurs at 13:47. The period is the time interval between these two values.
period = 13:47−1:23 = 12:24

The period is approximately 12 h and 24 min.

If the height of the tide defines a periodic function with respect to time, calculate the amplitude of the function, to the nearest tenth of a metre.

Solution

Calculate the amplitude, $|a|$, of the periodic function.

$$|a| = \frac{|\text{maximum} - \text{minimum}|}{2}$$

$$|a| = \frac{|7.3-0.3|}{2}$$

$$|a| = 3.5$$

The amplitude of the periodic function is 3.5 m.

Use the following information to answer the next question.

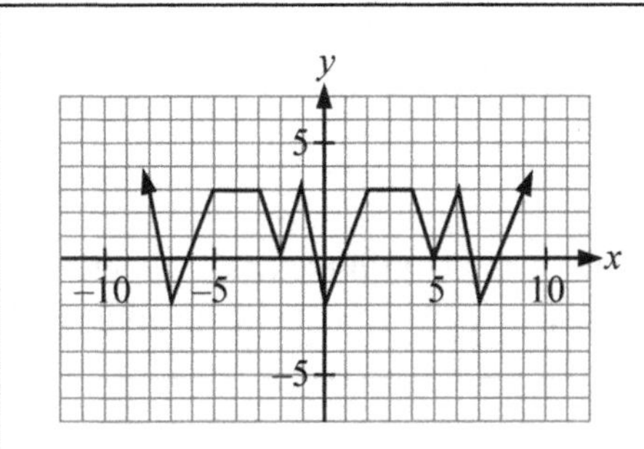

The graph of a function is given.

15. What is the period of the given function?

A. 3 units **B.** 5 units

C. 7 units **D.** 8 units

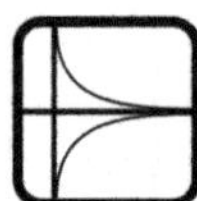

Use the following information to answer the next multipart question.

16. The table shows the water usage in a home in Ontario over a 12-month period.

Month	Usage (m^3)
Jan	12.0
Feb	11.5
Mar	10.5
Apr	10.2
May	11.2
Jun	12.4
Jul	13.2
Aug	13.0
Sep	12.4
Oct	11.2
Nov	9.8
Dec	11.4

Open Response

a) What is the expected amount of water that would be used the following August?

b) What is the average amount of water usage throughout the year?

c) What is the amplitude of the function represented by the data in the given table?

TR2.2 predict, by extrapolating, the future behaviour of a relationship modelled using a numeric or graphical representation of a periodic function

Extrapolating Periodic Functions

Since a periodic function is repetitive, you can predict particular x- and y-values beyond the given values that are specified for a particular situation. This method of predicting beyond the given information or the known facts is called **extrapolating**.

Example

The graph of a periodic function is shown.

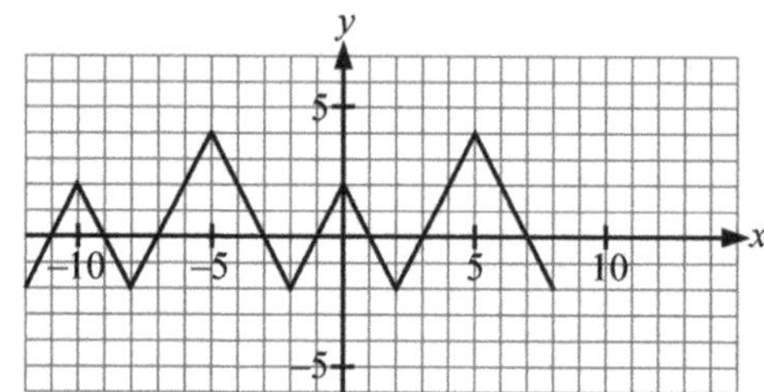

Extrapolate the given curve, and determine the y-value at $x = 10$.

Solution

In order to properly extrapolate the curve, observe that the period of the function is 10 units. In other words, the pattern repeats itself every 10 units.

The curve can be extrapolated as follows.

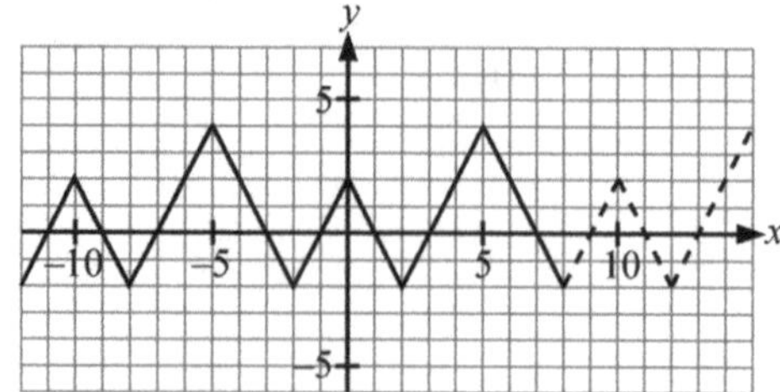

From the extrapolated portion of the graph, the y-value at $x = 10$ is $y = 2$. This can be verified by observing that since the period is 10 units, the y-value at $x = 10$ is the same as at $x = 0$ and $x = -10$. At both of these known points, $y = 2$.

Therefore, the y-value at $x = 10$ is 2.

Example

Kayla has an investment plan in which she makes a deposit into a savings account each month. The amounts of the deposits for the first six months of the previous year are shown in the table.

Month	Amount Deposited ($)
January	450
February	425
March	400
April	350
May	350
June	375

If the deposit amounts are modelled by a periodic function with a period of six months, determine the amount that Kayla deposited in September.

Solution

Since the period of the function is six months, Kayla deposits the same amounts in the second half of the year as she did in the previous six-month period. September is the third month in the second six-month period, so the amount deposited is the same as in March.

Kayla deposited an amount of $400 in September.

Use the following information to answer the next question.

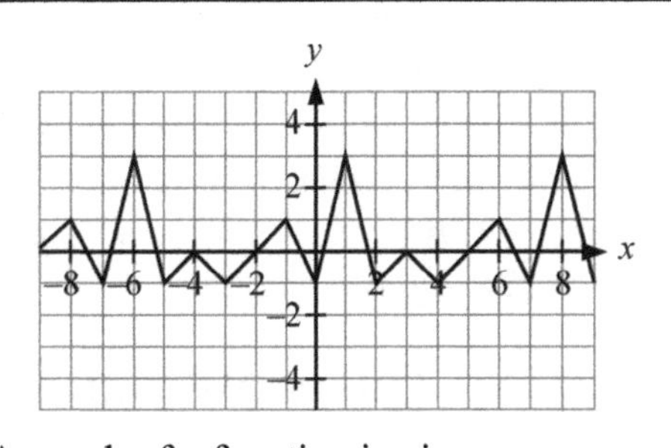

A graph of a function is given.

17. If the function existed for values of the domain less than −9, what would the predicted y-value be in the given graph at $x = -15$?

A. −1 **B.** 0

C. 1 **D.** 3

Use the following information to answer the next question.

The pendulum on a grandfather clock takes 2.0 s to swing from one side to the other and back again. The given table represents data for when the pendulum is on the far right side of its swing.

Time (s)	0.0	0.5	1.0	1.5	2.0	2.5	3.0
Distance from far right side (cm)	0	300	600	300	0	300	600

Numerical Response

18. After 4.5 s, the pendulum's distance from the far right side will be _________ cm. (Record your answer to the nearest centimetre.)

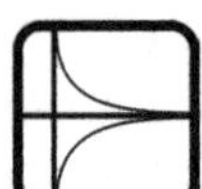

TR2.3 make connections between the sine ratio and the sine function and between the cosine ratio and the cosine function by graphing the relationship between angles from 0° to 360° and the corresponding sine ratios or cosine ratios, with or without technology defining this relationship as the function f(x) = sinx or f(x) = cosx, and explaining why the relationship is a function

CONNECTING TRIGONOMETRIC RATIOS WITH THEIR CORRESPONDING FUNCTIONS

For right-triangle trigonometry, the sine ratio of **acute** angle A is defined as $\sin A = \dfrac{\text{opposite}}{\text{hypotenuse}}$ and $\cos A = \dfrac{\text{adjacent}}{\text{hypotenuse}}$.

To include angles of any measure, other definitions are helpful.

If you are given an angle θ drawn in standard position on the Cartesian plane with $P(x, y)$ on the terminal arm of angle θ, use $\sin \theta = \dfrac{y}{r}$ and $\cos \theta = \dfrac{x}{r}$, where $r = \sqrt{x^2+y^2}$.

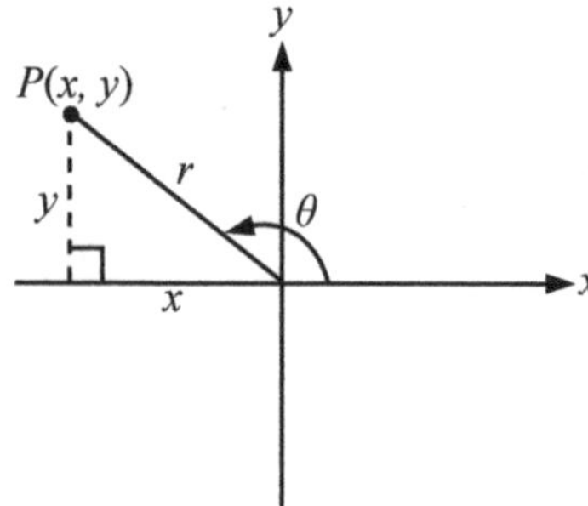

If $r = 1$, then point P will be on a unit circle. For this situation, use $\sin \theta = \dfrac{y}{1} = y$ and $\cos \theta = \dfrac{x}{1} = x$.

Example

For the relation $y = \sin x$, x represents an angle of any measure and y is the y-coordinate of a point P that is on the terminal arm of the angle and also on the unit circle.

Determine if the relation $y = \sin x$ is a function.

Solution

Use a calculator to determine the sine ratio values, y-coordinates for angles x (in degrees between 0° and 360° inclusive) that are multiples of 30°. The resulting values are given in the table.

Angle Measure (*x*)	Sine Ratio (*y*)
0 °	0
30 °	0.5
60 °	0.866
90 °	1
120 °	0.866
150 °	0.5
180 °	0
210 °	−0.5
240 °	−0.866
270 °	−1
300 °	−0.866
330 °	−0.5
360 °	0

From the table of values shown, $y = \sin x$ seems to be a function because for every angle measure x in degrees, there is a single unique sine ratio value y.

If you place these values on the Cartesian plane and connect them with a smooth curve, the graph of $y = \sin x$ is formed for all angles from 0 ° to 360 °.

The y-value on the unit circle corresponds to its angle x, as seen at 210°.

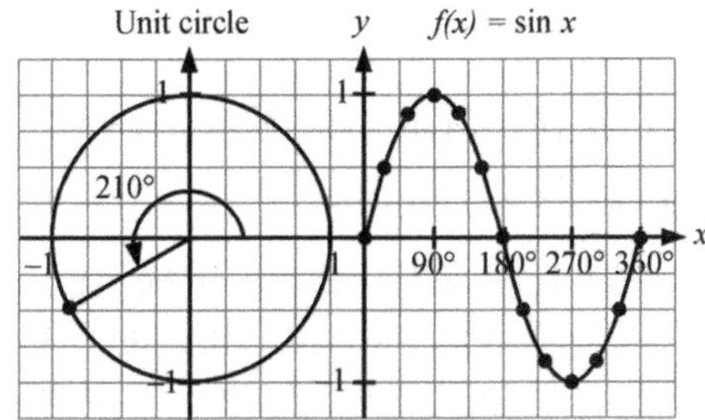

Since the graph passes the vertical line test, the relation $y = \sin x$ is a function and can be written as $f(x) = \sin x$.

Example

For the relation $y = \cos \theta$, θ represents an angle of any measure and y is the x-coordinate of a point P that is on the terminal arm of the angle and also on the unit circle.

Determine whether the relation $y = \cos \theta$ is a function.

Solution

Use the unit circle to determine the cosine ratio values, x-coordinates for angles θ (in degrees between 0° and 360° inclusive) that are multiples of 30°. The resulting values are given in the table.

Angle Measure (θ)	Cosine Ratio (*y*)
0 °	1
30 °	$\frac{\sqrt{3}}{2}$
60 °	$\frac{1}{2}$
90 °	0
120 °	$-\frac{1}{2}$
150 °	$-\frac{\sqrt{3}}{2}$
180 °	−1
210 °	$-\frac{\sqrt{3}}{2}$
240 °	$-\frac{1}{2}$
270 °	0
300 °	$\frac{1}{2}$
330 °	$\frac{\sqrt{3}}{2}$
360 °	1

From the table of values, $y = \cos \theta$ seems to be a function because for every angle measure θ in degrees, there is a single unique cosine ratio value y.

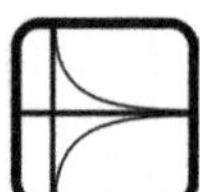

If you place these values on the Cartesian plane and connect them with a smooth curve, the graph of $y = \cos\theta$ is formed for all angles from 0 ° to 360 °.

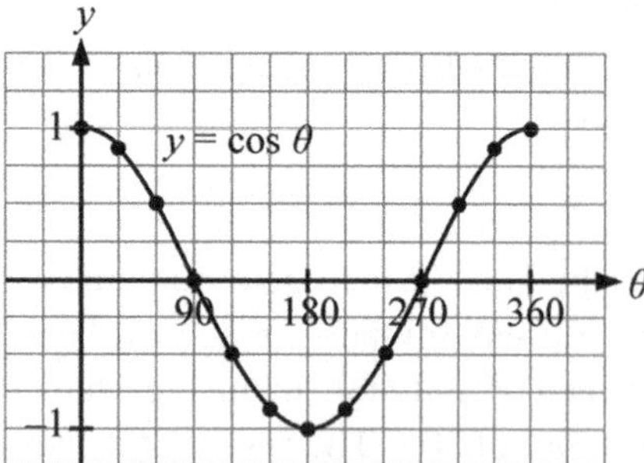

Since the graph passes the vertical line test, the relation $y = \cos\theta$ is a function and can be written as $f(\theta) = \cos\theta$.

---

19. The expression $f(x) = \cos x$ is a function because every value of

A. x is paired with exactly one value of $\cos x$

B. $\cos x$ is paired with exactly one value of x

C. x is paired with at least one value of $\cos x$

D. $\cos x$ is paired with at least one value of x

Use the following information to answer the next question.

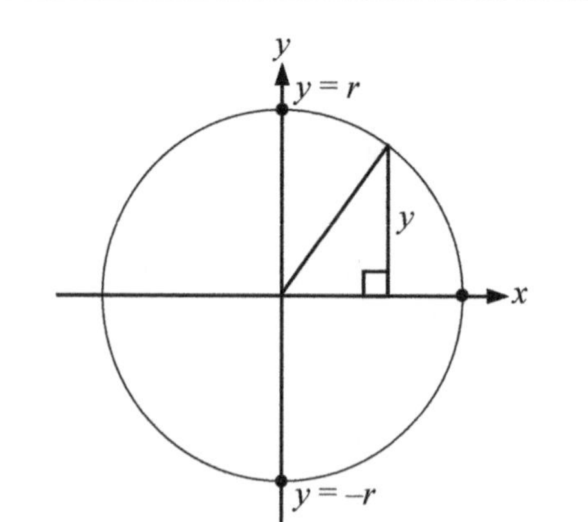

The graph of a circle with its centre located at the origin and a radius of r is given.

Open Response

20. Explain why the maximum value of $\sin\theta$ is 1 and the minimum value is -1.

TR2.4 sketch the graphs of f(x) = sinx and f(x) = cosx for angle measures expressed in degrees, and determine and describe their key properties (i.e., cycle, domain, range, intercepts, amplitude, period, maximum and minimum values, increasing/ decreasing intervals)

The Graphs of the Sine and Cosine Functions

The sine and cosine functions can be sketched for a domain outside of 0° to 360°. If you use the unit circle and angles in standard position, you can see that the sine and cosine ratios repeat as the terminal arm is rotated past 360° in a counterclockwise direction or past 0° in a negative or clockwise direction. The result is the periodic functions $f(x) = \sin x$ and $f(x) = \cos x$, each with a period of 360°.

These are two methods of sketching the graphs of the sine and cosine functions:

- Use a table of values, and draw a freehand curve.
- Use the graph illustrated on your graphing calculator after entering sin(x) or cos(x) into $Y_1 =$.

Key Properties of the Sine Function

The sine function has several key properties that you will be required to describe and identify from a graph of the function.

The graph shows the function $y = \sin x$, where $-360° \le x \le 360°$. The graph follows a smooth, wavy curve and is defined as sinusoidal.

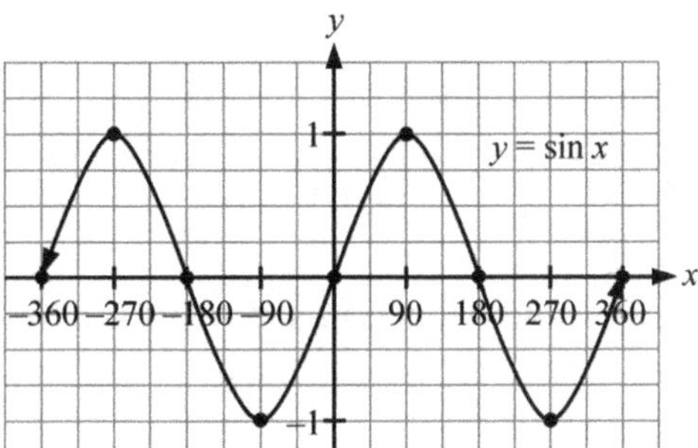

By examining the graph of the sine function, it is possible to describe the key properties of $y = \sin x$ (or $f(x) = \sin x$) that include the period, domain, maximum and minimum values, amplitude, equation of horizontal axis, range, intercepts, and increasing or decreasing intervals.

- The period is 360°, which is the length of one cycle.
- The domain is $x \in R$. (The function is defined for all real measures of angle x.)
- The maximum value is +1, and the minimum value is −1.
- The amplitude, $|a|$, is 1. (The distance from the horizontal axis to the maximum or minimum.) The amplitude can be determined from the maximum and minimum values by $|a| = \frac{|\max - \min|}{2} = \frac{|1-(-1)|}{2} = 1.$
- The equation of the horizontal axis is $d = 0$. (This represents the average value of the function.) It is determined by $d = \frac{\max + \min}{2} = \frac{1+(-1)}{2} = 0.$
- For a sinusoidal function, the range is defined as $\min \le f(x) \le \max$; the range of $f(x) = \sin x$ is $-1 \le f(x) \le 1$.
- For the intercepts of the function, the y-intercept is 0 and the x-intercepts are … −360°, −180°, 0°, 180°, 360° ….
These x-intercepts can be described as multiples of 180° using the formula $x = 180°n, n \in I$.
- The increasing and decreasing intervals are read from the graph. Observe that the function is increasing for x-values between −360° and −270°, −90° and 90°, and between 270° and 360°. Similarly, the function is decreasing between −270° and −90° and between 90° and 270°. Since the function is periodic with a period of 360°, it can be said that the function is increasing for
$(-90+360n)° < x < (90+360n)°, n \in I$ and decreasing for
$(90+360n)° < x < (270+360n)°, n \in I$.

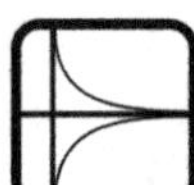

KEY PROPERTIES OF THE COSINE FUNCTION

The cosine function has several key properties that you will be required to describe and identify from a graph of the function.

The graph of $y = \cos x$, where $-360° \leq x \leq 360°$, is shown. The graph follows a smooth, wavy curve and is defined as sinusoidal.

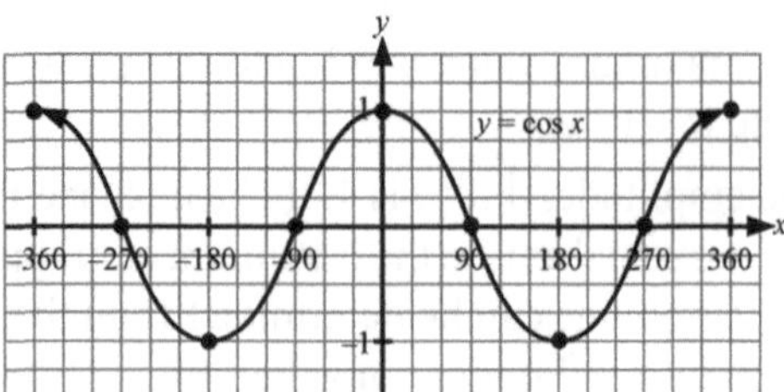

By examining the graph of the cosine function, it is possible to describe the key properties of $y = \cos x$ (or $f(x) = \cos x$) that include the period, domain, maximum and minimum values, amplitude, equation of horizontal axis, range, intercepts, and increasing or decreasing intervals.

- The period is 360°, which is the length of one cycle.
- The domain is $x \in R$. (The function is defined for all real measures of angle x.)
- The maximum value is +1, and the minimum value is −1.
- The amplitude, $|a|$, is 1. (The distance from the horizontal axis to the maximum or minimum.) The amplitude can be determined from the maximum and minimum values by $|a| = \frac{|\max - \min|}{2} = \frac{|1-(-1)|}{2} = 1.$
- The equation of the horizontal axis is $d = 0$. (This represents the average value of the function.) It is determined by $d = \frac{\max + \min}{2} = \frac{1+(-1)}{2} = 0.$
- For a sinusoidal function, the range is defined as $\min \leq f(x) \leq \max$; the range of $f(x) = \cos x$ is $-1 \leq f(x) \leq 1$.
- For the intercepts of the function, the y-intercept is 1 and the x-intercepts are … −270°, −90°, 90°, 270°, …. These intercepts can be described as multiples of 180°, starting at 90° and using the formula $x = 90° + 180°n$, $n \in I$.
- The increasing and decreasing intervals are read from the graph. The function is increasing for x-values between −180° and 0° and between 180° and 360°. Similarly, the function is decreasing between −360° and −180° and between 0° and 180°. Since the function is periodic with a period of 360°, it can be said that the function is increasing for $(-180 + 360n)° < x < (0 + 360n)°$, $n \in I$ and decreasing for $(0 + 360n)° < x < (180 + 360n)°$, $n \in I$.

21. Which of the following graphs **best** represents the graph of $f(x) = \cos x$?

A.

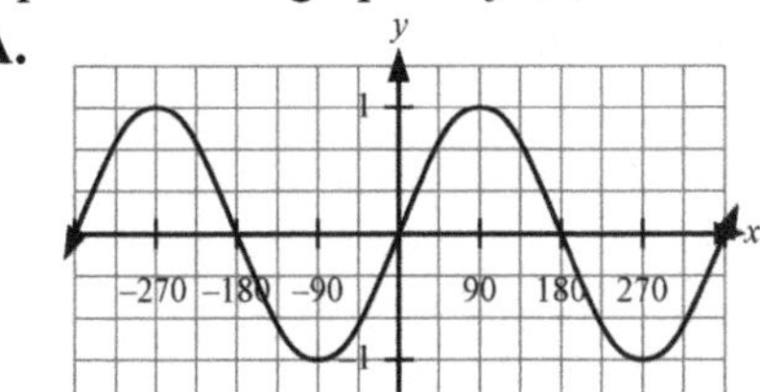

B.

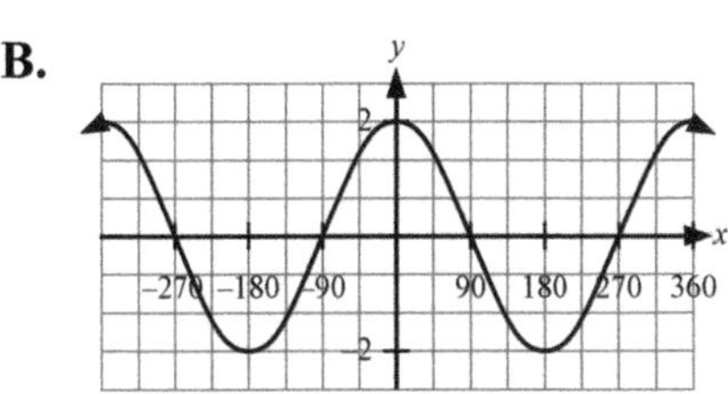

C.

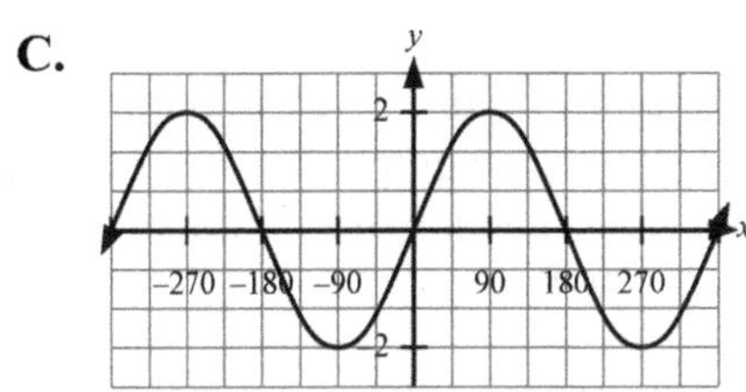

D.

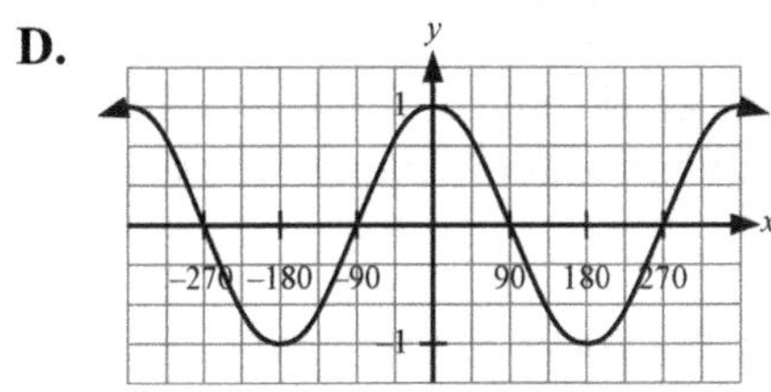

Use the following information to answer the next question.

The x-intercepts of $f(x) = \sin x$ can be described using $x = a°n,\ n \in I$.

Numerical Response

22. What is the value of a?__________

TR2.5 determine, through investigation using technology, the roles of the parameters a, k, d, and c in functions of the form y = af(k(x-d)) + c, where f(x) = sinx or f(x) = cosx with angles expressed in degrees, and describe these roles in terms of transformations on the graphs of f(x) = sinx and f(x) = cosx (i.e., translations; reflections in the axes; vertical and horizontal stretches and compressions to and from the x- and y-axes)

Transformations of Sinusoidal Functions

For a sinusoidal function of the form $y = af(k(x - d)) + c$, the parameters a, k, d, and c reveal important information about the transformations of the sinusoidal function. Through investigation, the effects of each parameter can be observed and generalized.

The Role of *a*

For either of the functions $y = a\sin(k(x - d)) + c$ or $y = a\cos(k(x - d)) + c$, changing the parameter a gives the following results:

- A vertical stretch or compression of the graph about the x-axis. If $a > 1$, there is a vertical stretch by a factor of a. If $0 < a < 1$, there is a vertical compression by a factor of a.
- When a is negative, there is a reflection in the x-axis.

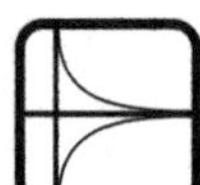

In the given diagram, the graphs of $y = 2\cos x$ and $y = -\frac{1}{2}\cos x$ are compared to the graph of $y = \cos x$.

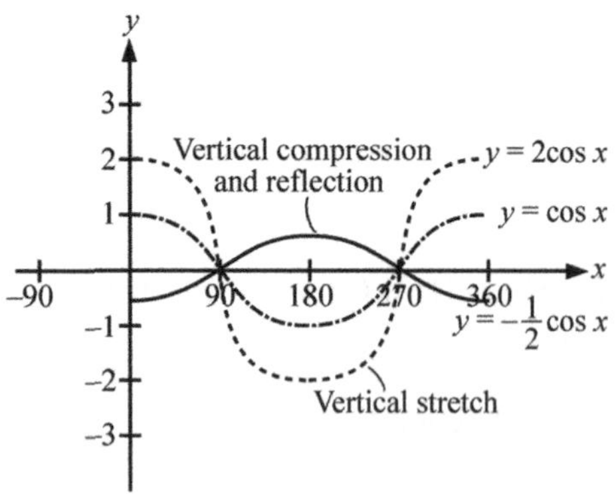

Notice the graph of $y = \cos x$ is vertically stretched by a factor of 2 to produce the graph of $y = 2\cos x$. The graph of $y = \cos x$ is vertically compressed by a factor of $\frac{1}{2}$ and reflected about the x-axis to produce the graph of $y = -\frac{1}{2}\cos x$.

The Role of *k*

In either the sine or cosine functions, the parameter k results in a horizontal stretch or compression about the y-axis by a factor of $\frac{1}{k}$. In the given graph, the graphs of $y = \sin\left(\frac{1}{2}x\right)$, $y = \sin x$ and $y = \sin(2x)$ are illustrated in the given graph.

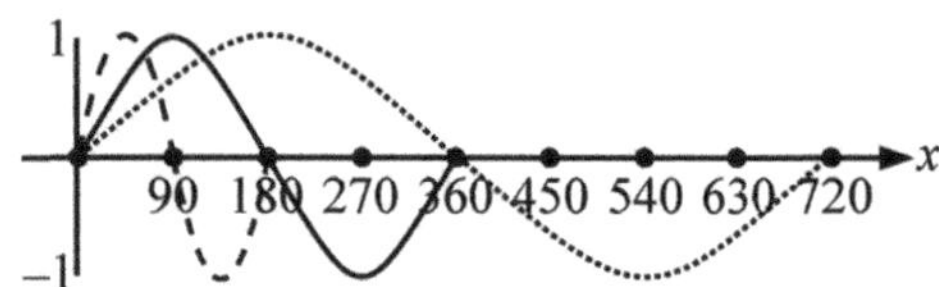

- If $|k| > 1$, there is a horizontal compression.
- If $0 < |k| < 1$, there is a horizontal stretch.
- If $k < 0$, there is a reflection in the y-axis.

The Role of *d*

For either of the sinusoidal functions, changing the parameter d results in the horizontal translation, or phase shift, of the function.

- If $d > 0$, the graph shifts d units to the right.
- If $d < 0$, the graph shifts $|d|$ units to the left.

In the given diagram, the graphs of $y = \sin(\theta - 45°)$ and $y = \sin(\theta + 30°)$ are compared to the graph of $y = \sin\theta$.

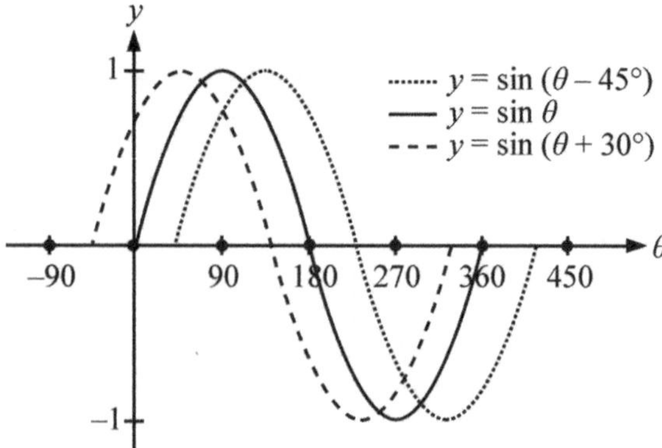

Notice that the graph of $y = \sin\theta$ is horizontally translated right 45° to produce the graph of $y = \sin(\theta - 45°)$. The graph of $y = \sin\theta$ is horizontally translated left 30° to produce the graph of $y = \sin(\theta + 30°)$.

The Role of *c*

The parameter c in either the sine or cosine functions affects the vertical translation of the graph of the function.

- If $c > 0$, the graph shifts upward c units.
- If $c < 0$, the graph shifts downward c units.

In the given diagram, the graphs of $y = \cos x + 1$ and $y = \cos x - 2$ are compared to the graph of $y = \cos x$.

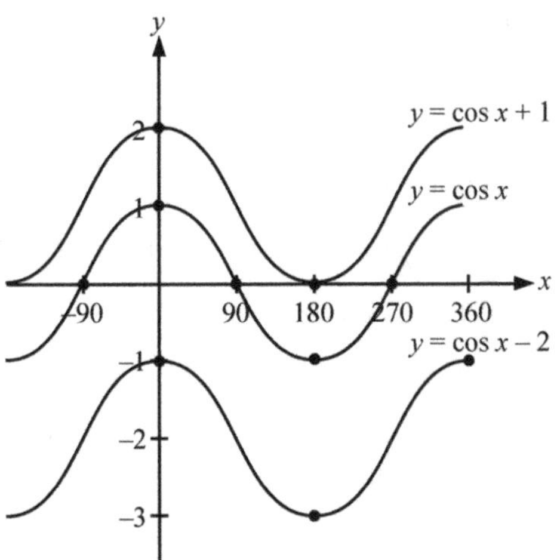

Notice that the graph of $y = \cos x$ is vertically translated upward 1 unit to produce the graph of $y = \cos x + 1$. The graph of $y = \cos x$ is vertically translated downward 2 units to produce the graph of $y = \cos x - 2$.

Example

Describe the transformations that need to be applied to the graph of $y = \cos x$ to obtain the graph of $y = -\frac{1}{2}\cos\left(\frac{1}{3}(x + 48°)\right) - 5$.

Solution

Comparing the equation $y = -\frac{1}{2}\cos\left(\frac{1}{3}(x + 48°)\right) - 5$ to the equation of the form $y = a\cos(k(x - d)) + c$ it can be seen that, $a = -\frac{1}{2}$, $k = \frac{1}{3}$, $d = -48°$ and $c = -5$.

Since $a = -\frac{1}{2}$, the graph is compressed vertically about the x-axis by a factor of $\frac{1}{2}$ and reflected in the x-axis.

The graph is stretched horizontally about the y-axis by a factor of 3.

The graph is translated 48° left (a phase shift of 48° left) and vertically translated 5 units down.

Use the following information to answer the next question.

> The given transformations are applied to the graph of $y = \sin x$.
> - The graph is compressed vertically about the x-axis by a factor of $\frac{1}{2}$ and then reflected in the x-axis.
> - The graph is stretched horizontally about the y-axis by a factor of 5.
> - The graph is translated 55° left and translated 5 units down.

23. Which of the following functions will be obtained once the transformations have been applied to the graph of $y = \sin x$?

A. $y = -\frac{1}{2}\sin\frac{1}{5}(x - 55°) + 5$

B. $y = -\frac{1}{2}\sin\frac{1}{5}(x + 55°) - 5$

C. $y = \frac{1}{2}\sin\left(-\frac{1}{5}(x - 55°)\right) - 5$

D. $y = \frac{1}{2}\sin\left(-\frac{1}{5}(x + 55°)\right) - 5$

Use the following information to answer the next question.

> The function $y = \cos x$ undergoes a phase shift of 30° to the right, a vertical stretch by a factor of 6, and a vertical shift of 2 units upward.

Numerical Response

24. If the transformed function is written in the form $y = a\cos(k(x - d)) + c$, what is the value of $a + (c \times d)$?_________

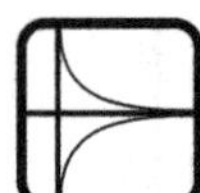

TR2.6 determine the amplitude, period, phase shift, domain, and range of sinusoidal functions whose equations are given in the form f(x) = asin(k(x-d)) + c or f(x) = acos(k(x-d)) + c

Sinusoidal Function Features Related to Parameters

Recall that the parameters a, k, d, and c each affect the graphs of sinusoidal functions in terms of transformations applied to the functions.
These parameters are also used to describe specific features of transformed sinusoidal functions.

For the functions $y = a\sin(k(x-d)) + c$ and $y = a\cos(k(x-d)) + c$, the relationship between the parameters and the corresponding key features can be summarized as follows:

- Amplitude = $|a|$
- Period = $\frac{360°}{|k|}$
- Horizontal phase shift = dRight if $d > 0$
  Left if $d < 0$
- Vertical displacement = cUp if $c > 0$
  Down if $c < 0$
- Domain: $x \in \mathbb{R}$
- Range: Recall that for sinusoidal functions, the range is defined as minimum $\leq y \leq$ maximum. The minimum and maximum values can be determined using amplitude and vertical displacement: $-|a| + c$ = minimum value
  $|a| + c$ = maximum value
  Written in terms of its parameters, the range can be defined as: $-|a| + c \leq y \leq |a| + c$.

Example

Determine the amplitude, period, phase shift, vertical displacement, domain, and range for the function $y = \frac{1}{2}\cos\left(\frac{5}{6}(x - 18°)\right) - 3$.

Solution

Compare the equation $y = \frac{1}{2}\cos\left(\frac{5}{6}(x - 18°)\right) - 3$ to the equation of the form $y = a\cos(k(x-d)) + c$.

The amplitude is

$$|a| = \left|\frac{1}{2}\right| = \frac{1}{2}$$

The period is

$$\frac{360°}{|k|} = \frac{360°}{\frac{5}{6}} = 432°$$

The phase shift is $d = 18°$. The phase shift is $18°$ to the right.

The vertical displacement is $c = -3$, which is 3 units down.

The domain is $x \in \mathbb{R}$.

The range is $-|a| + c \leq y \leq |a| + c$.

$$|a| = \left|\frac{1}{2}\right| = \frac{1}{2}$$

and $c = -3$

$$-\frac{1}{2} + (-3) \leq y \leq \frac{1}{2} + (-3)$$

$$-\frac{7}{2} \leq y \leq -\frac{5}{2}$$

---

25. Which of the following angles is the **least positive** period of the function $y = 4\cos(2(x-3)) + 5$?

A. 60° **B.** 120°

C. 180° **D.** 360°

Open Response

26. For the trigonometric function $y = -2\cos\left(\frac{2}{3}(x + 90°)\right) - 2$, determine the amplitude, period, phase shift, and vertical displacement.

TR2.7 sketch graphs of y = af(k(x – d)) + c by applying one or more transformations to the graphs of f(x) = sinx and f(x) = cosx, and state the domain and range of the transformed functions

Sketching the Graphs of Sinusoidal Functions

In order to sketch the graphs of $y = a\sin(k(x - d)) + c$ and $y = a\cos(k(x - d)) + c$ by hand, transformations can be applied to the graphs of $y = \sin x$ and $y = \cos x$. All points on the transformed graph must satisfy the given transformations. For example, consider these graphs.

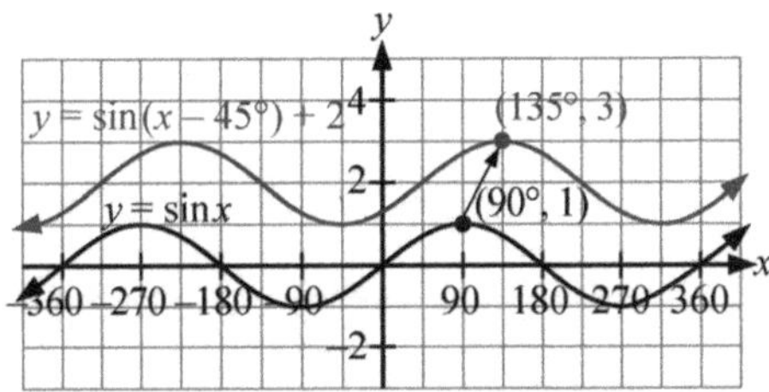

Compared to the graph of $y = \sin x$, the graph of the function $y = \sin(x - 45°) + 2$ has been translated 45° right and 2 units up. Similarly, the point (90°, 1), which is on the graph of $y = \sin x$, will become the point (135°, 3) on the graph of $y = \sin(x - 45°) + 2$. This is because 135° is 45° right of 90° and 3 is 2 units up from 1.

Order of Transformations for Sine and Cosine Functions

When you are sketching the graph of $y = af(k(x - d)) + c$ by applying transformations to the graphs of $y = \sin x$ or $y = \cos x$, the order of transformations should be as follows:

1. Vertical and horizontal stretches in either order
2. Reflections in either axis
3. Vertical and horizontal translations in either order

Steps 1 and 2 can be reversed.

Sometimes, the word stretch is used in place of the words expansion and compression. In these situations, find the value of the factor to determine whether the stretch is in fact an expansion or a compression.

Example

Sketch the graph of $y = -\cos(3(x + 90°)) - 2$, over the domain $-180° \leq x \leq 180°$, by applying transformations to the graph of $y = \cos x$, and verify using technology.

Solution

Compared to the graph of $y = \cos x$, the graph of $y = -\cos(3(x + 90°)) - 2$ has the following transformations applied:

1. Horizontal stretch by a factor of $\frac{1}{3}$
2. Reflection in the x-axis
3. Vertical translation 2 units down
4. Horizontal translation 90° left

Use these transformations to sketch the graph by hand.

The graph shows the transformations of the graph of $y = \cos x$ given in order.

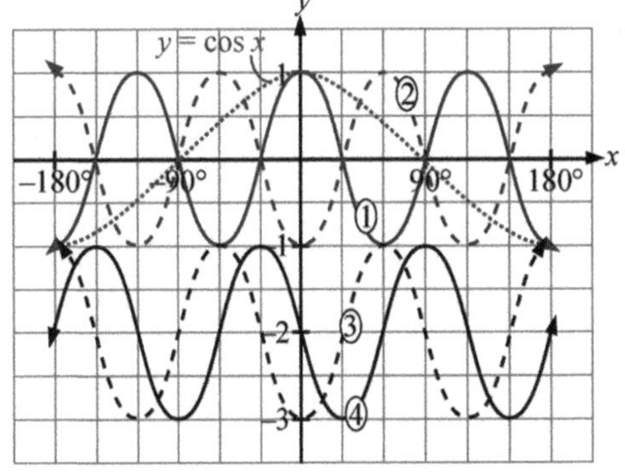

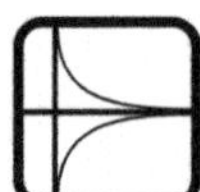

To verify with technology, enter the function $y = -\cos(3(x + 90°)) - 2$ into the $Y =$ feature of a TI-83 or similar graphing calculator. Be sure it is set to DEGREE mode. For an initial image, use ZOOM 7 ↓ ZTrig. The graph displayed uses the window setting x:[−210, 210, 30] y:[−3.5, 1.5, 0.5].

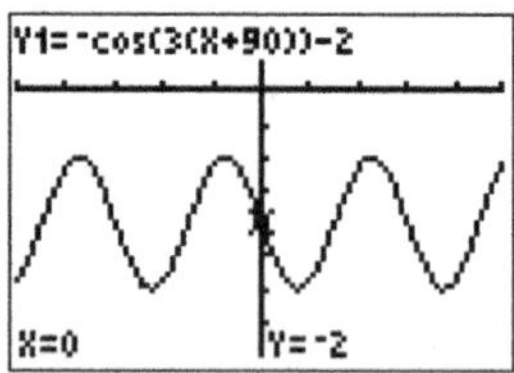

Rather than sketching the full curve at each transformation stage, three or four key points can be transformed and the final curve drawn using the final set of transformed points.

Use the following information to answer the next question.

A student performed a series of transformations on the graph of $y = \cos x$ to produce the graph of $y = \frac{1}{2}\cos\left(-\frac{3}{4}(x + 60°)\right) + 1.$

27. Which of the following graphs represents one of the transformation steps and the final graph of $y = \frac{1}{2}\cos\left(-\frac{3}{4}(x + 60°)\right) + 1$?

A.

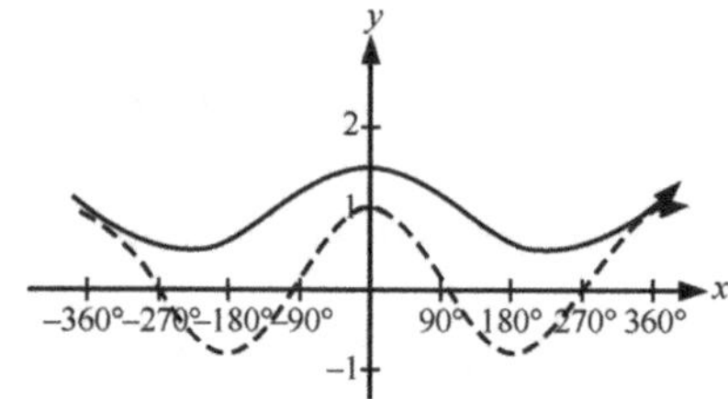

B.

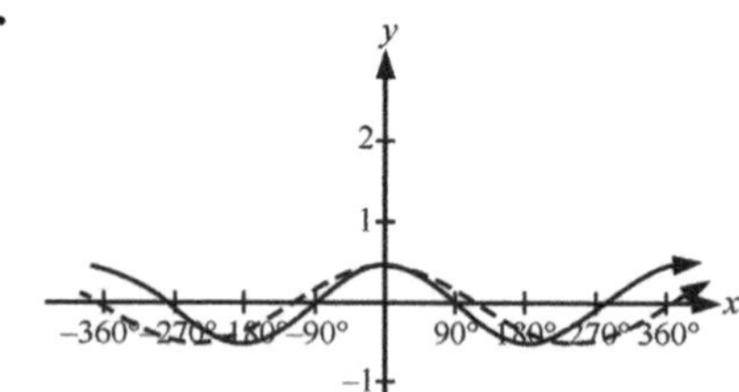

C.

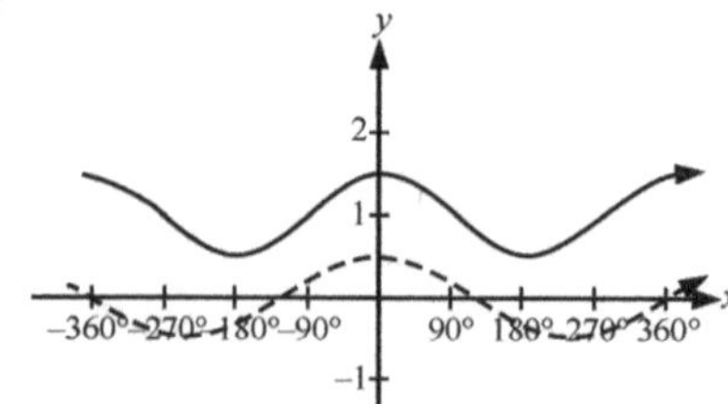

D.

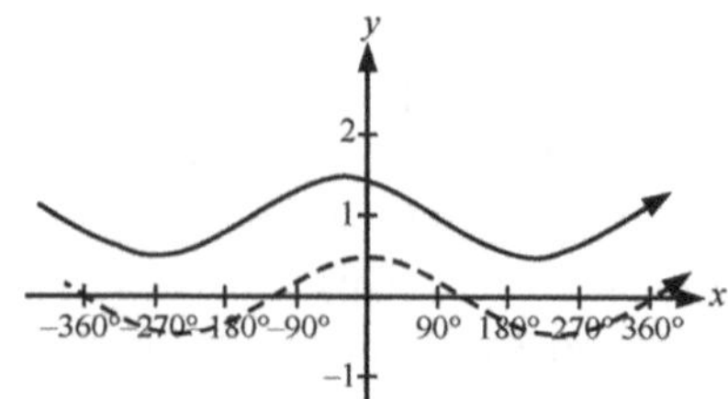

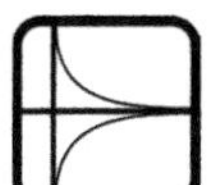

28. For the function $f(x) = \cos x - 15$, what is the domain and the range?

A. $x \in \mathbb{R}$ and $f(x) \geq -16$

B. $x \in \mathbb{R}$ and $-16 \leq f(x) \leq -14$

C. $-360° \leq x \leq 360°$ and $f(x) \geq -16$

D. $-360° \leq x \leq 360°$ and $-16 \leq f(x) \leq -14$

TR2.8 represent a sinusoidal function with an equation, given its graph or its properties

Representing Sinusoidal Functions with an Equation

To determine the equation of a sinusoidal function in the form $y = af[k(x-d)] + c$, in which $f(x) = \sin x$ or $f(x) = \cos x$, it is necessary to determine the values of the parameters a, k, d, and c, which represent amplitude, period, phase shift, and vertical displacement, respectively. Once the values of these parameters have been determined, substitute the values into the appropriate sinusoidal function equation.

Example

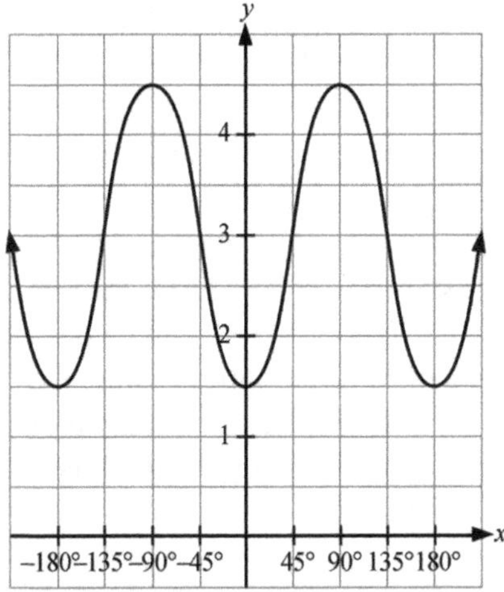

A graph of a function is given.

Determine the equation of the function that is represented by the graph. Write the function in the forms $y = a\sin[k(x-d)] + c$ and $y = a\cos[k(x-d)] + c$, when $a > 0$ and with the smallest possible phase shift.

Solution

Step 1

Determine the maximum and minimum value for each function.

Regardless of its form, the function has a maximum of 4.5 and a minimum of 1.5.

Therefore, $a = \dfrac{4.5 - 1.5}{2} = 1.5$.

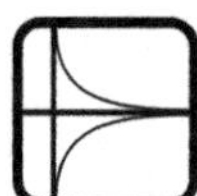

Step 2

Determine the period of each function.

From the graph, the period is 180°. Therefore,

$$180° = \frac{360°}{k}$$
$$k = \frac{360°}{180°}$$
$$k = 2$$

Step 3

Determine the equation of the graph in the form $y = a\sin[k(x - d)] + c$.

As a sine function, the graph is displaced 3 units up, and $c = 3$. From the new horizontal mid-line axis ($y = 3$), it can be determined that the smallest phase shift possible is 45° right, so $d = 45°$. Therefore, the equation of the sine function representing the graph is $y = 1.5\sin[2(x - 45°)] + 3$.

Step 4

Determine the equation of the graph in the form $y = a\cos[k(x - d)] + c$.

As a cosine function, the graph is also displaced 3 units up, and $c = 3$. From the new horizontal mid-line axis ($y = 3$), it can be determined that the smallest phase shift possible is 90° right, so $d = 90°$. Therefore, the equation of the cosine function representing the graph is $y = 1.5\cos[2(x - 90°)] + 3$.

Example

A student graphs the function $y = \cos\theta$, which has a period of 270°.

Assuming k is a positive number, determine the function that describes $y = \cos\theta$ after it has been stretched vertically about the θ-axis by a factor of 3, reflected in the θ-axis, translated 30° to the left, and displaced 2 units down.

Solution

The vertical stretch by a factor of 3 and a reflection in the θ-axis gives $a = -3$. Since the period is 270°,

$$\frac{360}{k} = 270$$
$$k = \frac{360}{270}$$
$$k = \frac{4}{3}$$

A translation (phase shift) of 30° left means that $d = -30°$. A vertical displacement of 2 units down means that $c = -2$. Therefore, the function is $y = -3\cos\left[\frac{4}{3}(\theta - (-30°))\right] - 2$ or

$$y = -3\cos\left[\frac{4}{3}(\theta + 30°)\right] - 2.$$

Use the following information to answer the next question.

> The graph of $y = f(x)$ is a cosine function that has a period of 12°, a vertical compression by a factor of $\frac{1}{7}$, a phase shift of 45° to the left, and a vertical displacement of 3 down.

29. Which of the following equations could represent this function?

A. $y = \frac{1}{7}\cos[3(x - 45°)] - 3$

B. $y = \frac{1}{7}\cos[30(x + 45°)] - 3$

C. $y = -\frac{1}{7}\cos[30(x - 45°)] + 3$

D. $y = \frac{1}{7}\cos[-30(x + 45°)] + 3$

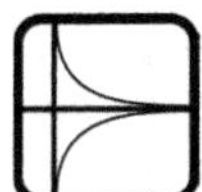

Use the following information to answer the next question.

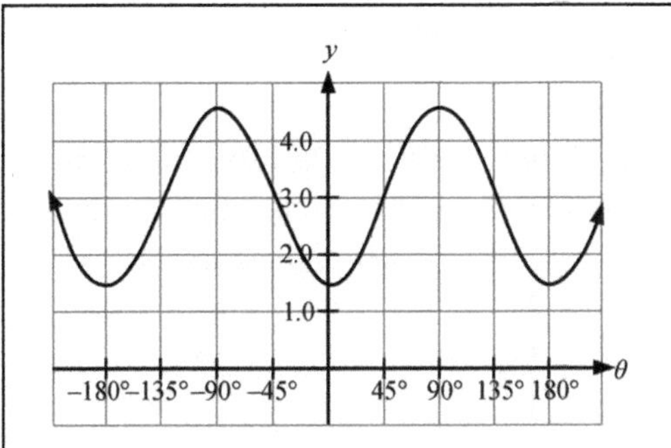

Open Response

30. Determine the equation of the function that is represented by the graph shown. Write the function in the form $y = a\sin[k(x-d)] + c$, where $a > 0$ and with the smallest possible phase shift.

TR3.1 collect data that can be modelled as a sinusoidal function through investigation with and without technology, from primary sources, using a variety of tools or from secondary sources and graph the data

TR3.2 identify periodic and sinusoidal functions, including those that arise from real-world applications involving periodic phenomena, given various representations (i.e., tables of values, graphs, equations), and explain any restrictions that the context places on the domain and range

Modelling Sinusoidal Functions

In certain scenarios, real life data can resemble periodic functions. Researchers collect and analyze this data, and they use tables of values, graphs, or equations to represent this data. The features of the periodic pattern can be identified from these models. Restrictions on the domain and range can also be defined by recognizing the limitations of the values set out by the context of the given scenario. A special type of periodic function, whose graph is a transformation of the sine or cosine functions, is called a **sinusoidal** function.

Example

In a physics lab, the centre of a bicycle pedal mechanism is 30 cm above the ground. Each pedal is 22 cm from this centre point. The pedal mechanism is rotated at a constant speed by a small motor. A student then uses a motion sensor to record the vertical height, h, in centimetres, of one pedal above the ground over a time of 2.0 s. The sensor records the heights every 0.1 s.

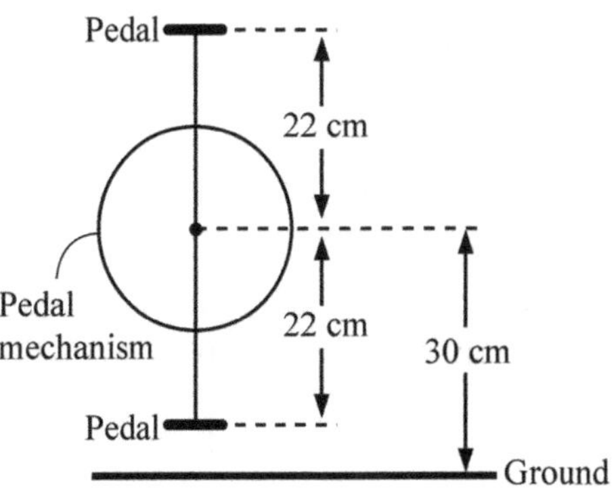

The given table lists the heights, h, in centimetres, of the pedal above the ground over time, t, in seconds.

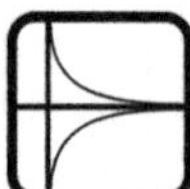

t (s)	h (cm)	t (s)	h (cm)
0	52.0	1.1	48.8
0.1	49.0	1.2	51.8
0.2	40.2	1.3	49.2
0.3	30.0	1.4	40.0
0.4	18.6	1.5	29.0
0.5	10.8	1.6	18.8
0.6	8.0	1.7	10.1
0.7	10.0	1.8	8.2
0.8	19.0	1.9	10.5
0.9	30.6	2.0	19.9
1.0	41.8		

Graph the data from the table, draw a smooth curve of best fit through the data points, and analyze the maximum, minimum, amplitude, and period of the periodic sinusoidal motion.

Solution

The maximum height of the pedal is about 52 cm, and the minimum height is about 8 cm above the ground.

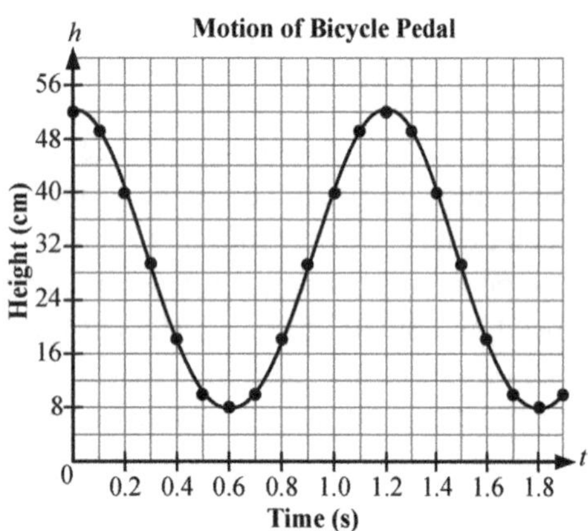

The horizontal axis of the graph runs through a y-value of $\frac{\max + \min}{2} = \frac{52+8}{2} = 30$ cm.

The amplitude of the graph is 22 cm, the length of each pedal arm.

Since the first maximum starts at $t = 0$ s and occurs again for the first time at $t = 1.2$ s, the period of the graph is 1.2 s. This means that the pedal rotates once every 1.2 s.

State the domain and range of the periodic function within the context of this investigation.

Solution

Step 1

Graph the data from the table, and draw a smooth curve of best fit through the data points.

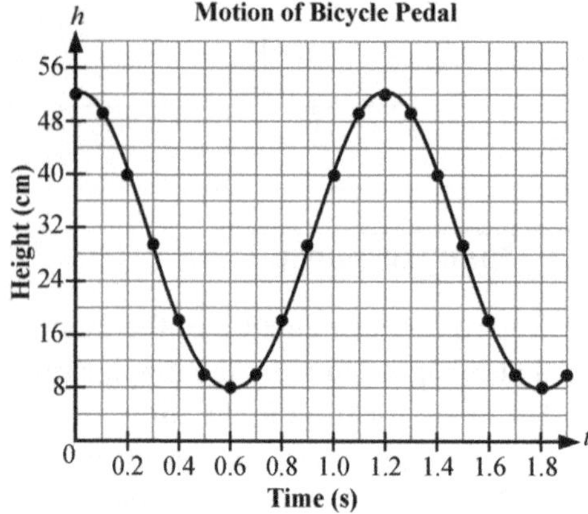

Step 2

Determine the domain of the graph.

The experiment started at $t = 0$ s. The motion sensor recorded data for 2 s, so the experiment ended at $t = 2$ s. Therefore, the domain in this context is $0 \leq t \leq 2$. However, if the sensor were set for a longer time period, T, then the domain would be $0 \leq t \leq T$.

Step 3

Determine the range of the graph.

In this experiment, the range is the h-values between the maximum and minimum values of the graph. Therefore, the range is $8 \leq h \leq 52$. However, if the bicycle was set closer or further from the ground, the range would change relative to the new position.

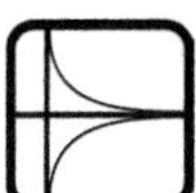

Use the following information to answer the next question.

At 7 A.M. on a Saturday morning, a person measured the distance between the bottom of his boat dock and the top of the water. He measured this distance again every 10 h over a 60 h period and recorded his data in the given table.

Time (h)	0	10	20	30	40	50	60
Distance (m)	2.7	1.3	2.1	2.1	1.3	2.7	1.3

31. Which of the following graphs **best** models the given sinusoidal data?

A.

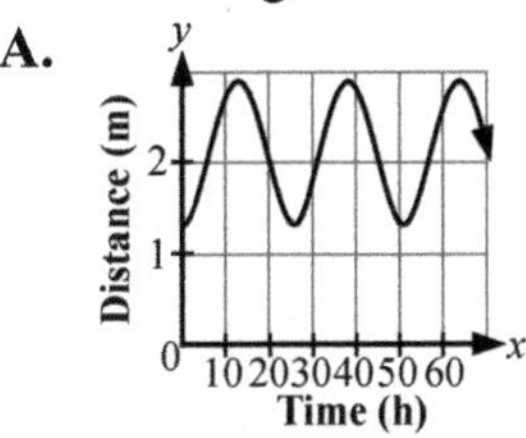

B.

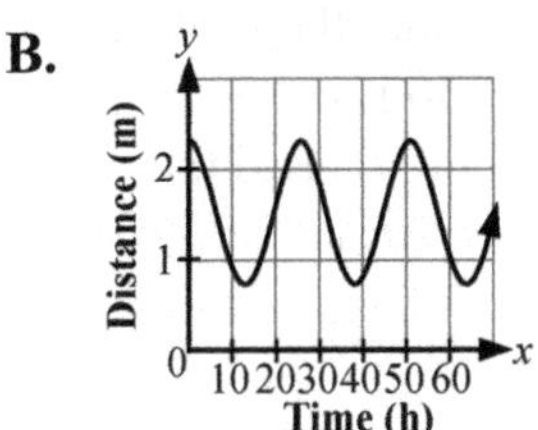

C.

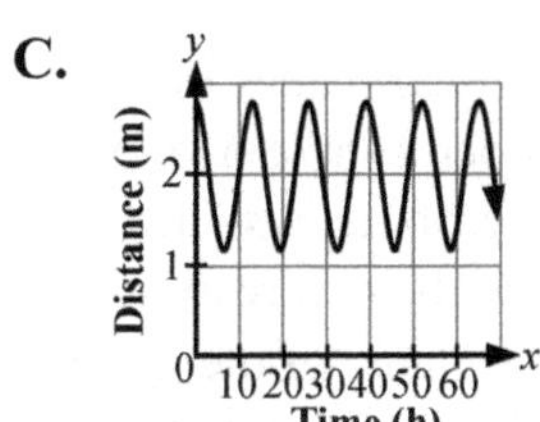

D.

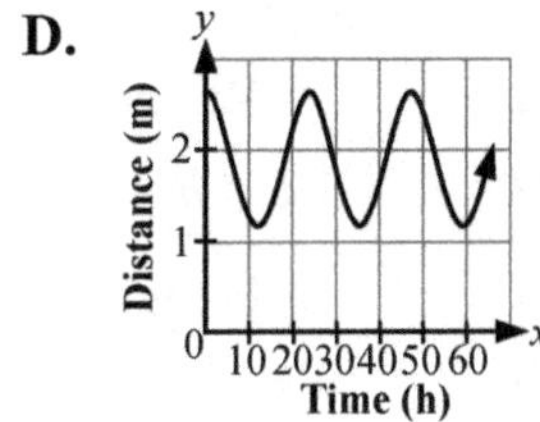

Use the following information to answer the next question.

The blades on a wind turbine are mounted on top of a 3.5 m tall shaft. When measured from the shaft to the tip of the blade, each blade is 1.5 m long.

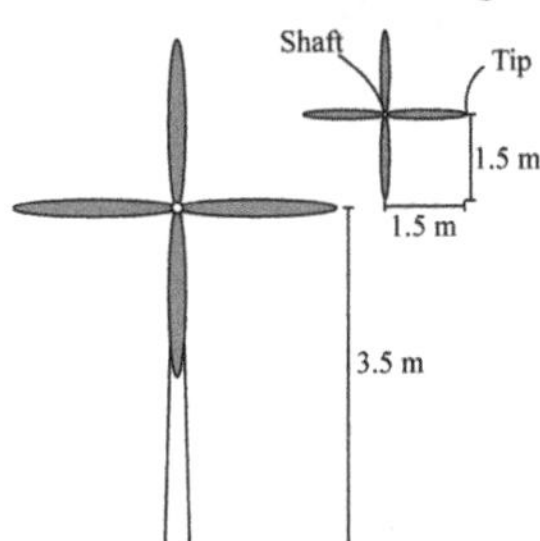

A student observed the motion of the blades and realized that they rotated in a periodic pattern of 30 revolutions per minute. The student graphed the height, h, in metres for one of the blades above the ground with respect to time, t, in seconds.

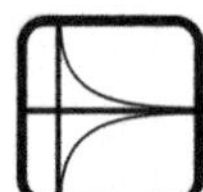

32. If the blade was at its maximum height when $t = 0$, which of the following graphs shows the motion the student observed?

A.

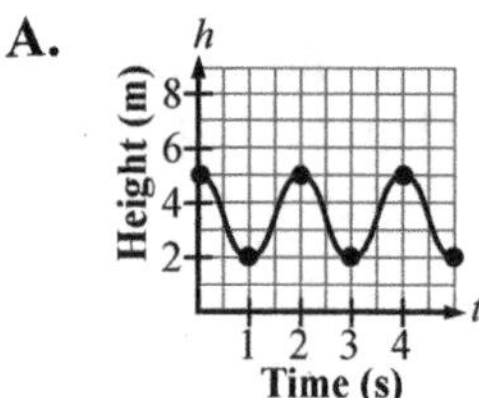

B.

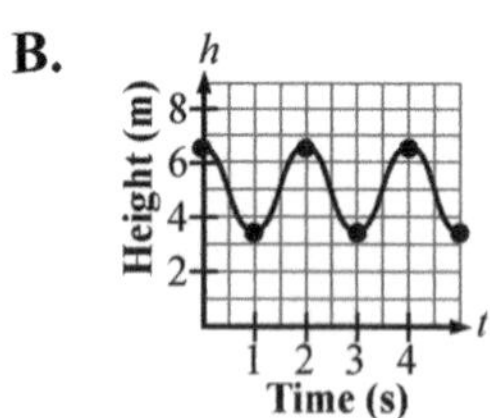

C.

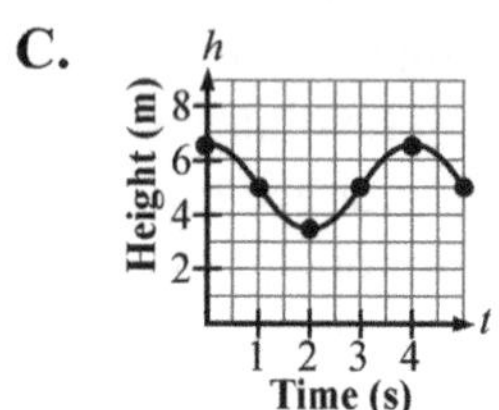

D.

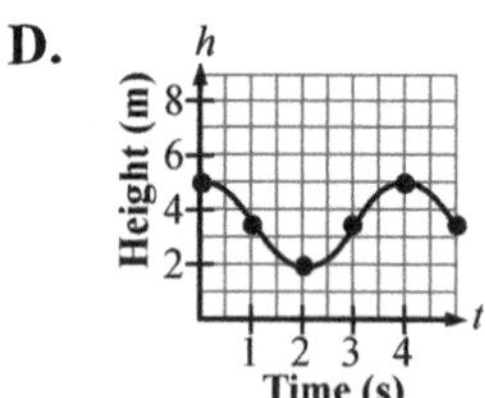

Use the following information to answer the next multipart question.

33. The blades on a wind turbine are mounted on top of a 3.5 m tall shaft. When measured from the top of the shaft to the tip of the blade, each blade is 1.5 m long.

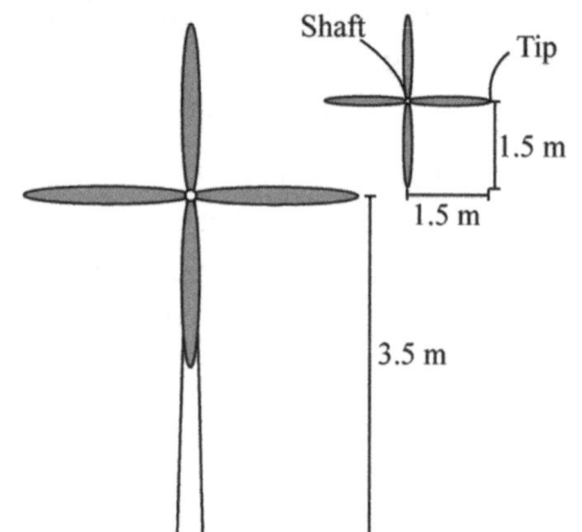

A student observed the motion of the blades and realized that they rotated in a periodic pattern of 30 revolutions per minute. The student graphed the height, h, in metres for one of the blades above the ground with respect to time, t, in seconds.

a) If four new 1.9 m long blades that rotate at 30 revolutions per minute over a total time of 50 min were to replace the original blades, what would the new restrictions be on the domain and range of the graph of the height, h, in metres of one of these blades with respect to time, t, in seconds?

A.

Domain	Range
$0 \leq t \leq 50$	$1.6 \leq h \leq 5.4$

B.

Domain	Range
$0 \leq t \leq 50$	$3.1 \leq h \leq 3.9$

C.

Domain	Range
$0 \leq t \leq 3\ 000$	$1.6 \leq h \leq 5.4$

D.

Domain	Range
$0 \leq t \leq 3\ 000$	$3.1 \leq h \leq 3.9$

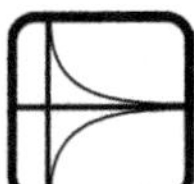

34. Which of the following scenarios would result in a sinusoidal function?

A. A rubber ball is dropped from an initial height and bounces five times before it begins to roll.
The independent variable is distance, and the dependent variable is the bounce height.

B. A rocket is launched from a platform and returns to the ground after 25 s. The independent variable is time, and the dependent variable is the height of the rocket.

C. The population of an ant colony doubles every 3 hrs. The independent variable is time, and the dependent variable is the ant population.

D. Teagan is doing pushups.
The independent variable is time, and the dependent variable is Teagan's height above the ground.

TR3.3 determine, through investigation, how sinusoidal functions can be used to model periodic phenomena that do not involve angles

USING SINUSOIDAL FUNCTIONS TO MODEL PERIODIC PHENOMENA

Periodic phenomena can be modelled using sinusoidal functions. A particular function can be determined and then used to approximate a set of data that models a specific periodic situation.

Example

The table shown gives the average monthly temperature in degrees Celsius in Timmins, Ontario, for 15 months, starting with January 2007.

Year	**Month**	**Month Numb er**	**Average Temperature (°C)**
2007	January	1	–8.2
	February	2	–7.1
	March	3	–2.4
	April	4	4.4
	May	5	11.7
	June	6	17.4
	July	7	20.0
	August	8	18.9
	September	9	14.2
	October	10	7.4
	November	11	0.1
	December	12	–5.6
2008	January	13	–8.2
	February	14	–7.1
	March	15	–2.4

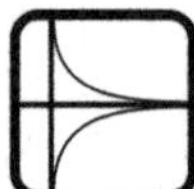

From a sketch, determine an approximate sine function for the data, and verify using technology.

Solution

Sine functions have the form
$y = a\sin(k(x - c)) + d$.

Step 1
Plot the points given in the table.
The points in the table are represented as (month number, average temperature). Draw a smooth curve through the points.

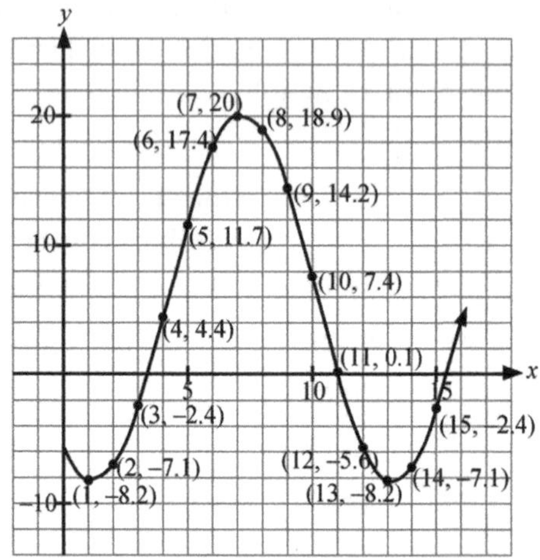

Step 2
Determine the approximate minimum and maximum values of the function that correspond to the given data.
The lowest point on the graph appears to be at (1, −8.2), and the highest point appears to be at (7, 20). As such, the minimum value of the function is approximately −8.2, and the maximum value is approximately 20.

Step 3
Determine the amplitude of the graph ($|a|$-value of the function) using the minimum and maximum function values.

$$\begin{aligned}|a| &= \frac{|\text{max} - \text{min}|}{2}\\ &= \frac{|20 - (-8.2)|}{2}\\ &= 14.1\end{aligned}$$

Step 4
Determine the period of the graph using the points (1, −8.2) and (13, −8.2).
Since these points represent consecutive minimum points on the graph of the function, they represent one full cycle. The period of the graph is 13 − 1 = 12. Find the value of k.

$$k = \frac{360°}{12} = 30°$$

Step 5
Determine the vertical displacement, d, using the minimum and maximum function values.

$$\begin{aligned}d &= \frac{\text{max} + \text{min}}{2}\\ &= \frac{20 + (-8.2)}{2}\\ &= 5.9\end{aligned}$$

The vertical displacement corresponds to the equation of the horizontal axis of the graph. For the graph of $y = \sin x$, the vertical displacement is $d = 0$ because the horizontal axis of the graph is the x-axis. The given graph has a horizontal axis at $y = 5.9$.

Step 6
Determine the horizontal phase shift.
To determine the horizontal phase shift, approximate the x-value for the point (x, 5.9).
From the graph, the value of x at $y = 5.9$ can be approximated as 4.2. Therefore, $c \approx 4.2$.
Substituting each value into the equation $y = a\sin(k(x - c)) + d$ gives an approximate sine function of
$y = 14.1\sin(30°(x - 4.2)) + 5.9$.

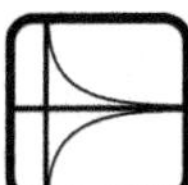

Step 7
Verify this equation using technology.
Enter the data into L_1 and L_2 of a TI-83 graphing calculator by pressing STAT and selecting 1:Edit.
Turn the stat plot option on by pressing 2nd Y = and selecting 1:Plot 1…. After selecting option 1, select On.
Press Y = , and enter the equation by using a window setting of X:[0, 17, 2]Y:[−15, 30, 5].
Graph with the calculator in degree mode.
The result should be a smooth curve that passes through the given data points.

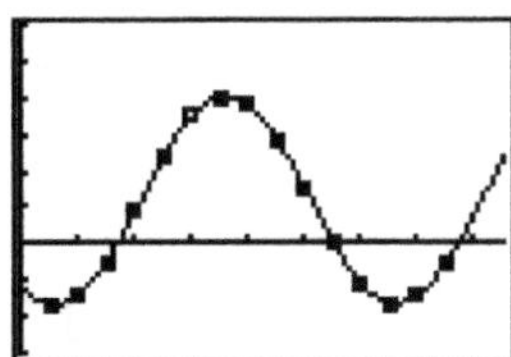

Therefore, the equation $y = 14.2\sin(30°(x - 4.2)) + 5.9$ is an appropriate approximation for the average monthly temperature in Timmins, Ontario.

Use the following information to answer the next question.

The given data represents the change in the sound pitch of a siren over time.

Time (s)	Frequency (Hz)
0	640.0
2	706.6
4	681.1
6	598.9
8	573.4
10	640.0
12	706.6
14	681.1
16	598.8
18	573.4
20	640.0

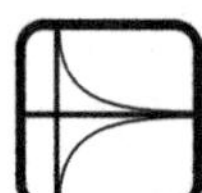

35. Which of the following graphs and corresponding equations **best** represents the given data?

A.

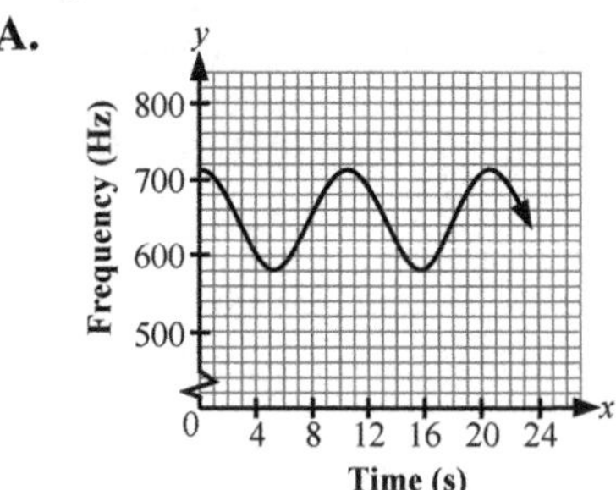

$y = 70\cos(36°x) + 640$

B.

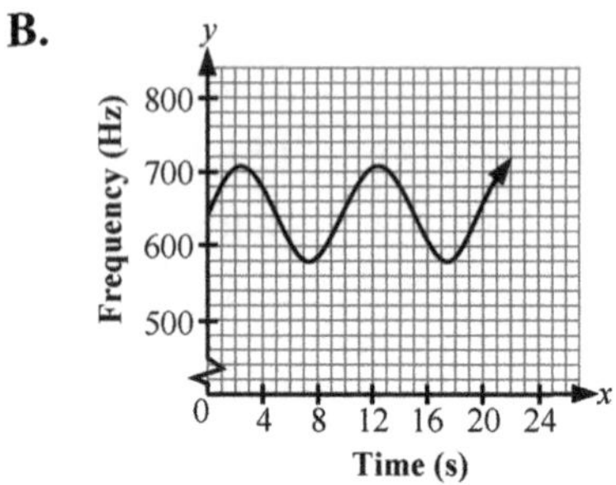

$y = 70\sin(36°x) + 640$

C.

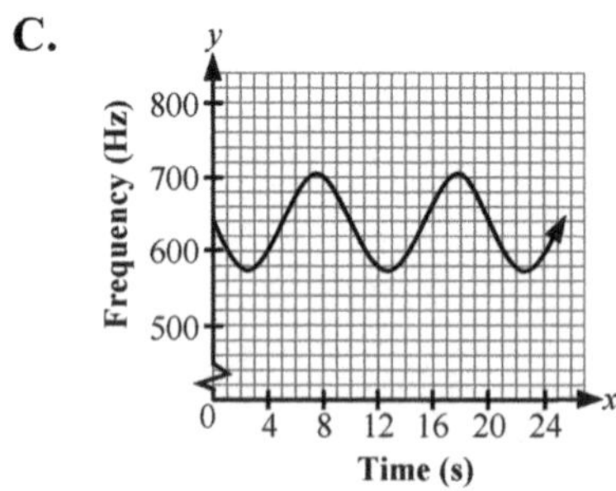

$y = 70\cos(36°(x + 2.57)) + 640$

D.

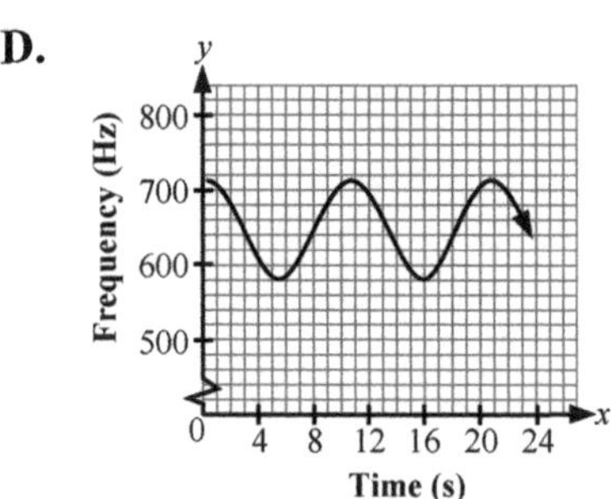

$y = 70\sin(36°(x + 2.57)) + 640$

Use the following information to answer the next question.

At 9 A.M. on a Saturday morning, a person measured the distance between the bottom of his boat dock and the top of the water. He measured this distance again every 10 h over a 60 h period and recorded his data in the given table.

Time (h)	Distance between Dock and Water (m)
0	2.7
10	1.3
20	2.2
30	2.1
40	1.3
50	2.7
60	1.3

36. Which of the following equations **best** models the given periodic data?

A. $D(t) = 0.77\sin(7.2°(t - 18.5)) + 1.91$

B. $D(t) = 0.77\sin(14.4°(t - 18.5)) + 1.91$

C. $D(t) = 0.77\cos(14.4°(t - 18.5)) + 1.91$

D. $D(t) = 0.77\cos(14.4°(t + 18.5)) + 1.91$

TR3.4 predict the effects on a mathematical model (i.e., graph, equation) of an application involving periodic phenomena when the conditions in the application are varied

Using Periodic Function Transformations to Solve Problems

The properties and behaviours of periodic functions can describe real-world situations. In addition, when the conditions of periodic phenomena are varied, the effects of the variations can be predicted using the knowledge of transformations of sinusoidal functions.

Example

A group of football players are running wind sprints before practice. Ryan repeatedly runs from the goal-line to the 20-yard line and back to the goal-line. Matt runs the same 20-yard sprints as Ryan, but he starts 6 seconds later than Ryan. Matt completes one cycle of his run in the same time as Ryan completes one cycle of his run.

Sam also runs a 20-yard sprint, but he runs from the 10-yard line to the 30-yard line and back. He completes one cycle of his run in the same time as Ryan completes one cycle of his, and he starts at the same time as Ryan.The given graph represents the position, s (in yards), that Ryan is from the goal-line t seconds after he starts his run.

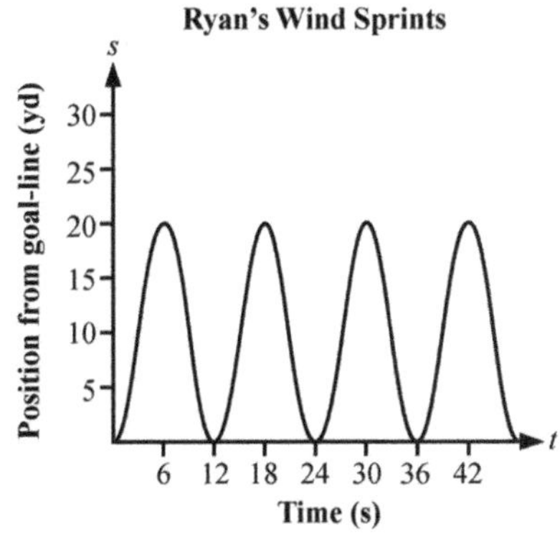

Sketch the graphs for both Matt's run and Sam's run on the same set of axes as the graph of Ryan's run.

Solution

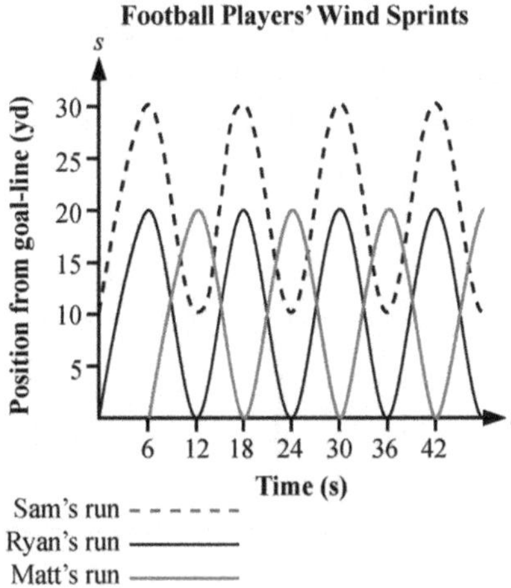

If another player, Larry, runs the same sprints as Ryan but runs only half as quickly, how would the graph of his run compare to the graph of Ryan's run?

Solution

The graph of Larry's run would be stretched horizontally, so that it takes 24 s to complete one cycle rather than 12 s. The period of the function would change from 12 s to 24 s.

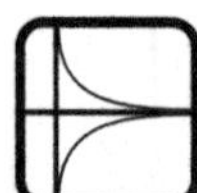

Use the following information to answer the next question.

Kyle rides his motorcycle at a constant speed over a series of hills. The hills are all the same size. Kyle starts his ride at the top of the first hill. The given graph shows his height, h, in metres above the ground t seconds after he starts the ride.

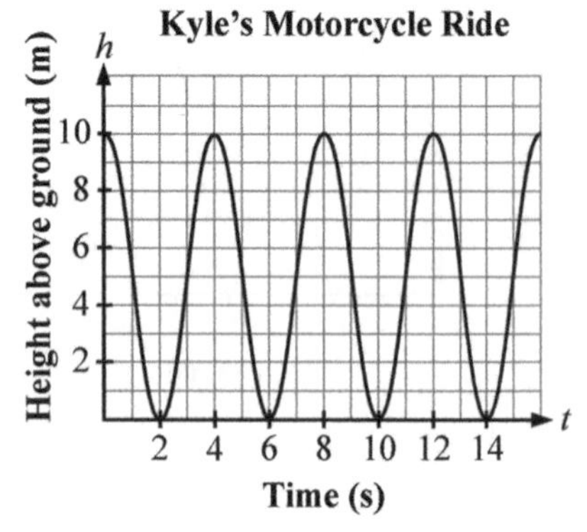

37. If Kyle started his ride at the bottom of the second hill, how would this affect the given graph?

A. There would be a vertical translation of 2 units up.

B. There would be a vertical translation of 2 units down.

C. There would be a horizontal translation of 2 units to the left.

D. There would be a horizontal translation of 2 units to the right.

Use the following information to answer the next question.

Britney ran laps at an indoor circular track so that her position, r, from the starting line t seconds after starting was given by the periodic function $r = f(t)$. Britney returned the next day and ran the same laps, but she ran at a faster pace.

38. What must be done to the graph of the first run, $r = f(t)$, to produce the graph of the second run?

A. Stretch the graph of $r = f(t)$ vertically.

B. Stretch the graph of $r = f(t)$ horizontally.

C. Compress the graph of $r = f(t)$ vertically.

D. Compress the graph of $r = f(t)$ horizontally.

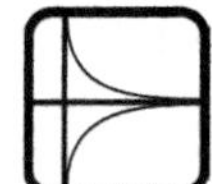

TR3.5 pose problems based on applications involving a sinusoidal function, and solve these and other such problems by using a given graph or a graph generated with technology from a table of values or from its equation

Solving Problems Involving Sinusoidal Motion

Periodic motion can often be described by sinusoidal behaviour. Graphs, tables of values, or equations can represent or model this sinusoidal behaviour. These models can then be used to solve problems relating to the context of that event. Technology, such as a graphing calculator, is frequently used for solving problems that involve sinusoidal motion.

Example

A piston in the engine of a car moves up and down in its cylinder in a periodic fashion. The motion of the piston can be described by the equation $h = 5\sin(157.08t) + 15$, where h is the height of the piston head in centimetres and t is the time in seconds.

Calculate the minimum and maximum heights the piston head reaches while moving up and down in the cylinder.

Solution

In the equation $h = 5\sin(157.08t) + 15$, the number 15 describes the horizontal axis of the graph of the sine function, and the number 5 describes the amplitude of the sinusoidal motion. The maximum and minimum values can be determined as follows:

- The maximum value is horizontal axis + amplitude = 15 + 5 = 20 cm.
- The minimum value is horizontal axis − amplitude = 15 − 5 = 10 cm.

The maximum height of the piston head is 20 cm, and the minimum height of the piston head is 10 cm.

Using a graphing calculator in radian mode, determine the graph represented by the given equation.

Solution

Step 1
For many real-life problems involving sinusoidal motion, the equation is usually defined with respect to angles measured in **radians**. A radian is simply another unit used to define the change in angle of the periodic (circular) motion of the event. Therefore, the graphing calculator needs to be changed from degree to radian by pressing [MODE]. Then, use the down arrow ∇ to highlight RADIAN, and press [ENTER].

Step 2
Enter the given equation in [Y =] as $Y_1 = 5\sin(157.08X) + 15$.

Step 3
Press the [WINDOW] button, and set the domain as x:[0, 0.10, 0.01] and the range as y:[0, 25, 5].

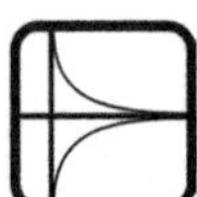

Step 4

Press GRAPH. Your calculator should draw this graph.

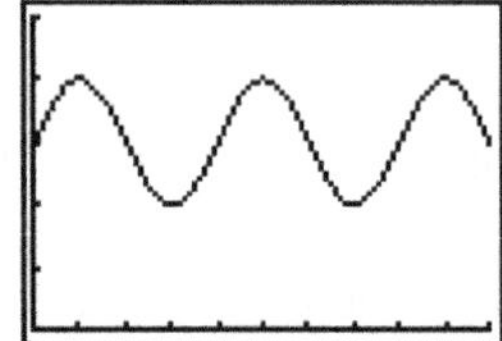

Use a graphing calculator to find the period of the given function, and explain the meaning of this value in terms of the context of this problem.

Solution

Press 2nd TRACE, and select the 4:maximum feature from the list to find the times at which the first two maximum values of the graph occur. These values are highlighted on the two screens shown.

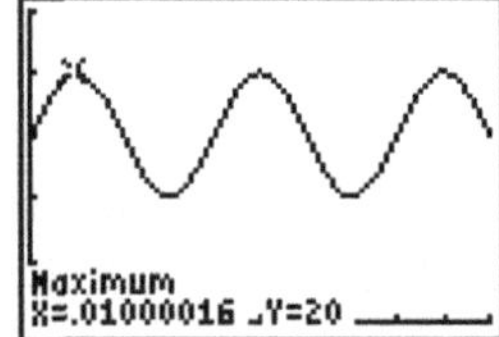

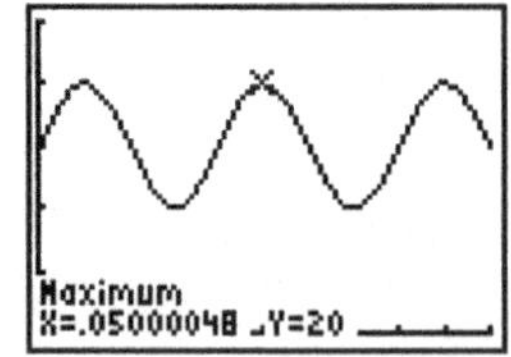

The two values that represent the times at which these two maximums occur are $x \approx 0.010\ 00$ and $x \approx 0.050\ 00$.

The period of a graph is the length of the x-interval of one cycle. In this case, the period occurs between the two repeated maximum values. Rounded to the nearest hundredth, the period of the x-values is $0.05 - 0.01 = 0.04$ seconds.

The period 0.04 s describes the time needed for the piston to go up and down through one cycle within the cylinder.

Calculate the number of complete cycles the piston makes if the piston operates steadily for one hour.

Solution

One cycle takes 0.04 s (calculated by finding the values of the two maximums and subtracting one from the other). The number of cycles made in 1 h (or $60 \times 60 = 3\ 600\text{s}$) can be found as follows:

$$\frac{3\ 600\text{ s}}{x} = \frac{0.04\text{ s}}{1\text{ cycle}}$$

$$\frac{(3\ 600\text{ s})(1\text{ cycle})}{0.04\text{ s}} = x$$

$$x = 90\ 000\text{ cycles}$$

The piston makes 90 000 complete cycles in one hour.

If necessary, you could also determine other features of the piston's motion, such as heights at different times and changes to the graph for pistons moving in other engines.

Use the following information to answer the next multipart question.

39. The function $T(d) = 3.5\sin(0.0172d + 1.76) + 6.75$, where T is the time of sunrise and d is the day of the year (starting with January 1 as day 1), can be used to predict the time of sunrise in a particular region.

Numerical Response

a) The sun will first rise at 7 A.M. on day ________.

b) What time will the sun rise on May 11 (the 131st day)?

A. 4:04 A.M. **B.** 4:07 A.M.

C. 4:17 A.M. **D.** 4:20 A.M.

c) How many days in one year will the sun rise earlier than 8 A.M.?

A. 59 **B.** 225

C. 284 **D.** 343

Numerical Response

d) The sun will rise the earliest on day __________ .

Use the following information to answer the next question.

The height, h, in metres above the ground of a person on a ferris wheel ride is a sinusoidal function with respect to the time, t, in seconds. The given graph illustrates a person's height above the ground from the time the ferris wheel begins moving until the end of the ride.

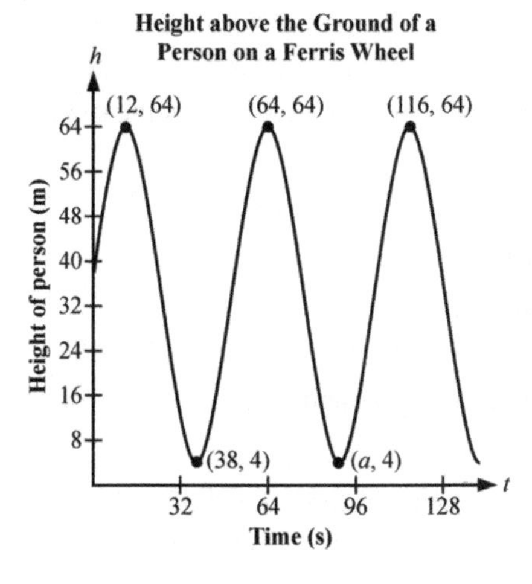

Open Response

40. Determine the height, h, above the ground when the person is halfway to the top of the ferris wheel, the period of the graph, and the radius of the ferris wheel.

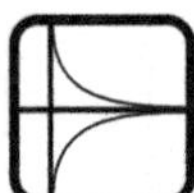

ANSWERS AND SOLUTIONS
TRIGONOMETRIC FUNCTIONS

1. D	**10. OR**	**17. C**	**26. OR**	**35. B**
2. 2	**11. C**	**18. 300**	**27. D**	**36. B**
3. A	**12. 22.9**	**19. A**	**28. B**	**37. C**
4. OR	**13. D**	**20. OR**	**29. B**	**38. D**
5. C	**14. 48.1**	**21. D**	**30. OR**	**39. a) 76**
6. D	**15. C**	**22. 180**	**31. D**	**b) A**
7. A	**16. a) OR**	**23. B**	**32. A**	**c) B**
8. B	**b) OR**	**24. 66**	**33. a) C**	**d) 172**
9. C	**c) OR**	**25. C**	**34. D**	**40. OR**

1. D

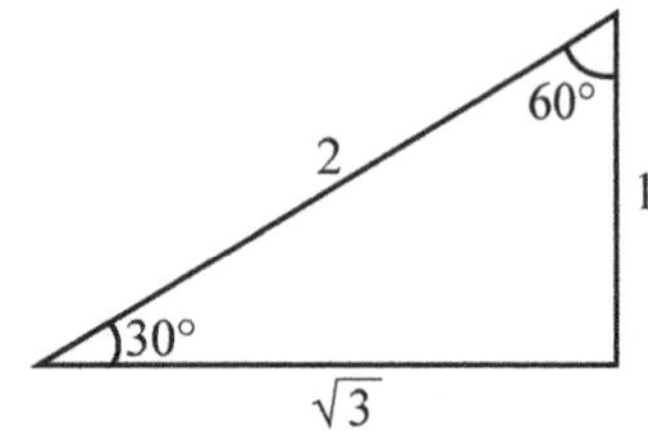

Use the special triangle to evaluate the angle ratios for the given angles.

$$\sin\theta = \frac{\text{opposite}}{\text{hypotenuse}} \therefore \sin 60° = \frac{\sqrt{3}}{2}$$
$$\cos\theta = \frac{\text{adjacent}}{\text{hypotenuse}} \therefore \cos 60° = \frac{1}{2}$$
$$\tan\theta = \frac{\text{opposite}}{\text{adjacent}} \therefore \tan 30° = \frac{1}{\sqrt{3}}$$

2. 2

Step 1
Use a calculator to find cos 0°.
$\cos 0° = 1$

Step 2
Use the 45-45-90 triangle and the definition of the tangent ratio to find the exact value of tan 45°.

$$\begin{aligned}\tan 45° &= \frac{\text{opposite}}{\text{adjacent}}\\ &= \frac{1}{1}\\ &= 1\end{aligned}$$

Step 3
Calculate the value of $a + c$.

$$\begin{aligned}a + c &= (1) + (1)\\ &= 2\end{aligned}$$

3. A

The y-coordinate of point P is equal to the sine ratio for 314°. According to a graphing calculator, $\sin 314° \approx -0.719$. Therefore, to the nearest thousandth, the y-coordinate of point P is −0.719.

4. OR

Step 1
Find the decimal equivalent of cos 64°.

Type in [6][4], and then press [cos] or [cos][6][4] [ENTER], depending on your calculator.

The screen will show 0.438 371 1468. A number to three decimal places is all that is required: 0.438. The value of cos 64°, to three decimal places, is 0.438.

5. C

Step 1
In degree mode, enter $\tan^{-1}(4.474)$ into a scientific calculator to determine the first solution to the nearest tenth.

$\theta_1 = 77.4°$

Step 2
Referring to the CAST rule, the second solution is found in quadrant III. Determine the second solution.

$$\begin{aligned}\theta_2 &= 180° + \theta_1\\ &\approx 180° + 77.4°\\ &\approx 257.4°\end{aligned}$$

To the nearest tenth, $\theta = 77.4°$ or $257.4°$.

6. D

Remember that $\sin 210° = -\frac{1}{2}$.

An angle of 210° terminates in quadrant III.
The reference angle is 30°. As such, the other angle must also have a reference angle of 30°.
Since the sine ratio is negative, the other angle must terminate in quadrant IV.

The angle must be 360° – 30° = 330°.

7. A

Step 1
Draw a diagram of the given triangle.

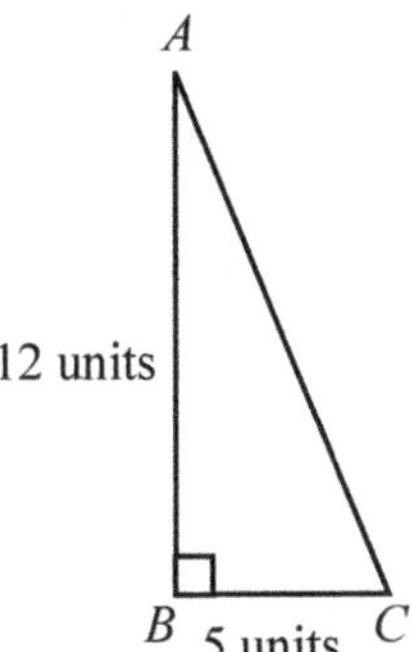

Step 2
Since ΔABC is right-angled, use the Pythagorean theorem to determine the value of the hypotenuse, AC.

$$\begin{aligned} AC^2 &= AB^2 + BC^2 \\ &= (12)^2 + 5^2 \\ &= 144 + 25 \\ &= 169 \\ AC &= 13 \end{aligned}$$

Step 3
Determine the value of csc A.

$$\begin{aligned} \csc A &= \frac{\text{hypotenuse}}{\text{opposite}} \\ &= \frac{AC}{BC} \\ &= \frac{13}{5} \end{aligned}$$

8. B

Since $\cot \theta = \frac{1}{\tan \theta}$, the same logic can be applied to cot 240°.

$$\cot 240° = \frac{1}{\tan 240°}$$

Using a scientific calculator gives the value as $\tan 240° \approx 1.732$.

Therefore, cot 240° is equal to 1 over approximately 1.732.

$$\begin{aligned} \cot 240° &= \frac{1}{1.732} \\ &\approx 0.577 \end{aligned}$$

To the nearest hundredth, cot 240° = 0.58.

9. C

An identity is a statement that is true for all values of x in the domain.

If $\frac{\tan^2 x + 1}{\cot^2 x + 1} = B$, then $\frac{\sec^2 x}{\csc^2 x} = B$ (by the Pythagorean identity).

Step 1
Apply the reciprocal identity.

$$\frac{\frac{1}{\cos^2 x}}{\frac{1}{\sin^2 x}} = B$$

Step 2
Invert and multiply.

$$\frac{1}{\cos^2 x} \times \frac{\sin^2 x}{1} = B$$

Step 3
Simplify.

$$\begin{aligned} \frac{\sin^2 x}{\cos^2 x} &= B \\ \tan^2 x &= B \end{aligned}$$

For the equation $\frac{\tan^2 x + 1}{\cot^2 x + 1} = B$, the value of B would need to be $\tan^2 x$ (or some other expression equivalent to $\tan^2 x$).

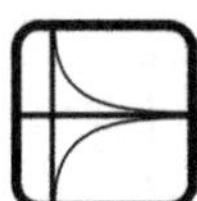

10. OR

LHS

$\tan A + \cot A$

Quotient identities	$= \dfrac{\sin A}{\cos A} + \dfrac{\cos A}{\sin A}$
Find a common denominator.	$= \dfrac{\sin^2 A}{\sin A\cos A} + \dfrac{\cos^2 A}{\sin A\cos A}$
Simplify.	$= \dfrac{\sin^2 A + \cos^2 A}{\sin A\cos A}$
Pythagorean identity	$= \dfrac{1}{\sin A\cos A}$
	$=$ RHS

RHS

$\csc A\sec A$

Quotient identities	$= \dfrac{1}{\sin A} \times \dfrac{1}{\cos A}$
Simplify.	$= \dfrac{1}{\sin A\cos A}$
	$=$ LHS

Since RHS = LHS, the identity $\tan A + \cot A = \csc A\sec A$ is proven.

11. C

Since there is no known pair (a known side with its corresponding opposite angle) given, use the cosine law to solve for a.

$a^2 = b^2 + c^2 - 2bc(\cos A)$
$a^2 = (6.2)^2 + (4.8)^2 - 2(6.2)(4.8)(\cos 74°)$
$a^2 = 45.074\ 064\ 58$
$a = 6.713\ 722\ 111$
$a \approx 6.7$

To the nearest tenth, the distance between ships B and C is 6.7 km.

12. 22.9

Step 1
Determine the sports car's horizontal distance, x_1, from the apartment building.

$\tan\theta = \dfrac{\text{opposite}}{\text{adjacent}}$
$\tan 18° = \dfrac{35}{x_1}$
$(\tan 18°)x_1 = 35$
$(0.3249\ldots)x_1 \approx 35$
$x_1 \approx \dfrac{35}{0.3249}$
$x_1 \approx 107.7$ m

Step 2
Determine the police car's horizontal distance, x_2, from the apartment building.

$\tan\theta = \dfrac{\text{opposite}}{\text{adjacent}}$
$\tan 15° = \dfrac{35}{x_2}$
$(\tan 15°)x_2 = 35$
$(0.2679\ldots)x_2 \approx 35$
$x_2 \approx \dfrac{35}{0.2679}$
$x_2 \approx 130.6$ m

Step 3
Subtract the sports car's horizontal distance from the police car's horizontal distance.

$x_2 - x_1 = 130.6 - 107.7$
$= 22.9$ m

The sports car and the police car are 22.9 m apart.

13. D

Step 1
Draw and Label a diagram based off the information given.

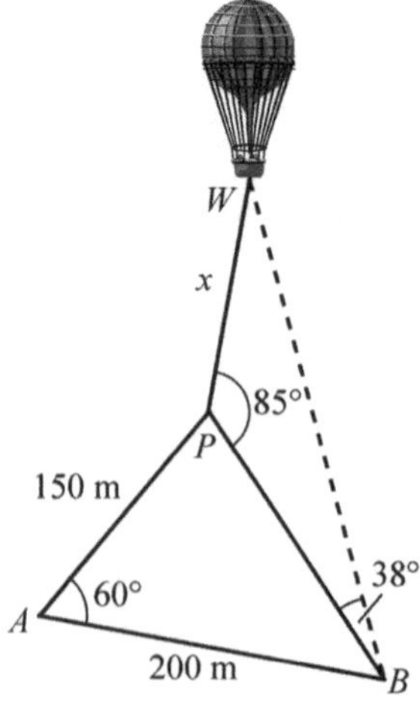

Step 2
Determine the length of side PB.
Use the cosine law in ΔABP.

$(PB)^2 = (AP)^2 + (AB)^2 - 2(AP)(AB)\cos A$

Substitute 150 m for AP, 200 m for AB, and 60° for A.

$(PB)^2 = 150^2 + 200^2 - 2(150)(200)\cos 60°$
$= 22\ 500 + 40\ 000 - 30\ 000$
$= 32\ 500$
$PB = \sqrt{32\ 500}$
$PB \approx 180.28$ m

Step 3
Determine the measure of $\angle BWP$.

$\angle BWP = 180° - 85° - 38° = 57°$

Step 4

Use the law of sines to find the measure of WP.

$$\frac{PB}{\sin \angle BWP} = \frac{WB}{\sin \angle WPB}$$
$$\frac{180.28}{\sin 57°} = \frac{WB}{\sin 85°}$$
$$WB \times \sin 57° = 180.28 \times \sin 85°$$
$$WB = \frac{180.28 \times \sin 85°}{\sin 57°}$$
$$WB = 214.14$$

To the nearest metre, the distance from the weather balloon to point B is 214 m.

14. 48.1

Step 1

Determine the lengths of the bases of the vertical triangles using the tangent ratio.

$$\tan 42° = \frac{25}{y}$$
$$y = \frac{25}{\tan 42°}$$
$$y \approx 27.77$$

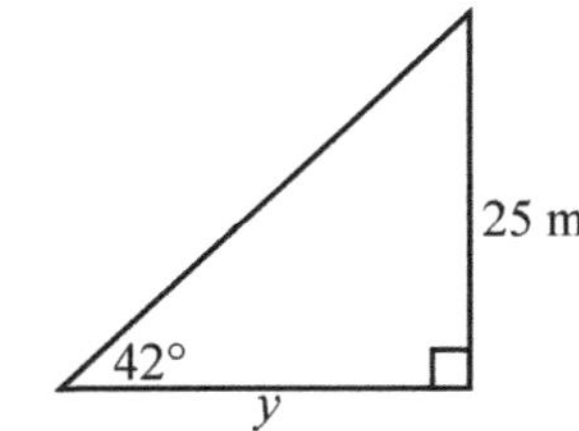

$$\tan 38° = \frac{25}{z}$$
$$z = \frac{25}{\tan 38°}$$
$$z \approx 32.00$$

25 m
38°
z

Step 2

Determine x using the cosine law.

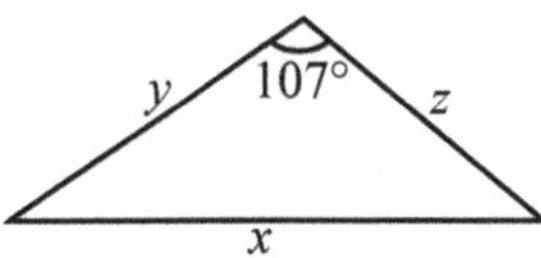

$$a^2 = b^2 + c^2 - 2bc\cos A$$
$$x^2 = y^2 + z^2 - 2(y)(z)\cos 107°$$
$$x \approx \sqrt{(27.77)^2 + (32.00)^2 - 2(27.77)(32.00)\cos 107°}$$
$$x \approx 48.1$$

15. C

The y-values on the graph repeat across an x-interval of 7 units. For example, the minimum y-value of -2 occurs at x-values of -7, 0, and 7. The difference between these values is always 7. Therefore, the period of the graph is 7 units.

16. a) OR

Since the given data represents a periodic function and the period is about 6 months, the expected water usage for the following August would be about the same as it is for August in the given data (6 months + 6 months). The expected amount of water used the following August would be approximately 13.0 m^3.

b) OR

The average amount of water usage throughout the year is defined by the equation of the horizontal axis of the sinusoidal function that could model the given data.

$$y = \frac{\text{maximum} + \text{minimum}}{2}$$
$$= \frac{13.2 + 9.8}{2}$$
$$= 11.5$$

The average amount of water usage throughout the year is 11.5 m^3.

c) OR

To find the amplitude, a, substitute the minimum and maximum y-values into the amplitude equation.

$$a = \frac{\text{maximum} - \text{minimum}}{2}$$
$$= \frac{13.2 - 9.8}{2}$$
$$= 1.7$$

The amplitude of the function is 1.7 m^3.

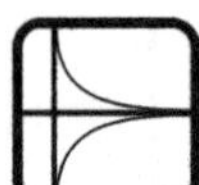

17. C

Step 1
Determine the period of the given function.

The maximum, $y = 3$,of the graph happens at the x-coordinates of -6, 1 and 8. Finding the difference between the consecutive points will give the period of the function.

$$8 - 1 = 7$$
$$1 - (-6) = 7$$

Step 2
Since the function has a period of 7, the y-value at $x = -15$ can be predicted by determining the y-values for the graph located exactly one or more periods to the right of $x = -15$.

$x = -15 + 7 = -8 \rightarrow y = 1$
$x = -15 + 2(7) = -1 \rightarrow y = 1$
$x = -15 + 3(7) = 6 \rightarrow y = 1$

Since $y = 1$ at each of the x-values given on the graph, it can be predicted that $y = 1$ when $x = -15$.

18. 300

Method 1
Follow the periodic pattern of the given table, extend it, and complete the table of values.

Time (s)	1.5	2.0	2.5	3.0	3.5	4.0	4.5
Distance from far right side (cm)	300	0	300	600	300	0	300

After 4.5 s, the pendulum will be 300 cm from the right side of its swing.

Method 2
Use the data points that are one or more periods under 4.5 s.

The data in the table starts repeating itself after 2.0 s, so the period is 2.0 s.

$t = 4.5 - 2.0$
$ = 2.5 \rightarrow d = 300$
$t = 4.5 - 2(2.0)$
$ = 0.5 \rightarrow d = 300$

Since $d = 300$ at each of the corresponding times, it is possible to predict that at a time of 4.5 s, the pendulum has a distance of 300 cm from the far right side.

19. A

One definition of a function is that every element of the domain is paired with exactly one element of the range. For $f(x) = \cos x$, the domain consists of all angles, x, which are uniquely paired with the corresponding cosine values, y, of the range.

20. OR

Step 1
State the definition of $\sin\theta$ for acute angles.

$$\sin\theta = \frac{\text{opposite}}{\text{hypotenuse}}$$
$$= \frac{y}{r}$$

Step 2
Determine the maximum value of $\sin\theta$.

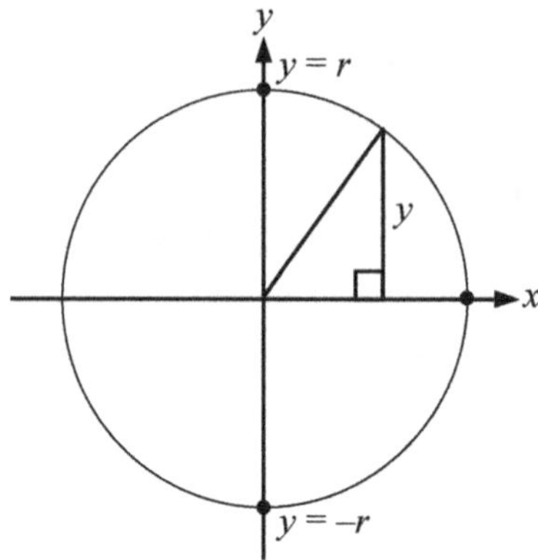

In the given diagram, y is on the circle, so y cannot be greater than the radius of the circle r.

At the maximum of the circle, $y = r$.

$$\sin\theta = \frac{y}{r}$$
$$= \frac{r}{r}$$
$$= 1$$

The maximum value of $\sin\theta$ will never be greater than 1.

Step 3
Determine the minimum value of $\sin\theta$.

At the minimum of the circle, $y = -r$.

$$\sin\theta = \frac{y}{r}$$
$$= \frac{-r}{r}$$
$$= -1$$

The minimum value of $\sin\theta$ will never be less than -1.

21. D

The graph of $f(x) = \cos x$ has the following characteristics that distinguish it from other graphs:

- The y-intercept is $(1, 0)$.
- The period is 360°.
- The maximum value is $+1$, and the minimum value is -1.
- The amplitude, a, can be determined from the maximum and minimum values as follows:

$$\begin{aligned} a &= \frac{\text{max}-\text{min}}{2} \\ &= \frac{1-(-1)}{2} \\ &= 1 \end{aligned}$$

Graph D intercepts the y-axis at $(1, 0)$, it has a maximum of $+1$ and a minimum of -1, and a period of 360°. This graph best represents the graph of $f(x) = \cos x$.

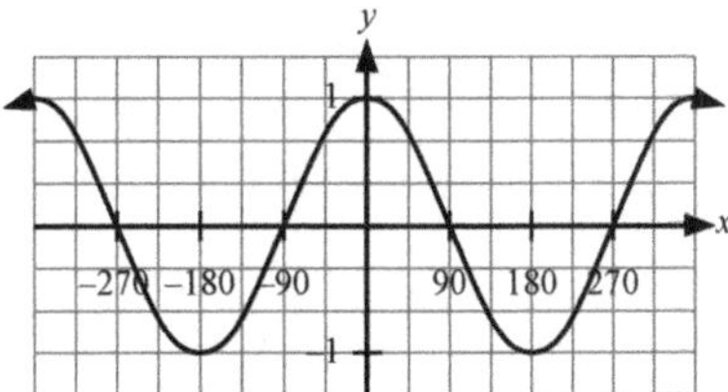

Graph B has a maximum value of $+2$ and a minimum value of -2, so it has an amplitude of 2. Therefore, this choice is incorrect.

Both graphs Aand C have an x- and y-intercept at $(0, 0)$, so these graphs more likely represent graphs of sine functions and not cosine functions.

22. 180

The x-intercepts of $f(x) = \sin x$ are multiples of 180°: …, −180°, 0°, 180°, …. As such, the x-intercepts can be described by $x = 180°n$, $n \in I$. And, given the form $x = a°n$, $n \in I$, $a = 180$.

23. B

The transformed graph of $y = \sin x$ will take the form $y = a\sin(k(x - d)) + c$.

When the graph is compressed vertically about the x-axis by a factor of $\frac{1}{2}$ and then reflected in the x-axis, $a = -\frac{1}{2}$.

The parameter k represents a horizontal stretch. When the graph is stretched horizontally about the y-axis by a factor of 5, $k = \frac{1}{5}$.

A horizontal translation is represented by the parameter d. The graph is translated 55° left. Therefore, since the graph has a phase shift of 55° left, $d = -55°$.

The parameter c represents a vertical translation. The graph is translated 5 units down, so $c = -5$.

Substituting each of the parameters into the equation $y = a\sin(k(x - d)) + c$ gives

$$y = -\frac{1}{2}\sin\frac{1}{5}(x + 55°) - 5.$$

24. 66

Step 1
Determine the value of a.

Since the graph is stretched vertically about the x-axis by a factor of 6, it follows that $a = 6$.

Step 2
Determine the value of d.

A horizontal translation is represented by the parameter d. The graph is translated 30° right. The graph has had a phase shift of 30° to the right, so $d = 30°$.

Step 3
Determine the value of c.

The parameter c represents a vertical translation. The graph is translated 2 units upward, so $c = 2$.

Step 4
Calculate the value of $a + (c \times d)$.

$$\begin{aligned} a + (c \times d) &= 6 + (2 \times 30) \\ &= 66 \end{aligned}$$

25. C

Comparing the function $y = 4\cos(2(x - 3)) + 5$ to the function of the form $y = a\cos(k(x - d)) + c$, it can be seen that $k = 2$. The period of a sinusoidal function is $\frac{360°}{|k|}$. Thus,

$$\begin{aligned} \text{period} &= \frac{360°}{|k|} \\ &= \frac{360°}{|2|} \\ &= 180° \end{aligned}$$

The least positive period of the function is 180°.

26. OR

Step 1
Compare the given function to the function $y = a\cos(k(x - d)) + c$.

Find the amplitude.

$$\begin{aligned} \text{amplitude} &= |a| \\ &= |-2| \\ &= 2 \end{aligned}$$

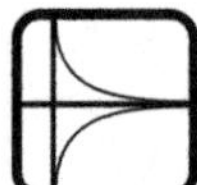

Step 2
Find the period.

$$\text{period} = \frac{360°}{|k|} = \frac{360°}{\frac{2}{3}} = 540°$$

Step 3
Find the phase shift.
phase shift $= d$
$= -90°$
The phase shift is 90° to the left.

Step 4
Find the vertical displacement.
vertical displacement $= c$
$= -2$
The vertical displacement is 2 units down.

27. D

Compared with the graph of $y = \cos x$, the graph of $y = \frac{1}{2}\cos\left(-\frac{3}{4}(x + 60°)\right) + 1$ has the following transformations applied.

1. Vertical stretch by a factor of $\frac{1}{2}$
2. Horizontal stretch by a factor of $\frac{4}{3}$
3. Reflection in the y-axis
4. Vertical translation 1 unit up
5. Horizontal translation 60° left

These graphs show the transformations of the graph $y = \cos x$ in order, as well as the final graph of $y = \frac{1}{2}\cos\left(-\frac{3}{4}(x + 60°)\right) + 1$.

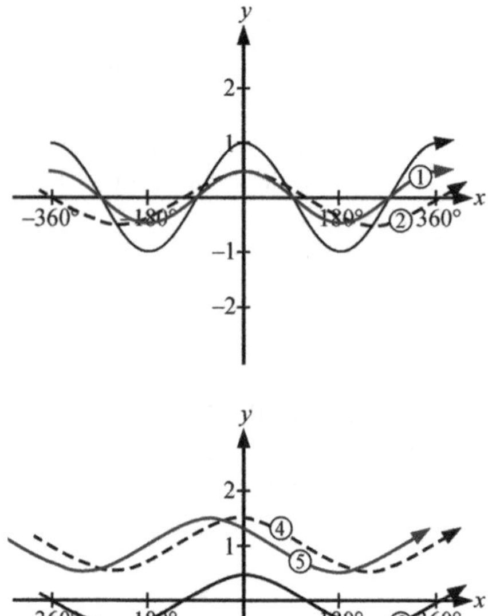

28. B

Step 1
Determine the domain of the function.

There is no restriction on the domain, so the domain is the set of real numbers, $x \in \mathbb{R}$.

Step 2
Determine the range of the function.

Since the graph of $f(x) = \cos x - 15$ is the graph of $f(x) = \cos x$ translated 15 units down, the maximum value of the graph would be $-15 + 1 = -14$, and the minimum would be $-15 - 1 = -16$. Therefore, the range of the graph is $-16 \leq f(x) \leq -14$.

29. B

When looking at a function of the form $y = a\cos(k(x - d)) + c$, the vertical compression by a factor of $\frac{1}{7}$ means that $a = \frac{1}{7}$.

Since the period is 12°, $12° = \frac{360°}{k}$. This means that k can be found by modifying the formula.

$$12° = \frac{360°}{k}$$
$$k = \frac{360°}{12°}$$
$$k = 30$$

The phase shift is 45° left; this means that $d = -45°$.

The vertical displacement is 3 units down, or $c = -3$.

Using all the given information, the function can be created.

$y = a\cos(k(x - d)) + c$

$y = \frac{1}{7}\cos[30(x - (-45°))] - 3$

$y = \frac{1}{7}\cos[30(x + 45°)] - 3$

30. OR

Step 1

Determine the value of a.

The function has a maximum of 4.5 and a minimum of 1.5, so $a = \frac{4.5 - 1.5}{2} = 1.5$.

Step 2

Determine the value of k.

The period is 180°, so $\frac{360°}{|k|} = 180°$. Therefore, $k = \frac{360°}{180°} = 2$.

Step 3

Determine the value of c.

The given graph has a horizontal midline axis at $y = \frac{1.5 + 4.5}{2} = \frac{6}{2} = 3$ and thus, $c = 3$.

Step 4

Determine the value of d.

From the new horizontal axis of $y = 3$, it can be determined that the smallest phase shift possible is 45° right. Therefore, $d = 45°$.

The function is $y = 1.5\sin[2(x - 45°)] + 3$.

31. D

Plotting the given data points and drawing a curve of best fit indicates that graph D best models the given data.

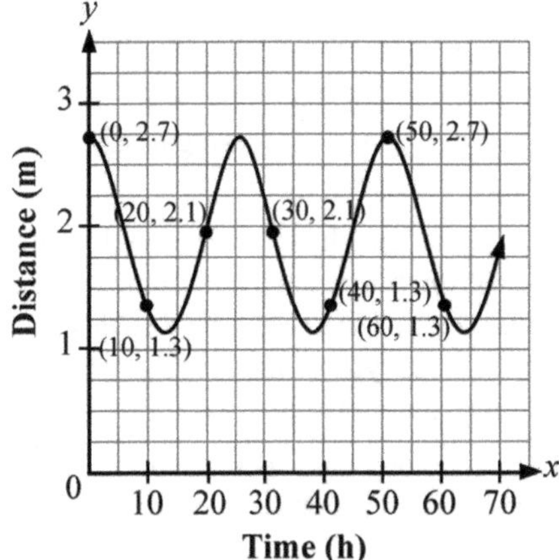

32. A

The maximum height of each blade above the ground would be 1.5 m above the top of the shaft (located 3.5 m above the ground), which is 1.5 + 3.5 = 5 m. The minimum height of each blade above the ground would be 1.5 m below the top of the shaft (located 3.5 m above the ground), which is 3.5 – 1.5 = 2 m. If the blade rotates 30 times each minute, or 30 times every 60 s, it means that the blade rotates once every $\frac{60}{30} = 2$ seconds, and one cycle takes 2 s. This is the period of the graph.

Graph Ashows the correct plotted points and curve of best fit.

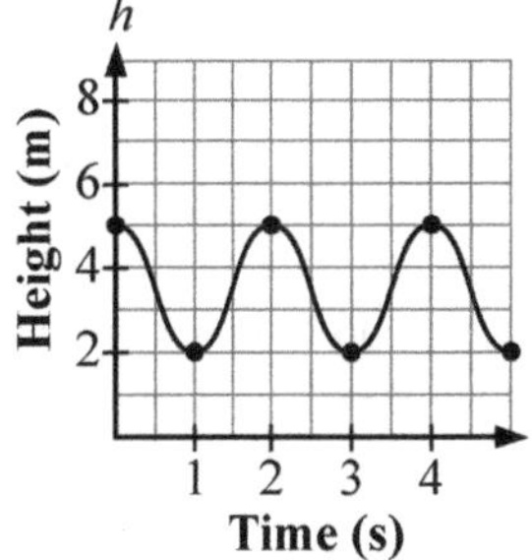

33. a) C

Since the total time is 50 min = 50 × 60 s = 3 000 s, the domain restriction, in seconds, would be $0 \leq t \leq 3\ 000$. The maximum height of the new blade would be 1.9 m higher than the top of the 3.5 m shaft, or 3.5 + 1.9 = 5.4 m. The minimum height of the new blade would be 1.9 m lower than the top of the 3.5 m shaft, or 3.5 – 1.9 = 1.6 m. Therefore, the restricted range would be $1.6 \leq h \leq 5.4$.

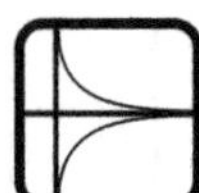

34. D

A sinusoidal function has a regular, repeating pattern over a constant interval.

Teagan's pushups are a change in height that will repeat in a regular pattern for an unspecified amount of time. This is consistent with periodic motion.

The bouncing of the rubber ball is a motion with a finite interval and decreasing height until there is no change in height.

The rocket launch is a motion with a definite path. The rocket will reach a maximum and a minimum height within the given time, but this action will not repeat. This type of motion is consistent with a quadratic relationship.

The ant colony has a population with a doubling period, which is consistent with exponential functions.

Therefore, Teagan's pushups is the scenario that will result in a sinusoidal function.

35. B

Step 1
Plot the given points, and draw a curve of best fit.

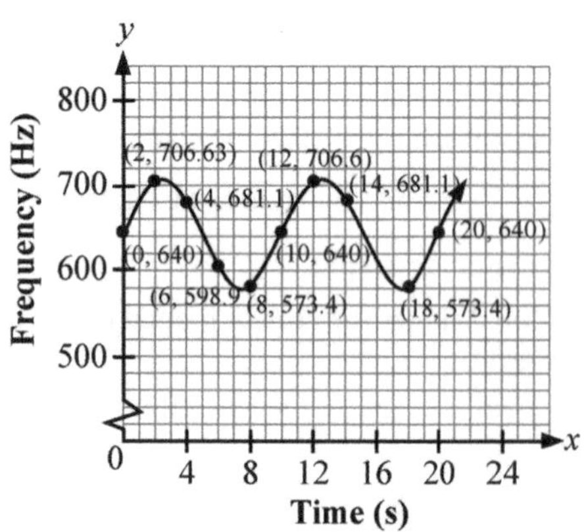

Step 2
Determine the approximate minimum and maximum values.
A sine function has the form
$y = a\sin(k(x - c)) + d$.
The minimum value is slightly lower than the given point (8, 573.4), and the maximum value is slightly higher than the given point (2, 706.6).
Therefore, approximate minimum and maximum values can be determined.
Minimum = 570
Maximum = 710

Step 3
Determine the amplitude, a, of the graph using the minimum and maximum values.

$$\begin{aligned} a &= \frac{\max - \min}{2} \\ &= \frac{710 - 570}{2} \\ &= 70 \end{aligned}$$

Step 4
The period of this graph can be determined using the points (0, 640) and (10, 640). Since this shows one cycle, the period is 10. Calculate the value of k.

$$\begin{aligned} k &= \frac{360°}{10} \\ &= 36° \end{aligned}$$

Step 5
Determine the vertical phase shift, d, using the minimum and maximum values.

$$\begin{aligned} d &= \frac{\max + \min}{2} \\ &= \frac{710 + 570}{2} \\ &= 640 \end{aligned}$$

Step 6
From the graph, there is no horizontal translation when compared to the graph of $y = \sin x$, so $c = 0$.

Substituting each value into the equation $y = a\sin(k(x - c)) + d$ gives an approximate sine function of $y = 70\sin(36°x) + 640$.

36. B

One method would be to graph each of the given functions and examine the table of values for each.

Step 1
Graph the equation
$D(t) = 0.77\sin(7.2°(t - 18.5)) + 1.91$, and examine the table of values.

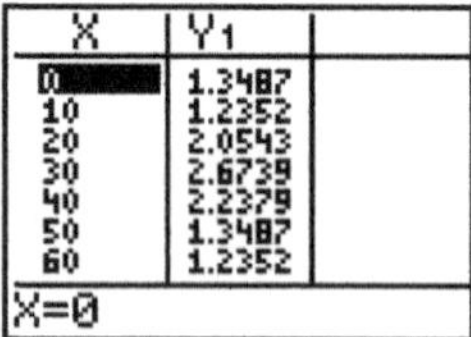

X	Y1
0	1.3487
10	1.2352
20	2.0543
30	2.6739
40	2.2379
50	1.3487
60	1.2352

X=0

Step 2
Graph the equation
$D(t) = 0.77\cos(14.4°(t - 18.5)) + 1.91$, and examine the table of values.

X	Y1
0	1.8617
10	1.4974
20	2.6259
30	1.1642
40	2.4008
50	1.8617
60	1.4974

X=0

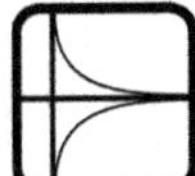

Step 3

Graph the equation
$D(t) = 0.77\sin(14.4°(t - 18.5)) + 1.91$, and examine the table of values.

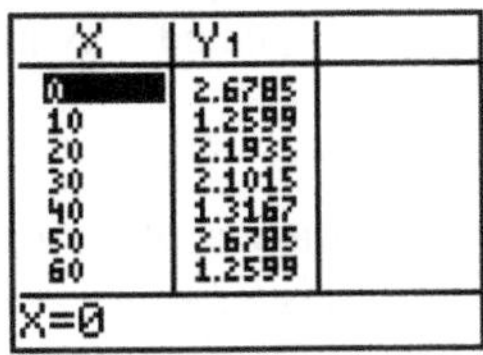

X	Y1
0	2.6785
10	1.2599
20	2.1935
30	2.1015
40	1.3167
50	2.6785
60	1.2599

X=0

Step 4

Graph the equation
$D(t) = 0.77\cos(14.4°(t + 18.5)) + 1.91$, and examine the table of values.

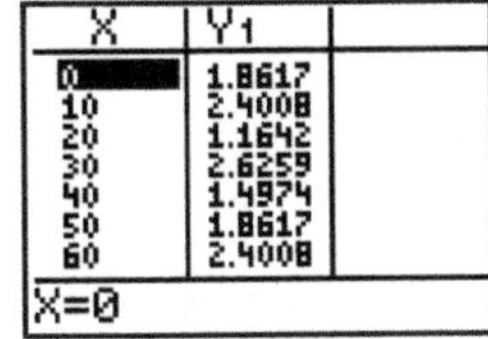

X	Y1
0	1.8617
10	2.4008
20	1.1642
30	2.6259
40	1.4974
50	1.8617
60	2.4008

X=0

The equation
$D(t) = 0.77\sin(14.4°(t - 18.5)) + 1.91$ produces the table of values that best corresponds with the initial table of values.

37. C

The bottom of the second hill is reached 2 s after Kyle starts riding, according to the original graph. However, if Kyle started at the bottom of the hill, the height of 0 m would occur at 0 s. To portray this change graphically, the original graph would be translated 2 units horizontally to the left:
$(2, 0) \rightarrow (0, 0)$.

38. D

Because Britney ran more quickly on the second day, she would have completed each cycle in a shorter time period. Therefore, the graph of $r = f(t)$ must be compressed horizontally to produce the graph of her second run.

39. a) 76

Graph Y1 = 3.5sin(0.0172X + 1.76) + 6.75 and 7 A.M.(Y2 = 7). Make sure the graphing calculator is in radian mode. Using the INTERSECTION feature, observe the first point of intersection, which is at 76.168 791.

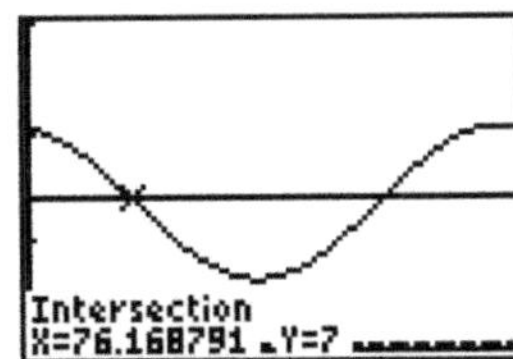

Therefore, the sun will rise at 7 A.M.. On day 76.

b) A

Step 1

Substitute $d = 131$ into the equation
$T(d) = 3.5\sin(0.0172d + 1.76) + 6.75$.

$T(d) = 3.5\sin(0.0172d + 1.76) + 6.75$
$T(131) = 3.5\sin(0.0172(131) + 1.76) + 6.75$
$T(131) = 4.071\ 22\ldots$

This means the sun will rise 0.071 22 h after 4 A.M.

Step 2

Calculate the number of minutes in 0.071 22 h.
$0.071\ 22\ldots \times 60 = 4.273$ min

The sun will rise at approximately 4:04 A.M. on the 131st day.

c) B

Graph the function
Y1 = 3.5sin(0.0172*X* + 1.76) + 6.75 along with Y2 = 8 using a TI-83 or similar graphing calculator.

Use the 2nd TRACE 5: intersect feature to determine that the two points of intersection occur on the 59th day and the 284th day.

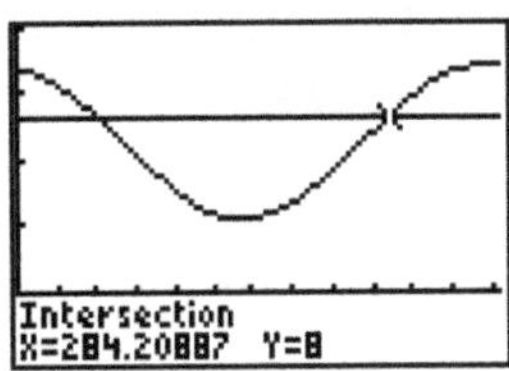

This leaves 284 – 59 = 225 days in between.

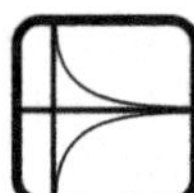

d) 172

Graph the given function using a TI-83 or similar graphing calculator and use the | 2nd | TRACE | 3: minimum feature to find the minimum value. This value represents the earliest sunrise.

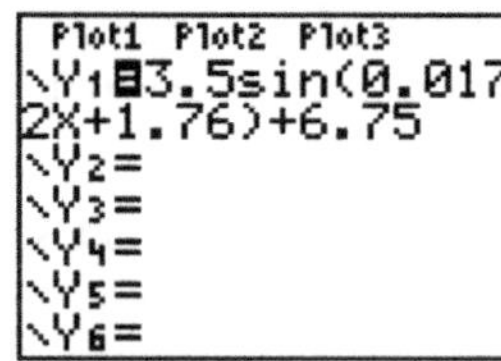

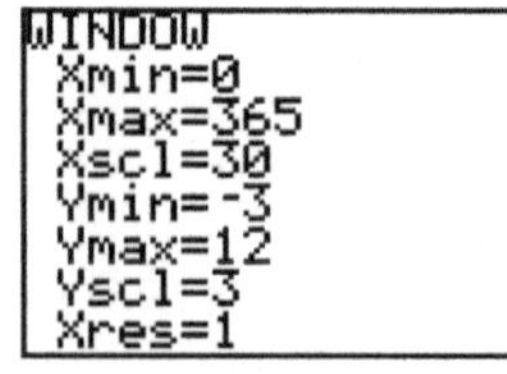

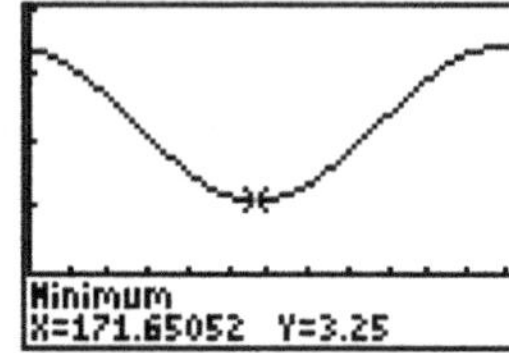

The minimum value occurs when $x = 171.650\ 52$.

Therefore, the 172nd day will have the earliest sunrise.

40. OR

Step 1

Determine the height, h, above the ground when the rider is halfway to the top of the ferris wheel.

Since the maximum height of the ride is 64 m above the ground and the minimum height is 4 m above the ground, the height above the ground when the person is halfway to the top would be located at the horizontal midline axis, h (halfway between the maximum and minimum).

$$h = \frac{\text{max} + \text{min}}{2}$$
$$= \frac{64 + 4}{2}$$
$$= \frac{68}{2}$$
$$= 34 \text{ m}$$

The person is 34 m above the ground at the halfway point.

Step 2

Determine the period of the graph.

The period of a graph is the length of the x-interval of one cycle of the graph. In this case, this occurs between the two repeated maximum (or minimum) values.

$64 - 12 = 52$

Using the x-coordinates of the first two maximum points, the period is 52 s.

Step 3

Determine the radius of the ferris wheel.

The radius can be determined by finding the amplitude of the graph.

$$a = \frac{\text{max} - \text{min}}{2}$$
$$= \frac{64 - 4}{2}$$
$$= 30 \text{ m}$$

The radius of the ferris wheel is 30 m.

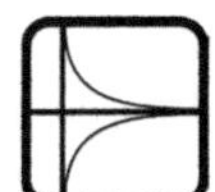

UNIT TEST — TRIGONOMETRIC FUNCTIONS

1. What is the exact value of sin 45°?

   A. 1 **B.** $\sqrt{2}$

   C. $\frac{1}{\sqrt{2}}$ **D.** $\frac{\sqrt{3}}{2}$

Use the following information to answer the next question.

The exact value of cos 240° is $-\frac{a}{b}$. Using the unit circle, the coordinates of this angle are $\left(-\frac{a}{b}, -\frac{\sqrt{c}}{d}\right)$.

Numerical Response

2. The value of *abcd* is __________.

3. What are the exact solutions to $\cos\theta = -\frac{1}{2}$, where $0° \leq \theta < 360°$?

   A. 60° and 240° **B.** 60° and 300°

   C. 120° and 60° **D.** 120° and 240°

4. What is the exact value of sec 30°?

   A. $\frac{\sqrt{3}}{2}$ **B.** $\frac{2\sqrt{3}}{2}$

   C. $\frac{2\sqrt{3}}{3}$ **D.** $2\sqrt{3}$

Open Response

5. Prove the identity $\frac{\sec x}{\sin x} - \frac{\sin x}{\cos x} = \cot x$.

Use the following information to answer the next question.

A child is flying two kites, as shown in the given diagram. Both kites are 8.3 m above the ground, and the child is holding the kite strings 0.5 m off the ground. One kite string is at an angle of elevation of 35°, and the other is at an angle of elevation of 45°. One kite is flying to the child's right, and the other is to the child's left.
The kites are 18 m apart.

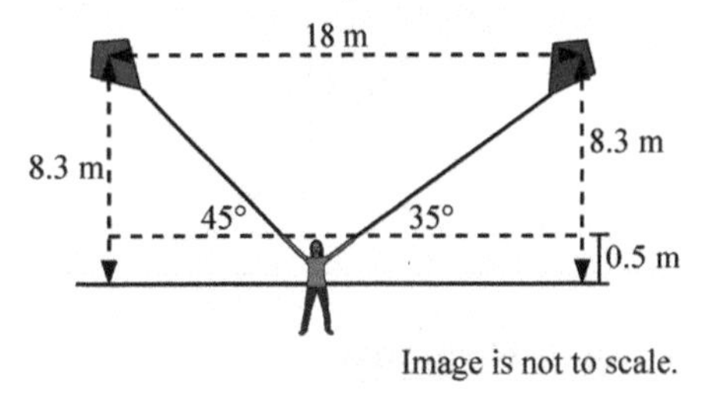

Image is not to scale.

Numerical Response

6. To the nearest tenth, the angle formed by the two kite strings is _________°.

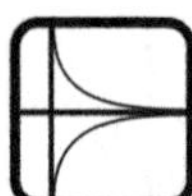

Use the following information to answer the next multipart question.

7. To navigate his sailboat home at night, a sailor uses a lighthouse as a reference point. He is 1 km away from the lighthouse, and the lighthouse is 2 km away from the harbour, as shown.

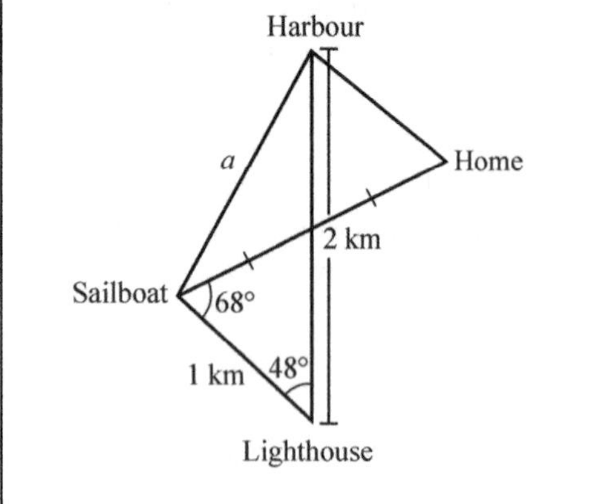

Open Response

a) To the nearest tenth of a kilometre, calculate how far the sailboat is from the sailor's home.

b) To the nearest tenth of a kilometre, calculate the distance from the sailboat to the harbour.

Use the following information to answer the next question.

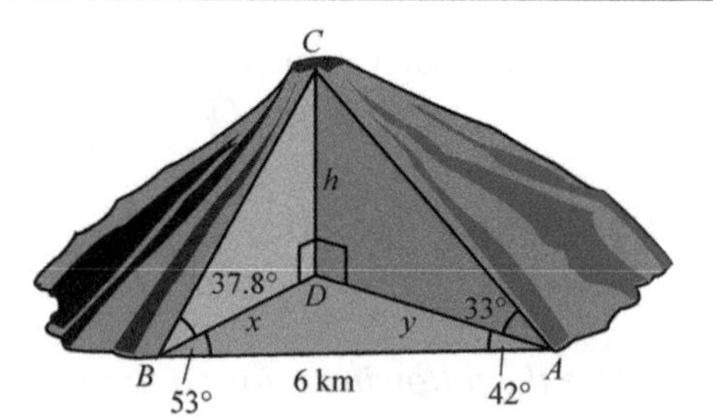

Using an instrument called a theodolite, a surveyor can determine the angles shown in the given picture and use them to calculate the height of the mountain.

8. Rounded to the nearest tenth, what are the lengths of sides x, y, and h?

A. 4.0 km, 4.8 km, and 3.1 km

B. 4.0 km, 4.8 km, and 8.8 km

C. 4.8 km, 3.1 km, and 2.4 km

D. 13.5 km, 31.2 km, and 44.7 km

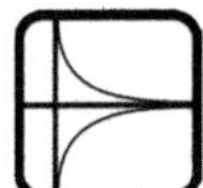

Use the following information to answer the next question.

The given graph can be used to predict the time of sunrise, T, for a certain location in the northern hemisphere on any particular day of the year, d, given that January 1st is day 1.

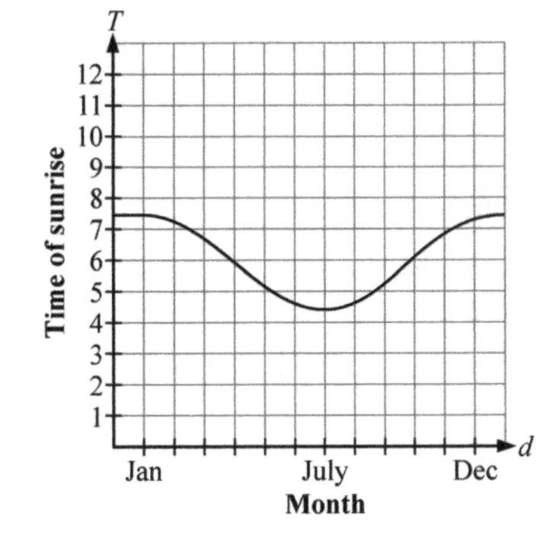

Open Response

9. Describe both the horizontal midline axis and the amplitude of the given periodic graph in terms of the time of sunrise and the days of the year.

Use the following information to answer the next question.

This table gives the average amount of daylight in Sudbury, Ontario, Canada, for approximately two recent consecutive years, neither of which were leap years. Day 1 is January 1 of year 1, day 213 is August 1 of year 1, and day 547 is July 1 of year 2.

Day	Hours of Daylight
1	8.6
60	11.0
121	14.4
182	15.7
213	14.9
274	11.7
305	10.0
366	8.6
397	9.6
456	12.9
486	14.5
547	15.9
609	13.3
639	11.7
700	8.8

10. Assuming the next consecutive year is not a leap year and that the given data represents a periodic function, approximately how much sunlight will there be on September 1 of year 3?

A. 11.5 h **B.** 13.5 h

C. 14.5 h **D.** 15.5 h

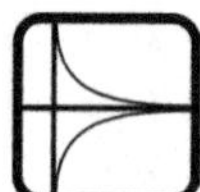

Use the following information to answer the next question.

Point P, with approximate coordinates ($a°$, 0.707), lies on the graph of the function $f(\theta) = \cos\theta$.

11. Which of the following equations could be used to represent the relationship between the given coordinates and the function $f(\theta) = \cos\theta$?

A. $\cos 0.707° = 45$

B. $\cos 45° = \dfrac{1}{0.707}$

C. $\cos 0.707° = \dfrac{1}{45}$

D. $\cos 45° = 0.707$

Use the following information to answer the next question.

A student examined the graph of $f(x) = \sin x$ and made the given observations.

1. One of the minimum points of the graph occurs at an angle of 1 350°.
2. The function increases between −450° and −270°.
3. An angle where the graph passes through its horizontal midline axis is at −620°.
4. The minimum and maximum values occur every 180°.

12. Which observation about the graph of $f(x) = \sin x$ is **false**?

A. 1 **B.** 2

C. 3 **D.** 4

13. When the graph of $f(x) = \cos x$ is transformed into $f(x) = -3\cos x$, it is

A. translated 3 units down.

B. stretched horizontally by a factor of −3.

C. reflected about the x-axis and translated 3 units down.

D. stretched vertically about the x-axis by a factor of 3 and reflected about the x-axis.

Open Response

14. Determine the amplitude, period, phase shift, domain, and range for the function $y = -\frac{2}{5}\sin(-3(x + 15°)) + 4$.

Use the following information to answer the next question.

Michelle searched a public sector employee database for statistical data that modelled a sine function. She found an example and recorded the data as a graph.

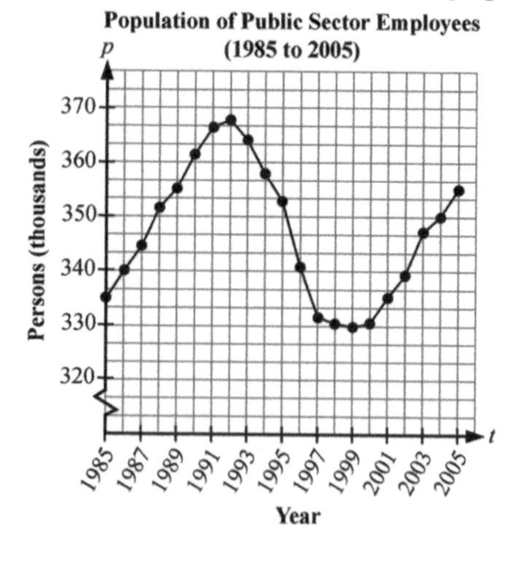

15. According to the approximate sinusoidal graph, the amplitude is about

A. 37 000 people **B.** 27 750 people

C. 18 500 people **D.** 9 250 people

Use the following information to answer the next question.

Tyra used several key points to draw the partial graph of the function $f(x) = \sin(x - 45°)$.

16. Which of the following graphs **best** represents this function?

A.

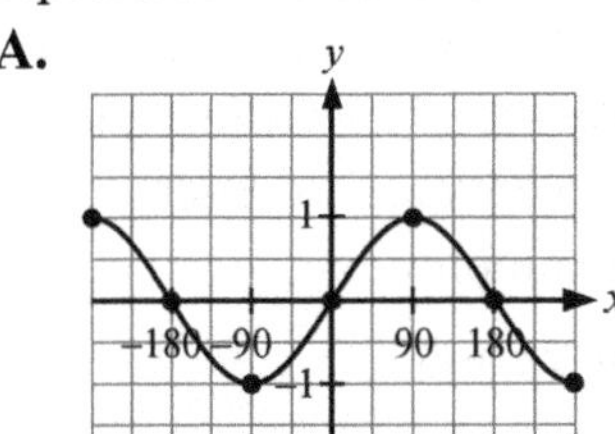

B.

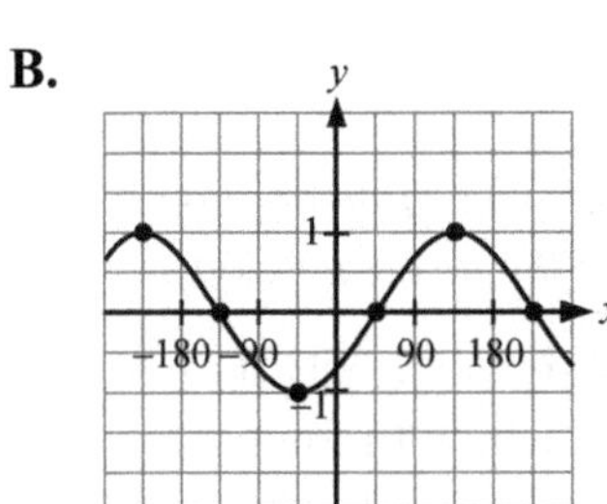

C.

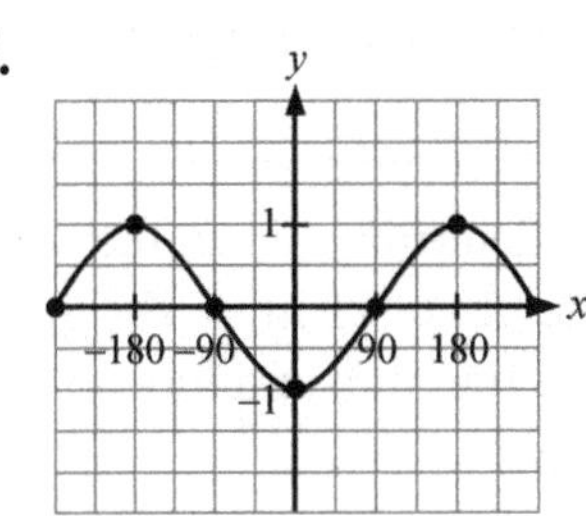

D.

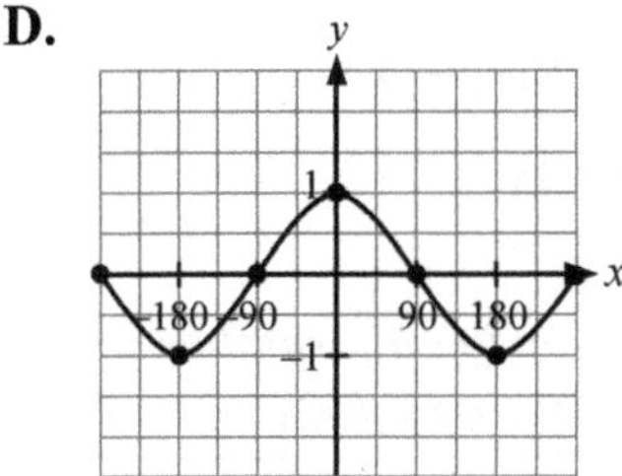

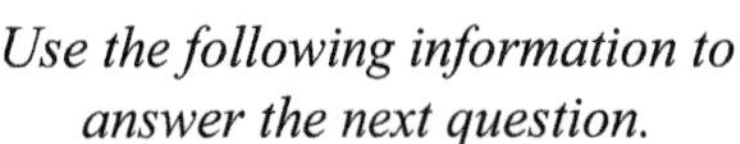

Use the following information to answer the next question.

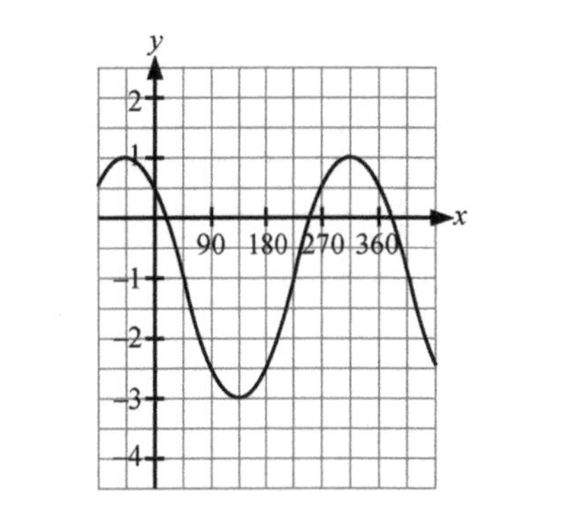

A graph of a function is given.

17. Which of the following equations **best** represents the given graph?

A. $y = -2\cos(x - 20°) - 1$

B. $y = -2\sin(x + 20°) - 1$

C. $y = 2\cos(x + 45°) - 1$

D. $y = 3\sin(x - 45°) - 1$

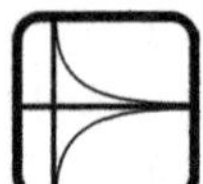

18. Which of the following graphs **best** represents a periodic function?

A.

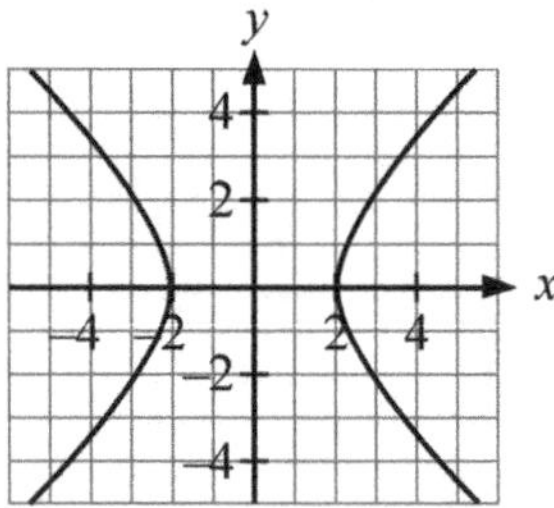

B.

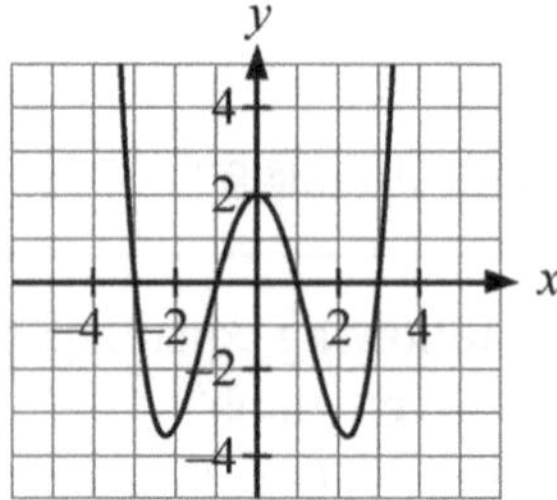

C.

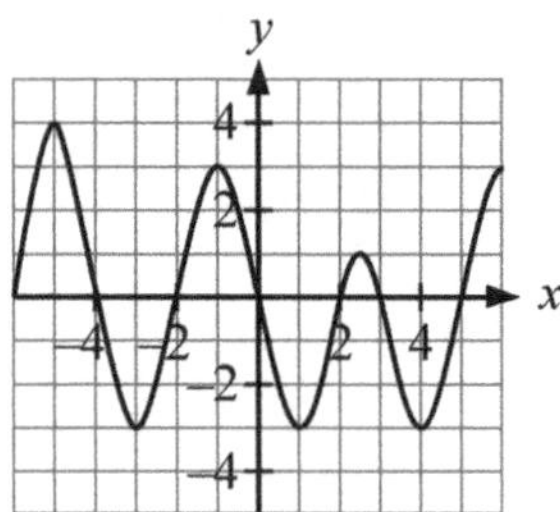

D.

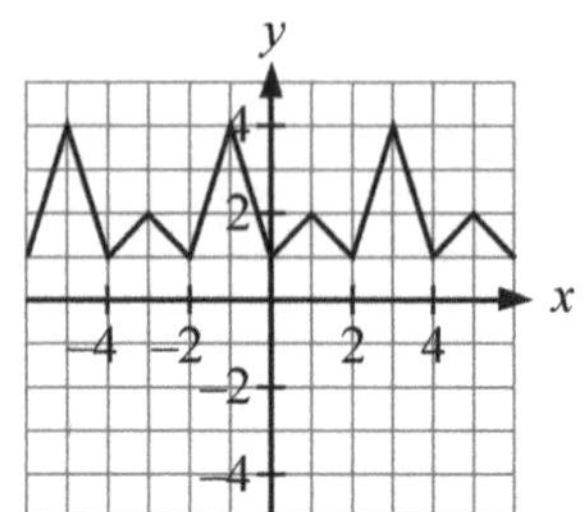

Use the following information to answer the next question.

The function $H(t) = 3\sin(0.52t - 1.57) + 2$ can be used to determine the height, H, in metres of a bucket on a water wheel over time, t, in seconds.

19. If this same wheel was moved farther down into the water, the corresponding sinusoidal curve would experience a

A. change in amplitude

B. change in period

C. horizontal shift

D. vertical shift

Use the following information to answer the next question.

Victoria was given the height of a chair on a ferris wheel which follows the equation $y = 5.7\sin(0.31x) + 7.9$ where y is the height (in metres) and x is the time (in seconds).

20. She wants to determine when the chair will be at a height of 15 m, so she graphed the given sine function and looked for the

A. x-intercepts

B. y-intercepts

C. points where $x = 15$

D. points where $y = 15$

Use the following information to answer the next question.

Tyson has been monitoring the amount of electricity he has been using at his business and has determined that the hourly usage during any business day can be modelled by a periodic function with a period of 24 hrs, an amplitude of 17 kW, and a maximum hourly usage of 39 kW.

Numerical Response

21. The minimum hourly usage is ______ kW.

ANSWERS AND SOLUTIONS — UNIT TEST

1. C	**6. 93.3**	**10. B**	**15. C**	**20. D**
2. 1232	**7. a) OR**	**11. D**	**16. B**	**21. 5**
3. D	**b) OR**	**12. C**	**17. C**	
4. C	**8. A**	**13. D**	**18. D**	
5. OR	**9. OR**	**14. OR**	**19. D**	

1. C

To find the exact value of sin 45°, use the 45-45-90 triangle and the definition of the trigonometric ratios.

$$\sin 45° = \frac{\text{opposite}}{\text{hypotenuse}} = \frac{1}{\sqrt{2}}$$

2. 1232

Consider the special angle 240° in the unit circle. It is an angle in standard position, and it corresponds to a tall triangle, with a reference angle of 60°, in quadrant III.

Label the sides of the triangle as x, y, and r. Because the unit circle has a radius of 1, $r = 1$.

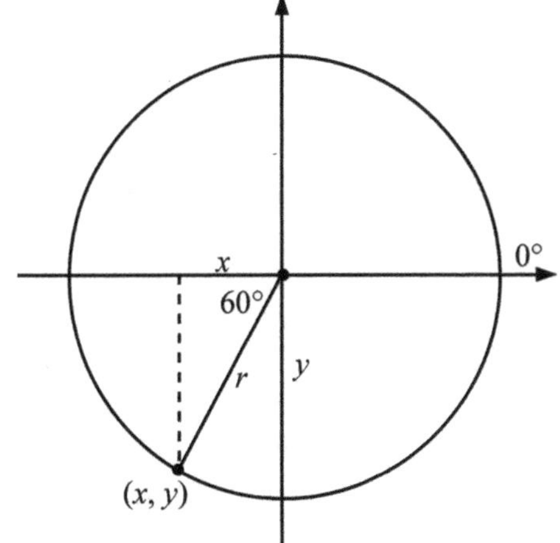

To find cos 240°, use a reference angle of 60°.

The coordinates of the point where the rotating arm intersects the circle are (x, y). Since this is a 60° triangle, the side opposite the 60° angle has a length of $\frac{\sqrt{3}}{2}$, and the side adjacent to the 60° angle has a length of $\frac{1}{2}$. Because point (x, y) is in quadrant III, its coordinates are $\left(-\frac{1}{2}, -\frac{\sqrt{3}}{2}\right)$.

The value of *abcd* is 1232.

3. D

On the unit circle, find the locations where $\cos\theta = -\frac{1}{2}$. This is equivalent to finding locations where $x = -\frac{1}{2}$.

Draw a vertical line at $x = -\frac{1}{2}$. This indicates the terminal points for the two angles that satisfy the equation.

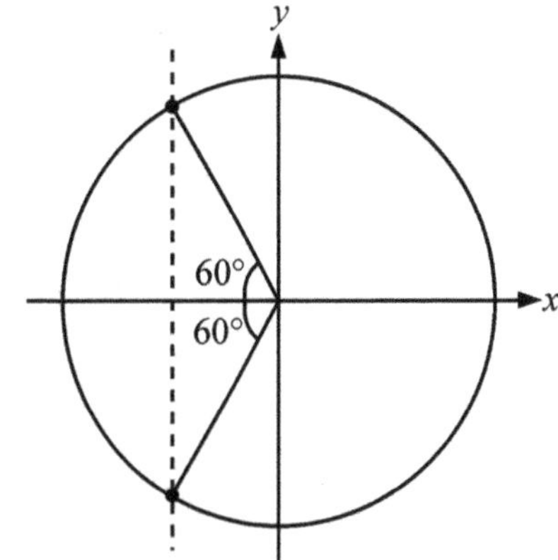

The reference angle is 60°. As a result, the solutions are $\theta = 180 - 60 = 120°$ or $\theta = 180 + 60 = 240°$.

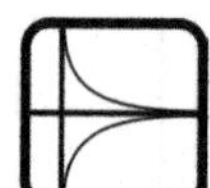

4. C

Remember that $\sec\theta = \frac{1}{\cos\theta}$. Therefore, it follows that $\sec 30° = \frac{1}{\cos 30°}$.

Since the answer must be an exact value, use the exact value for cos 30° from special triangles or the unit circle.

$$\sec 30° = \frac{1}{\cos 30°} = \frac{1}{\frac{\sqrt{3}}{2}}$$

Simplify, and rationalize the denominator.

$$\begin{aligned}\sec 30° &= \frac{1}{\frac{\sqrt{3}}{2}}\\ &= 1 \times \frac{2}{\sqrt{3}}\\ &= \frac{2}{\sqrt{3}}\\ &= \frac{2\sqrt{3}}{3}\end{aligned}$$

5. OR

	LHS	RHS
	$\frac{\sec x}{\sin x} - \frac{\sin x}{\cos x}$	$\cot x$
Apply the reciprocal identity	$\frac{\frac{1}{\cos x}}{\sin x} - \frac{\sin x}{\cos x}$	
Simplify	$\frac{1}{\sin x \cdot \cos x} - \frac{\sin x}{\cos x}$	
Find the common denominator and combine	$\frac{1 - \sin^2 x}{\sin x \cdot \cos x}$	
Apply the Pythagorean identity	$\frac{\cos^2 x}{\sin x \cdot \cos x}$	
Reduce (cos x)	$\frac{\cos x}{\sin x}$	
Apply the quotient identity	$\cot x$	
	LHS=	RHS

6. 93.3

Step 1
Begin by labelling the diagram.

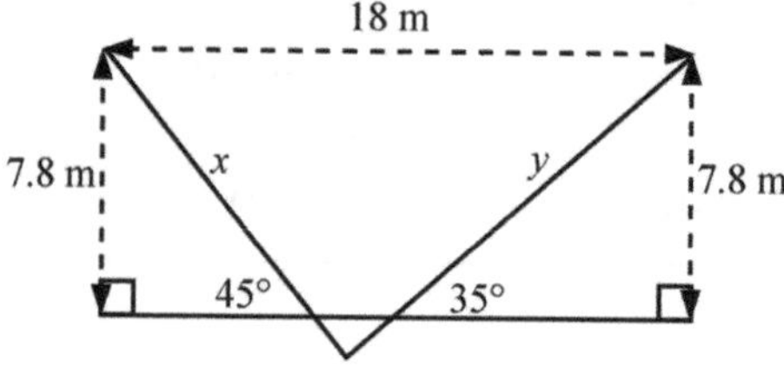

Image not drawn to scale.

Step 2
Apply the sine ratio.

$$\sin 45° = \frac{7.8}{x}$$
$$x = \frac{7.8}{\sin 45°}$$
$$\sin 35° = \frac{7.8}{y}$$
$$y = \frac{7.8}{\sin 35°}$$

Step 3

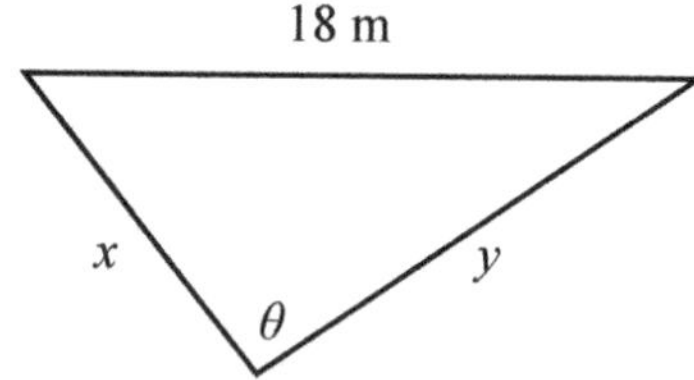

Now, use the cosine law to determine the angle, θ.

$$\cos A = \frac{b^2 + c^2 - a^2}{2bc}$$
$$\cos\theta = \frac{x^2 + y^2 - 18^2}{2xy}$$
$$\theta = \cos^{-1}\left(\frac{\left(\frac{7.8}{\sin 45°}\right)^2 + \left(\frac{7.8}{\sin 35°}\right)^2 - 18^2}{2\left(\frac{7.8}{\sin 45°}\right)\left(\frac{7.8}{\sin 35°}\right)}\right)$$
$$\theta \approx 93.3°$$

7. **a) OR**

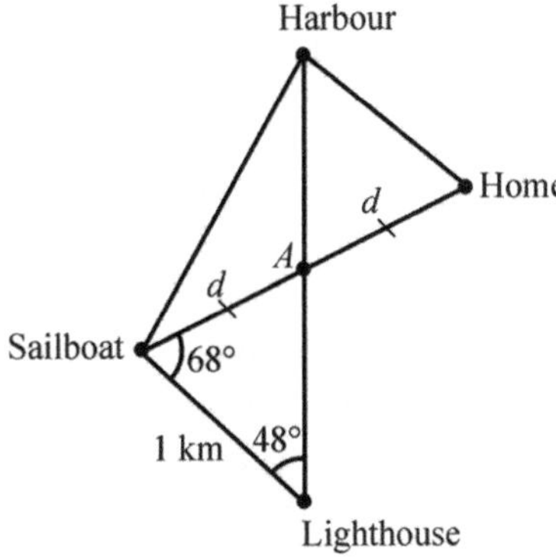

According to the diagram, the sailor is a distance of $2d$ from home. Since two angles and the length of one side is known, use the sine law to solve the problem.

Step 1
Find angle A.
Use the rule that the sum of the interior angles of a triangle is 180°.
$\angle A = 180° - 48° - 68° = 64°$

Step 2
Use the sine law to find side d.

$$\frac{a}{\sin A} = \frac{d}{\sin D}$$
$$\frac{1}{\sin 64°} = \frac{d}{\sin 48°}$$
$$(\sin 48°)1 = (\sin 64°)d$$
$$\frac{\sin 48°}{\sin 64°} = d$$
$$0.826\,824\ldots = d$$

Remember that the sailboat is a distance of $2d$ from home.
$2d \approx 2(0.8268) \approx 1.6536$
Therefore, the sailboat is approximately 1.7 km away from the sailor's home.

b) OR

Step 1
Draw a diagram.
The sailboat is denoted as B, the lighthouse as A, and the harbour as C.

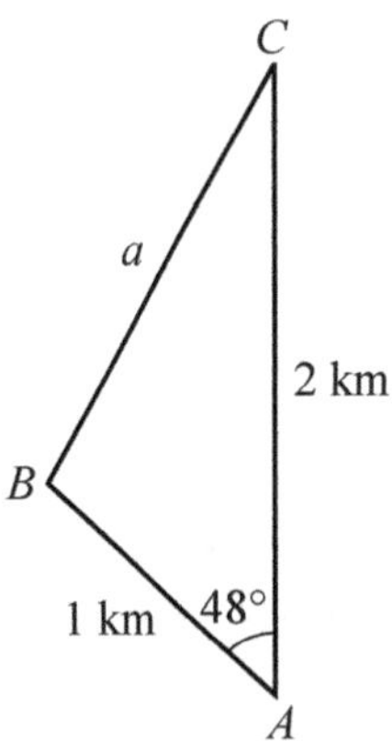

Step 2
Since the triangle is not a right triangle and the measures of two sides and an included angle are known, use the cosine law to solve for a.

$$a^2 = b^2 + c^2 - 2bc(\cos A)$$
$$a^2 = 2^2 + 1^2 - 2(2)(1)\cos 48°$$
$$a^2 \approx 2.3235$$
$$a \approx 1.5 \text{ km}$$

The distance from the sailboat to the harbour is approximately 1.5 km.

8. **A**

Step 1
Find the missing $\angle BDA$.
$180° - 53° - 42° = 85°$

Step 2
Determine the length of x.

$$\frac{\sin A}{a} = \frac{\sin B}{b}$$
$$\frac{\sin 42°}{x} = \frac{\sin 85°}{6}$$
$$6(\sin 42°) = x(\sin 85°)$$
$$\frac{6\sin 42°}{\sin 85°} = x$$
$$x \approx 4.0 \text{ km}$$

Step 3
Determine the length of y.

$$\frac{\sin A}{a} = \frac{\sin B}{b}$$
$$\frac{\sin 53°}{y} = \frac{\sin 85°}{6}$$
$$6(\sin 53°) = y(\sin 85°)$$
$$\frac{6\sin 53°}{\sin 85°} = y$$
$$y \approx 4.8 \text{ km}$$

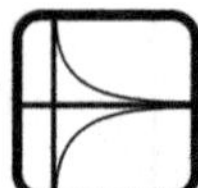

Step 4
Lastly, determine the height, h, using the value calculated for either x or y.

$$\tan\theta = \frac{\text{opposite}}{\text{adjacent}}$$
$$\tan 37.8° = \frac{h}{4}$$
$$(4)\tan 37.8° = h$$
$$3.1 \text{ km} \approx h$$

$$\tan\theta = \frac{\text{opposite}}{\text{adjacent}}$$
$$\tan 33° = \frac{h}{4.8}$$
$$(4.8)\tan 33° = h$$
$$3.1 \text{ km} \approx h$$

Therefore, the lengths of x, y, and h are, respectively, 4 km, 4.8 km, and 3.1 km.

9. OR

The horizontal midline axis is represented by the line $y = 6$ because it is the exact middle line between the maximum, 7.5, and the minimum, 4.5. Thus, the average time of sunrise is 6 A.M.

The amplitude of the graph can be calculated using the maximum and minimum values.

$$a = \frac{\text{max} - \text{min}}{2}$$
$$= \frac{7.5 - 4.5}{2}$$
$$= 1.5$$

The time of sunrise varies between 1.5 h before and 1.5 h after 6 A.M.

10. B

Step 1
Plot the given points on a graph, and draw a smooth sinusoidal curve to connect the data points.

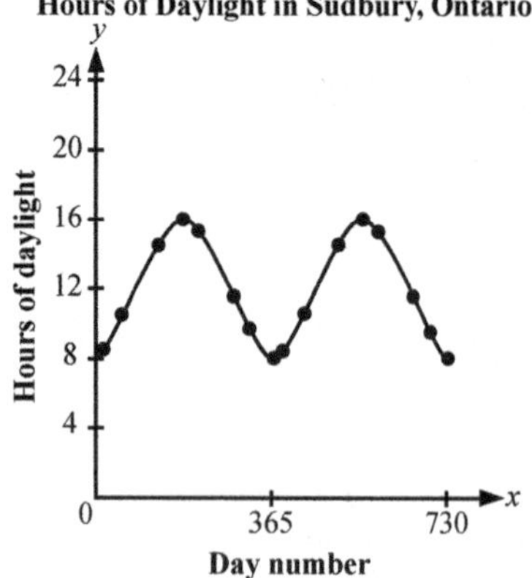

Step 2
Determine the period of the graph.

The greatest amount of daylight occurs on days 182 and 547, and the least amount of daylight occurs on days 1 and 366. Since 547 – 182 = 365 and 366 – 1 = 365, the data and graph have a period of 365 days.

Step 3
Using a period of 365 days, extrapolate the curve on the graph to the end of year 3, which is 1 095 days.

Use the graph to estimate the number of hours of daylight on day 974 (September 1 of year 3).

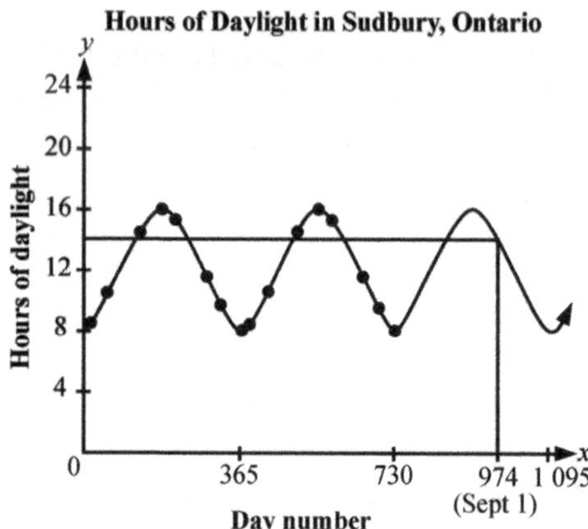

The approximate number of daylight hours on day 974 is 13.5.

11. D

Substitute the given coordinates ($a°$, 0.707) into the function $f(\theta) = \cos\theta$.
$f(a°) = \cos a°$
$\cos a° = 0.707$

Use the inverse cosine operation on your calculator, in degree mode, to find the value of a.

$\cos^{-1}(0.707) = 45°$

Therefore, the equation that represents the required relationship is $\cos 45° = 0.707$.

12. C

Observation 1 is true. Minimum points occur at angles of –90°, 270°, 630°,... or $(-90 + n360)°$, $n \in I$. When $n = 4$,
$\theta = (-90 + 4(360))°$
$= 1\ 350°$
Thus, there is a minimum point at 1 350°.

Observation 2 is true. The sine function increases for intervals $(-90 + 360n)° < x < (90 + 360n)°$, $n \in I$. When $n = -1$,
$(-90 - 360)° < x < (90 - 360)°$, or
$-450° < x < -270$.

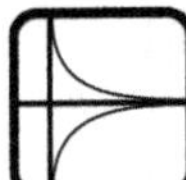

Observation 3 is false. The angles occurring on the horizontal midline axis, $y = 0$, are the x-intercepts. The x-intercepts occur when $x = 180°n$, $n \in I$. Thus, solve for n when $x = -620°$.

$$x = 180°n$$
$$-620° = 180°n$$
$$\frac{-620°}{180°} = n$$
$$n = -3.444...$$

Since n does not equal an integer, $-620°$ does not lie on the horizontal axis of the graph of $f(x) = \sin x$.

Observation 4 is true. The period is 630° for $f(x) = \sin x$, which indicates the interval between successive maximum or minimum values. Thus, the interval between minimum and maximum values would be $\frac{360°}{2} = 180°$.

13. D

The 3 in $f(x) = -3\cos x$ causes the graph of $f(x) = \cos x$ to stretch vertically about the x-axis by a factor of 3. The negative sign in front of the 3 means that the graph of $f(x) = \cos x$ will also be reflected about the x-axis.

14. OR

Step 1
Compare the given function to the function $y = a\sin(k(x-d)) + c$.
Find the amplitude.

$$\text{amplitude} = |a| = \left|-\frac{2}{5}\right| = \frac{2}{5}$$

Step 2
Find the period.

$$\text{period} = \frac{360°}{|k|} = \frac{360°}{|-3|} = 120°$$

Step 3
Calculate the phase shift.

$$\text{phase shift} = d = -15°$$

The phase shift is 15° to the left.

Step 4
Calculate the domain.

$$\text{domain} = x \in \mathbb{R}$$

Step 5
Find the range.

$$\text{range} = -|a| + c \le y \le |a| + c$$
$$|a| = \left|-\frac{2}{5}\right| = \frac{2}{5}$$
$$c = 4$$
$$-\frac{2}{5} + 4 \le y \le \frac{2}{5} + 4$$
$$\frac{18}{5} \le y \le \frac{22}{5}$$

15. C

Select a maximum point and a minimum point.

In this case, choose the maximum point to be in 1992 and the minimum point to be in 1999. Using the p-coordinate of each of these points, calculate the approximate amplitude. Note that the p-axis values represent thousands.

$$\frac{\text{max} - \text{min}}{2} \approx \frac{367\ 000 - 330\ 000}{2} \approx 18\ 500$$

The amplitude of the graph is about 18 500 people.

16. B

Since $f(x) = \sin(x - 45°)$ is in the form $f(x) = \sin(x - d)$, Tyra should have used angle values of $x = d + 90°n$, $n \in I$ to sketch her graph. These values can be generated using the recursive formula $x = 45° + 90°n$, $n \in I$. If Tyra substituted in $n = -2, -1, 0, 1, 2$, she would generate angle values of $-135°$, $-45°$, $45°$, $135°$, and $225°$. The given table of values shows the angles, x, and their corresponding $f(x)$ values.

x	$f(x) = \sin(x - 45°)$
$-135°$	$f(-135°)$ $= \sin(-135° - 45°)$ $= 0$
$-45°$	$f(-45°)$ $= \sin(-45° - 45°)$ $= -1$
$45°$	$f(45°)$ $= \sin(45° - 45°)$ $= 0$
$135°$	$f(135°)$ $= \sin(135° - 45°)$ $= 1$
$225°$	$f(225°)$ $= \sin(225° - 45°)$ $= 0$

Graph B best represents the function $f(x) = \sin(x - 45°)$ because it passes through all the points represented in the given table.

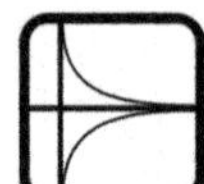

17. C

Step 1

Determine the maximum and minimum value for each function.

The function has a maximum of 1 and a minimum of -3. Therefore,

$$a = \frac{1-(-3)}{2} \\ = 2$$

Step 2

Determine the period of each function.

From the graph, the period is 360°. Therefore,

$\frac{360°}{k} = 360°$, and

$$360° = \frac{360°}{k}$$
$$k = \frac{360°}{360°}$$
$$k = 1$$

Step 3

Determine the vertical translation.

The horizontal midline axis for the function $y = \sin x$ or $y = \cos x$ is at $x = 0$. The given graph has a horizontal midline axis at the centre of the maximum and minimum. Thus, the horizontal midline axis of the given graph is

$$\frac{\max + \min}{2} = \frac{1+(-3)}{2} = \frac{-2}{2} = -1$$

The graph has been translated vertically 1 unit down. Therefore, $c = -1$.

Step 4

Determine the horizontal translation.

If the given graph is a sine function.

The graph of $y = \sin x$ has a y-intercept value of 0. Since the graph has been vertically translated down 1 unit, the new y-intercept is -1. Therefore, from the given graph it can be seen that the function has either been horizontally translated to the right 45° or to the left 315°.

If the given graph is a cosine function.

The graph of $y = \cos x$ has a y-intercept at the maximum value. From the given graph it can be seen that the function has been either horizontally translated to the left 45° or to the right 315°.

Of the options available there is only one that is a sine function with a horizontal translation to the right 45°, but it has $a = 3$ which is incorrect since it was already determined that $a = 2$. There is one option that is a cosine function with a horizontal translation to the left 45° with an appropriate value of a. Therefore, $d = -45°$.

Step 5

Determine the equation of the graph.

From the previous step it was determined that a cosine function is being used. Therefore, substitute 2 for a, 1 for k, -1 for c and $-45°$ for d into the equation $y = a\cos(k(x-d)) + c$.

$$y = a\cos(k(x-d)) + c$$
$$= 2\cos(1(x-(-45°))) - 1$$
$$= 2\cos(x+45°) - 1$$

18. D

To represent a periodic function, the vertical and horizontal changes must be consistent throughout the domain of the graph. In graph D, each tall peak is 3 units high and 2 units wide, and each neighbouring small peak is 1 unit high and 2 units wide. Each cycle of the graph (every 4 horizontal units) is the same. Therefore, graph D represents a periodic function.

19. D

Moving the wheel farther down into the water would cause a change in the vertical shift. The change in vertical displacement would lower all the values of maximum, horizontal axis, and minimum, which would mean the entire curve would be shifted vertically downward.

20. D

If the height, y, is given as a function of time, x, as in $y = 5.7\sin(0.31x) + 7.9$, then to find the points when the height of the chair is 15 m, look for points where $y = 15$.

21. 5

The amplitude, a, can be determined by finding the maximum and minimum values of usage.
Substitute x for the minimum, 39 for the maximum and 17 for a into the equation
$a = \frac{\text{maximum} - \text{minimum}}{2}$ and solve for x.

$$\begin{aligned} a &= \frac{\text{maximum} - \text{minimum}}{2} \\ 17 &= \frac{39 - x}{2} \\ 34 &= 39 - x \\ -5 &= -x \\ x &= 5 \end{aligned}$$

Therefore, the minimum hourly usage is 5 kW.

NOTES

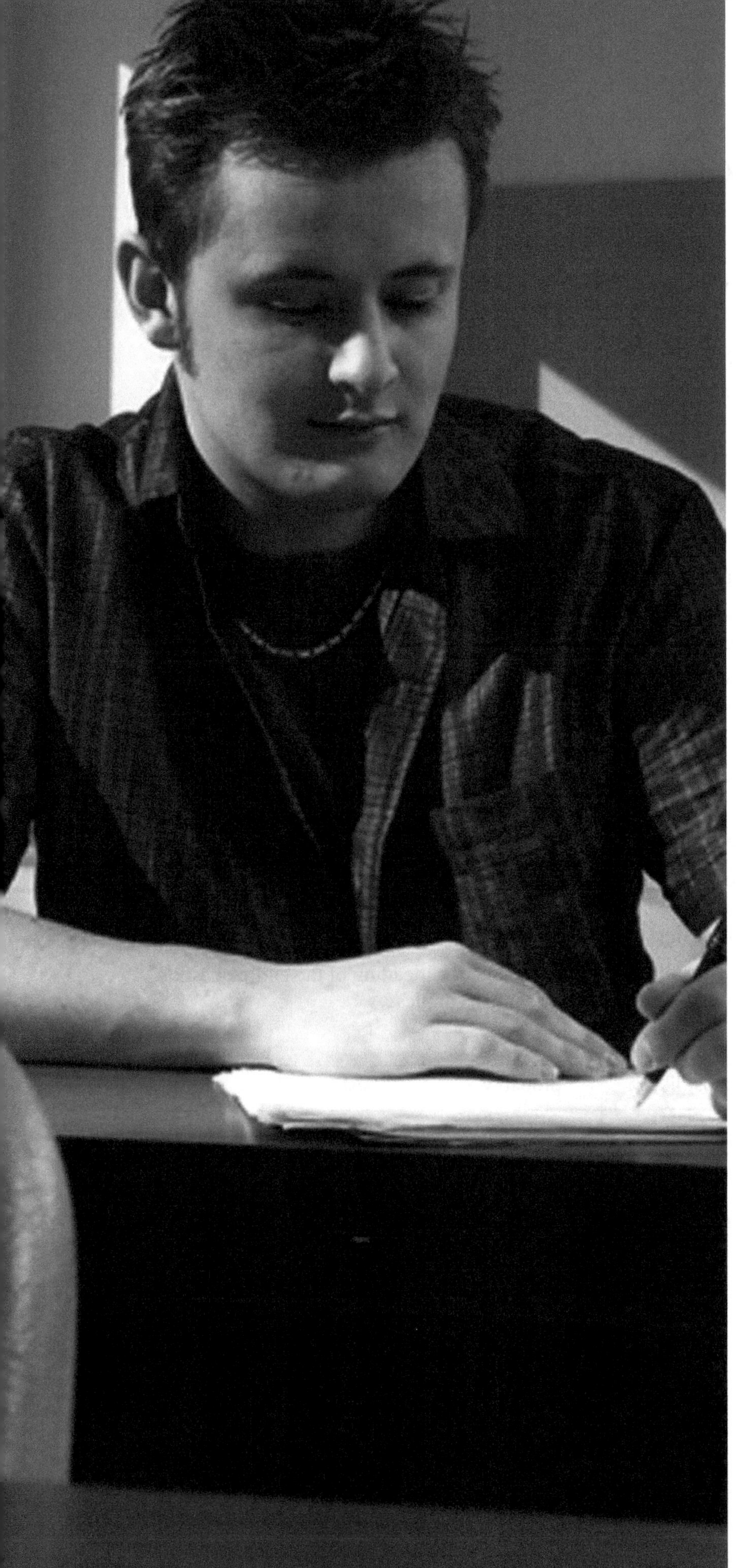

KEY Strategies for Success on Tests

KEY STRATEGIES FOR SUCCESS ON TESTS

THINGS TO CONSIDER WHEN TAKING A TEST

It is normal to feel anxious before you write a test. You can manage this anxiety by using the following strategies:

- Think positive thoughts. Imagine yourself doing well on the test.
- Make a conscious effort to relax by taking several slow, deep, controlled breaths. Concentrate on the air going in and out of your body.
- Before you begin the test, ask questions if you are unsure of anything.
- Jot down key words or phrases from any instructions your teacher gives you.
- Look over the entire test to find out the number and kinds of questions on the test.
- Read each question closely, and reread if necessary.
- Pay close attention to key vocabulary words. Sometimes, these words are **bolded** or *italicized*, and they are usually important words in the question.
- If you are putting your answers on an answer sheet, mark your answers carefully. Always print clearly. If you wish to change an answer, erase the mark completely, and ensure that your final answer is darker than the one you have erased.
- Use highlighting to note directions, key words, and vocabulary that you find confusing or that are important to answering the question.
- Double-check to make sure you have answered everything before handing in your test.
- When taking tests, students often overlook the easy words. Failure to pay close attention to these words can result in an incorrect answer. One way to avoid this is to be aware of these words and to underline, circle, or highlight them while you are taking the test.
- Even though some words are easy to understand, they can change the meaning of the entire question, so it is important that you pay attention to them. Here are some examples.

all	always	most likely	probably	best	not
difference	usually	except	most	unlikely	likely

Example

1. Which of the following expressions is **incorrect**?

A. $3 + 2 \geq 5$

B. $4 - 3 < 2$

C. $5 \times 4 < 15$

D. $6 \times 3 \geq 18$

TEST PREPARATION AND TEST-TAKING SKILLS

HELPFUL STRATEGIES FOR ANSWERING MULTIPLE-CHOICE QUESTIONS

A multiple-choice question gives you some information and then asks you to select an answer from four choices. Each question has one correct answer. The other choices are distractors, which are incorrect.

The following strategies can help you when answering multiple-choice questions:

- Quickly skim through the entire test. Find out how many questions there are, and plan your time accordingly.
- Read and reread questions carefully. Underline key words, and try to think of an answer before looking at the choices.
- If there is a graphic, look at the graphic, read the question, and go back to the graphic. Then, you may want to underline the important information from the question.
- Carefully read the choices. Read the question first and then each choice that goes with it.
- When choosing an answer, try to eliminate those choices that are clearly wrong or do not make sense.
- Some questions may ask you to select the best answer. These questions will always include words like *best*, *most appropriate*, or *most likely*. All of the choices will be correct to some degree, but one of the choices will be better than the others in some way. Carefully read all four choices before choosing the answer you think is the best.
- If you do not know the answer, or if the question does not make sense to you, it is better to guess than to leave it blank.
- Do not spend too much time on any one question. Make a mark (*) beside a difficult question, and come back to it later. If you are leaving a question to come back to later, make sure you also leave the space on the answer sheet, if you are using one.
- Remember to go back to the difficult questions at the end of the test; sometimes, clues are given throughout the test that will provide you with answers.
- Note any negative words like *no* or *not*, and be sure your answer fits the question.
- Before changing an answer, be sure you have a very good reason to do so.
- Do not look for patterns on your answer sheet, if you are using one.

HELPFUL STRATEGIES FOR ANSWERING WRITTEN-RESPONSE QUESTIONS

A written response requires you to respond to a question or directive indicated by words such as explain, predict, list, describe, show your work, solve, or calculate. The following strategies can help you when answering written-response questions:

- Read and reread the question carefully.
- Recognize and pay close attention to directing words such as *explain*, *show your work*, and *describe*.
- Underline key words and phrases that indicate what is required in your answer, such as *explain*, *estimate*, *answer*, *calculate*, or *show your work*.
- Write down rough, point-form notes regarding the information you want to include in your answer.
- Think about what you want to say, and organize information and ideas in a coherent and concise manner within the time limit you have for the question.
- Be sure to answer every part of the question that is asked.
- Include as much information as you can when you are asked to explain your thinking.
- Include a picture or diagram if it will help to explain your thinking.
- Try to put your final answer to a problem in a complete sentence to be sure it is reasonable.
- Reread your response to ensure you have answered the question.
- Ask yourself if your answer makes sense.
- Ask yourself if your answer sounds right.
- Use appropriate subject vocabulary and terms in your response.

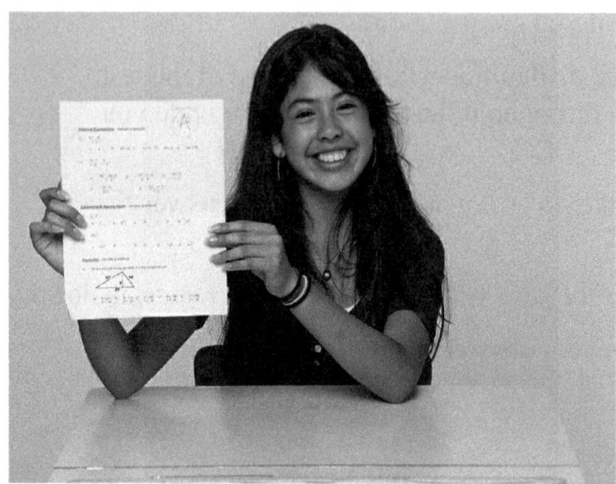

About Mathematics Tests

What You Need to Know about Mathematics Tests

To do well on a mathematics test, you need to understand and apply your knowledge of mathematical concepts. Reading skills can also make a difference in how well you perform. Reading skills can help you follow instructions and find key words, as well as read graphs, diagrams, and tables. They can also help you solve mathematics problems.

Mathematics tests usually have two types of questions: questions that ask for understanding of mathematics ideas and questions that test how well you can solve mathematics problems.

How You Can Prepare for Mathematics Tests

The following strategies are particular to preparing for and writing mathematics tests:

- Know how to use your calculator, and, if it is allowed, use your own for the test.
- Note taking is a good way to review and study important information from your class notes and textbook.
- Sketch a picture of the problem, procedure, or term. Drawing is helpful for learning and remembering concepts.
- Check your answer to practice questions by working backward to the beginning. You can find the beginning by going step by step in reverse order.
- Use the following steps when answering questions with graphics (pictures, diagrams, tables, or graphs):
  1. Read the title of the graphic and any key words.
  2. Read the test question carefully to figure out what information you need to find in the graphic.
  3. Go back to the graphic to find the information you need.
  4. Decide which operation is needed.
- Always pay close attention when pressing the keys on your calculator. Repeat the procedure a second time to be sure you pressed the correct keys.

TEST PREPARATION COUNTDOWN

If you develop a plan for studying and test preparation, you will perform well on tests.

Here is a general plan to follow seven days before you write a test.

COUNTDOWN: 7 DAYS BEFORE THE TEST

1. Use "Finding Out about the Test" to help you make your own personal test preparation plan.
2. Review the following information:
   - Areas to be included on the test
   - Types of test items
   - General and specific test tips
3. Start preparing for the test at least seven days before the test. Develop your test preparation plan, and set time aside to prepare and study.

COUNTDOWN: 6, 5, 4, 3, 2 DAYS BEFORE THE TEST

1. Review old homework assignments, quizzes, and tests.
2. Rework problems on quizzes and tests to make sure you still know how to solve them.
3. Correct any errors made on quizzes and tests.
4. Review key concepts, processes, formulas, and vocabulary.
5. Create practice test questions for yourself, and answer them. Work out many sample problems.

COUNTDOWN: THE NIGHT BEFORE THE TEST

1. Use the night before the test for final preparation, which includes reviewing and gathering materials needed for the test before going to bed.
2. Most importantly, get a good night's rest, and know you have done everything possible to do well on the test.

TEST DAY

1. Eat a healthy and nutritious breakfast.
2. Ensure you have all the necessary materials.
3. Think positive thoughts, such as "I can do this," "I am ready," and "I know I can do well."
4. Arrive at your school early, so you are not rushing, which can cause you anxiety and stress.

SUMMARY OF HOW TO BE SUCCESSFUL DURING A TEST

You may find some of the following strategies useful for writing a test:

- Take two or three deep breaths to help you relax.
- Read the directions carefully, and underline, circle, or highlight any important words.
- Look over the entire test to understand what you will need to do.
- Budget your time.
- Begin with an easy question or a question you know you can answer correctly rather than follow the numerical question order of the test.
- If you cannot remember how to answer a question, try repeating the deep breathing and physical relaxation activities. Then, move on to visualization and positive self-talk to get yourself going.
- When answering questions with graphics (pictures, diagrams, tables, or graphs), look at the question carefully, and use the following steps:
    1. Read the title of the graphic and any key words.
    2. Read the test question carefully to figure out what information you need to find in the graphic.
    3. Go back to the graphic to find the information you need.
- Write down anything you remember about the subject on the reverse side of your test paper. This activity sometimes helps to remind you that you do know something and are capable of writing the test.
- Look over your test when you have finished, and double-check your answers to be sure you did not forget anything.

NOTES

Practice Tests

PRACTICE TEST 1

1. Which of the following equations represents a relation that is **not** a function?

A. $y = x^2 + 4x$

B. $y = 4x - 5$

C. $y^2 = 4x$

D. $y = 4$

Numerical Response

2. For the function $f(x) = 8x^2 - 10x + 5$, the value of $f\left(-\frac{1}{2}\right)$ is ________. (Record your answer to the nearest tenth.)

3. The domain and range, respectively, of the function $f(x) = \frac{2}{x+3}$ are

A. $x \neq -3$ and $y \in R$

B. $x \in R$ and $y \in R$

C. $x \neq -3$ and $y \neq 0$

D. $x \neq 3$ and $y \neq 0$

Use the following information to answer the next question.

A function has a domain of $-2 \leq x \leq 6$ and a range of $y \geq 5$.

4. The domain and range of the inverse of this function are

A. $x \leq 5$ and $-2 \leq y \leq 6$

B. $x \geq 5$ and $-2 \leq y \leq 6$

C. $x \leq 5$ and $-6 \leq y \leq 2$

D. $x \geq 5$ and $-6 \leq y \leq 2$

5. The inverse of the quadratic function $f(x) = \frac{1}{2}(x+6)^2 - 5$ is

A. $y = \pm\sqrt{2x+5} - 6$

B. $y = \pm\sqrt{2x+10} - 6$

C. $y = \pm 2\sqrt{x+5} - 6$

D. $y = \pm 2\sqrt{x-6} + 5$

6. In order to vertically stretch the graph of the function $f(x) = \frac{1}{x}$ by a factor of 5 from the x-axis and then translate it 4 units horizontally left, the equation must be transformed into

A. $f(x) = \frac{5}{x-4}$

B. $f(x) = \frac{5}{x+4}$

C. $f(x) = \frac{1}{5(x-4)}$

D. $f(x) = \frac{1}{5(x+4)}$

Use the following information to answer the next question.

The function $f(x) = \sqrt{x}$ is transformed into the function $g(x) = \sqrt{-x} + 2$.

7. Which of the following graphs represents the transformed function $g(x)$?

A.

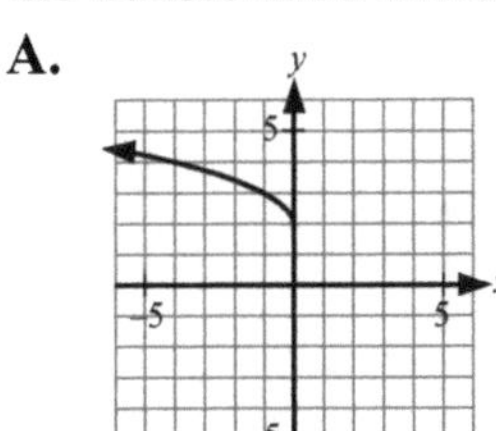

B.

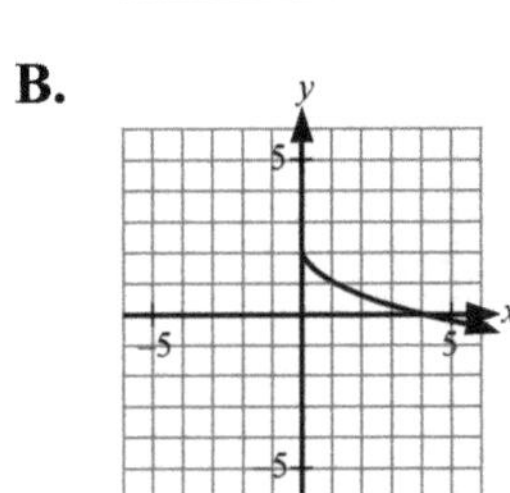

C.

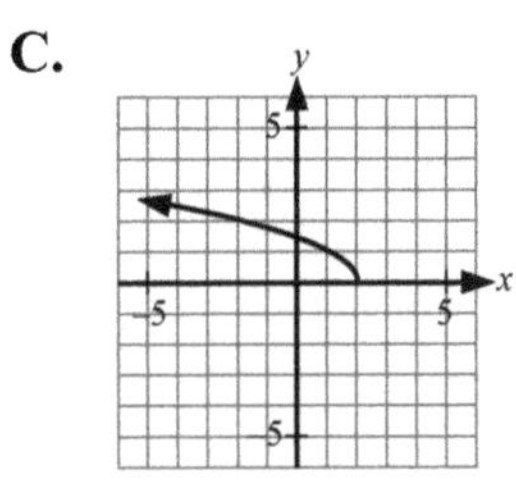

D.

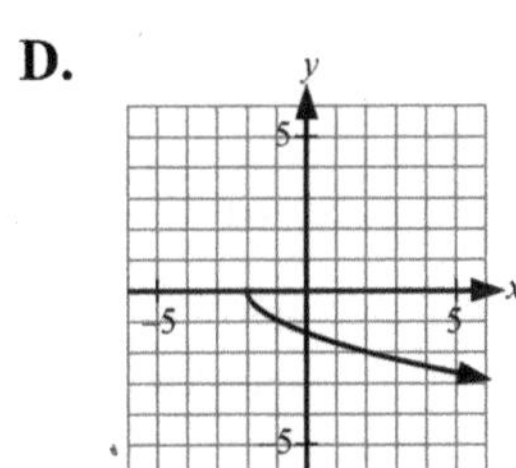

Numerical Response

8. The minimum value of the quadratic function $f(x) = 3x^2 + 12x + 20$ is __________.

Use the following information to answer the next question.

A farmer wishes to enclose a rectangular area to form two pens. He decides to use part of the wall of his barn as the length of the pen and part of an existing fence attached to the corner of his barn as the width of the pen. Then, he will divide the pens by erecting a fence perpendicular to the barn wall.

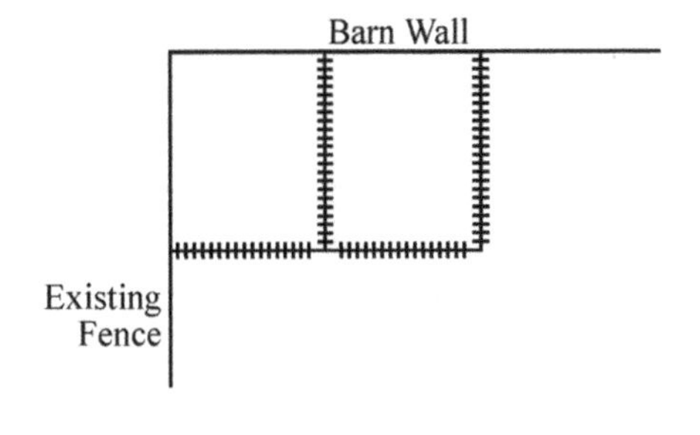

9. If the farmer has 200 m of fencing available to complete this project, the maximum area the farmer can enclose is

A. 4 000 m^2

B. 4 800 m^2

C. 5 000 m^2

D. 5 600 m^2

Open Response

10. If the roots of a corresponding quadratic equation are $2 + \sqrt{5}$ and $2 - \sqrt{5}$, what is the equation of the quadratic function that passes through the point (7, –40)?

Open Response

11. Determine the equations of the family of lines that have a slope of 2 and that intersect the graph of the quadratic function $f(x) = -x^2 + 8x$ once, twice, or never.

Open Response

12. Write and simplify an expression for the volume of a rectangular prism with a height of $2x + 3$, a length of $3x + 1$, and a width of $3x - 1$.

13. What is the simplified form of the rational expression $\frac{x-3}{x^2-4} + \frac{x-2}{x^2-x-6}$?

A. $\frac{2x^2 - 10x + 13}{(x-2)(x+2)(x-3)}$

B. $\frac{2x^2 + 13}{(x-2)(x+2)(x-3)}$

C. $\frac{2x-5}{2x^2 - x - 10}$

D. $\frac{2}{x+2}$

Open Response

a) Draw a sketch of the graph of $y = \left(\frac{1}{2}\right)^x$ on the grid given below, passing through the points with x-values of $-3, -2, -1, 0, 1, 2,$ and 3.

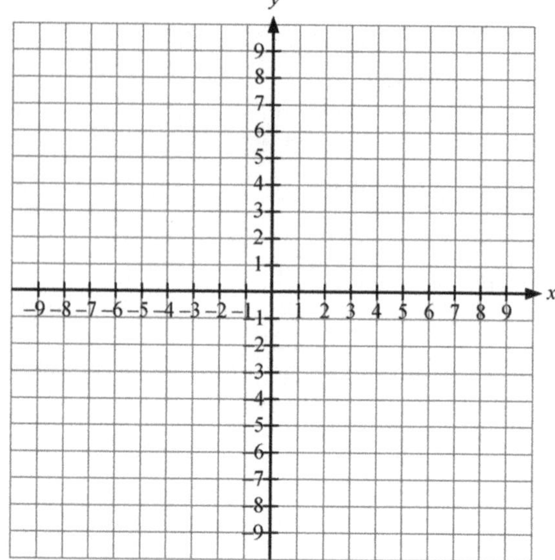

b) State the following features of the graph:

Domain: ________ y-intercept: ________

Range: ________ x-intercept: ________

Asymptote: ________

c) How is the graph of $y = \left(\frac{1}{2}\right)^x$ different from the graph of $y = \left(\frac{2}{3}\right)^x$? Explain.

15. What is the value of $(-64)^{-\frac{2}{3}}$?

A. $\frac{1}{512}$

B. $\frac{1}{16}$

C. 16

D. 512

Use the following information to answer the next question.

Four exponential functions are given.

1. $f(x) = 5^x$
2. $f(x) = \left(\frac{2}{3}\right)^x$
3. $f(x) = 3^x$
4. $f(x) = \left(\frac{1}{5}\right)^x$

Numerical Response

16. When these functions are ordered from the function whose graph is closest to the positive x-axis to the function whose graph is farthest from the positive x-axis, the order is __________. (Record your answer as a four-digit number.)

Use the following information to answer the next question.

A partial table of values is given.

x	y
−2	6
−1	8
0	10
1	12
2	14

17. This partial table of values is **most likely** from

A. a linear function

B. a quadratic function

C. an exponential-decay function

D. an exponential-growth function

Open Response

18. Describe the transformations that would change the graph of $f(x) = 3^x$ into the graph of $g(x) = 4(3)^{x+2} - 3$.

19. Which of the following graphs represents the function $f(x) = 3^{-x+3}$?

A.

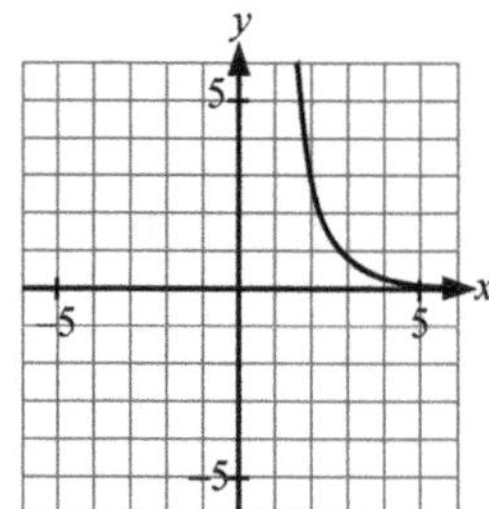

B.

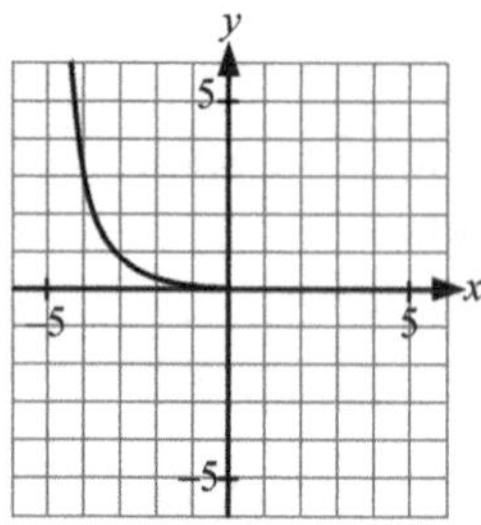

C.

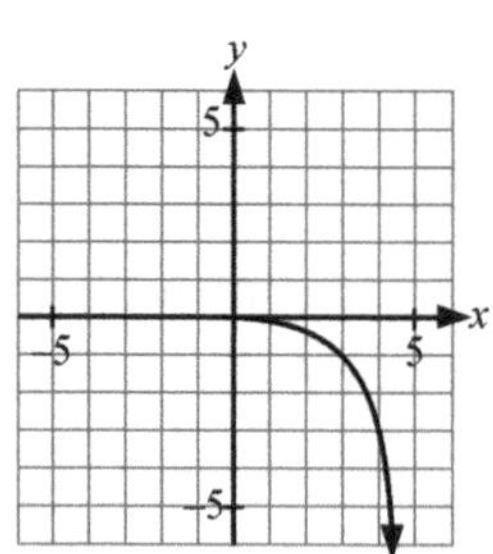

D.

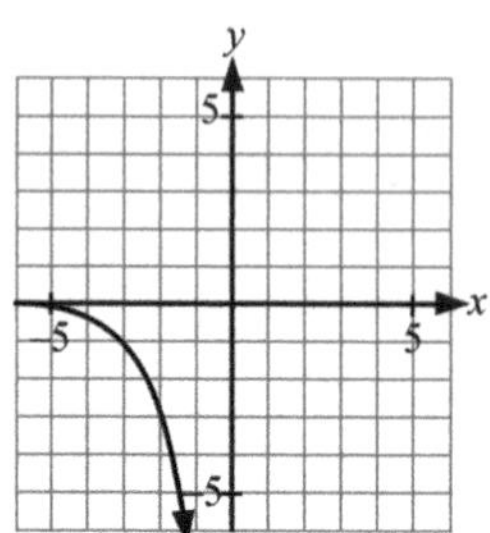

20. Which of the following functions is equivalent to $f(x) = 27^x$?

A. $g(x) = \left(\frac{1}{9}\right)^{-\frac{2}{3}x}$

B. $h(x) = 81^{\frac{1}{2}x}$

C. $p(x) = 9^{\frac{3}{2}x}$

D. $m(x) = 3^{2x}$

Use the following information to answer the next question.

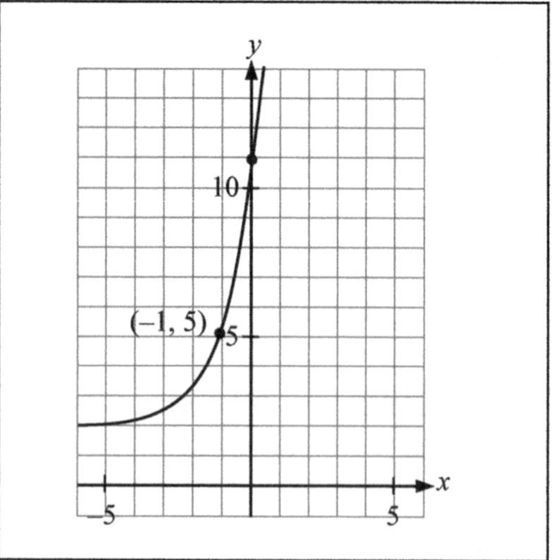

Open Response

21. Determine the equation for the exponential function of the form $f(x) = a(b)^x + c$ shown in the given graph, and explain your answer in terms of transformations.

Use the following information to answer the next multipart question.

22. For every metre that a diver descends below the water, the light intensity or percentage of sunlight is reduced by 2.5%. The function showing this exponential decay is $P = 100(0.975)^d$, where P is the percentage of sunlight and d is the distance below the water surface in metres.

Numerical Response

a) To the nearest hundredth, the percentage of sunlight found 100 m below the water surface is__________%.

b) A student graphed this function on his graphing calculator with the appropriate window settings. He found that the change in percentage of sunlight for a diver going from 40 to 60 m below the water surface is about

A. 14%

B. 17%

C. 22%

D. 36%

23. Which of the following functions would generate the sequence 4, 8, 12, 16, …?

A. $f(x) = 2^x, x \in N, x \geq 2$

B. $f(x) = 4(x + 1), x \in W$

C. $f(x) = 4x + 8, x \in W$

D. $f(x) = 2x^2, x \in N$

24. Which of the following sequences can be represented by the general term $t_n = 2(3)^{n-1}$?

A. 6, 18, 54,…

B. 2, 6, 18,…

C. 2, 6, 12,…

D. 1, 6, 36,…

Open Response

25. Determine a recursive formula to represent the sequence 5, 11, 21, 35, 53, …

Use the following information to answer the next question.

A Fibonacci-type sequence is recursively defined by $t_1 = 3$, $t_2 = 3$, $t_n = t_{n-1} + t_{n-2}$, $n > 2$.

Numerical Response

26. The 10th term in this sequence is_______.

27. Which of the following general terms would generate a geometric sequence?

A. $t_n = 4n$

B. $t_n = 4^n$

C. $t_n = 4n^2$

D. $t_1 = 4, t_n = 4t_{n-1} + 4, n > 1$

Open Response

28. Determine the general term of the sequence $\frac{1}{64}, \frac{1}{32}, \frac{1}{16}, \frac{1}{8}, \ldots$, and then find the 12th term.

Use the following information to answer the next multipart question.

29. The sum of the first 8 terms in an arithmetic series is 212. The sum of the first 12 terms in the same series is 438.

Open Response

a) Determine the first four terms in the series.

b) Determine the 20th term in the series.

c) Determine the sum of the first 20 terms in the given series.

Use the following information to answer the next question.

In order to get in shape for a marathon, Betty decides to run 4 000 m on the first day of a 30-day month. She then increases the distance she runs by 500 m each day.

30. To the nearest metre, what is the total distance Betty runs during that month?

A. 14 500 m

B. 18 500 m

C. 337 500 m

D. 675 000 m

Use the following information to answer the next question.

The yearly value for the first four years of an initial investment of \$800.00 is given by the
sequence \$824.00, \$848.72, \$874.18, and \$900.41.

31. Which of the following investments describes the sequence?

A. \$800 invested at simple interest of 3%/*a*

B. \$800 invested at simple interest of 1.03%/*a*

C. \$800 invested at 3%/*a* compounded annually

D. \$800 invested at 6%/*a* compounded semi-annually

Numerical Response

32. If \$600 is invested in an account paying monthly interest and grows to \$738 after 4 years, the yearly interest rate is ________%. (Record your answer to the nearest tenth of a percentage.)

Use the following information to answer the next question.

In order to save money for their newborn son's university education, the Smiths decide to start an ordinary simple annuity. They have two options. In the first option, at the end of each month, they would deposit \$150 into an account earning interest at 6%/*a* compounded monthly. In the second option, they would deposit \$1 800 at the end of each year into an account earning interest at 6%/*a* compounded annually.

33. At the end of the 18 years, what is the difference in value between the two options?

A. \$2 039

B. \$2 473

C. \$2 763

D. \$3 338

Use the following information to answer the next question.

The exact value of cos 30° is $\frac{\sqrt{a}}{b}$, and the exact value of sin 90° is c.

Numerical Response

34. The value of $a + b + c$ is __________.

35. To the nearest tenth, what are the solutions to the equation $\cos\theta = -0.266$, where $0° \leq \theta < 360°$?

A. 105.4° and 254.6°

B. 105.4° and 285.4°

C. 74.6° and 105.4°

D. 74.6° and 285.4°

36. If an angle θ in standard position terminates in quadrant II, and $\cos\theta = -\frac{1}{4}$, then what are the exact values of csc θ and cotθ, respectively?

A. $\frac{\sqrt{15}}{4}$ and $-\frac{\sqrt{15}}{15}$

B. $\frac{\sqrt{15}}{4}$ and $\frac{\sqrt{15}}{15}$

C. $-\frac{4\sqrt{15}}{15}$ and $\frac{\sqrt{15}}{15}$

D. $\frac{4\sqrt{15}}{15}$ and $-\frac{\sqrt{15}}{15}$

Open Response

37. Prove the identity $\sqrt{\frac{1-\sin\theta}{1+\sin\theta}} = \sec\theta - \tan\theta$.

Use the following information to answer the next question.

A light in the park illuminates up to a distance of 90 m. A point on a walking path is 144 m from the light. The angle between the point on the walking path and the light is 29.3°.

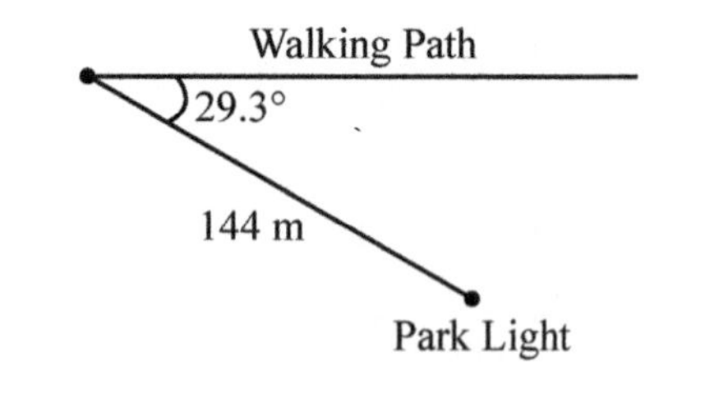

38. Rounded to the nearest tenth, how much of the walking path is illuminated by the light?

A. 69.5 m

B. 112.0 m

C. 181.5 m

D. 251.0 m

Use the following information to answer the next question.

As part of a weekend expedition, an adventure club proposes to climb a cliff overlooking a river. To plan for the climb, a surveyor takes some measurements to calculate the height of the cliff.
The surveyor draws the given diagram of the cliff.

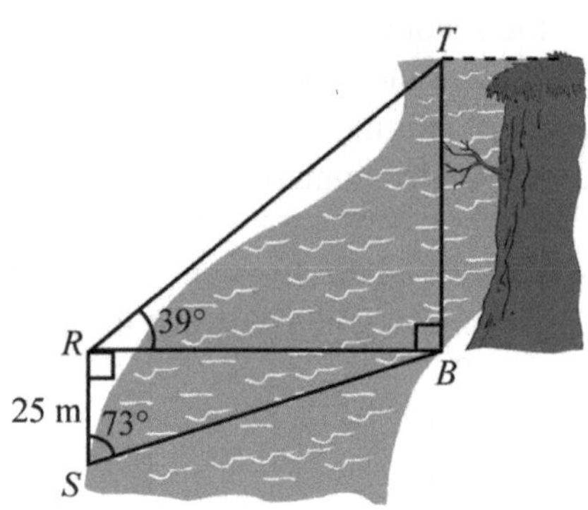

From a point R on the shore directly across the river from the base of the cliff, the angle of elevation to the top of the cliff is $\angle TRB = 39°$. Point S is located 25 m down the river. From point S, the angle between point R and point B, $\angle BSR$, has a measure of 73°.

39. To the nearest metre, what is the height of the cliff?

A. 107 m

B. 82 m

C. 66 m

D. 16 m

Use the following information to answer the next question.

A small boat has been spotted in rough seas, but rescuers are having difficulty keeping it in view because the boat is following the rhythm of the waves; it rises up on the crest of a wave and then falls down into the trough, where it is out of view. The boat reappears every 8 s as it hits the crest of a wave, which brings the boat 3 m above sea level. When the boat is down in the trough of a wave, it is 3 m below sea level. The graph shown illustrates the path of the boat.

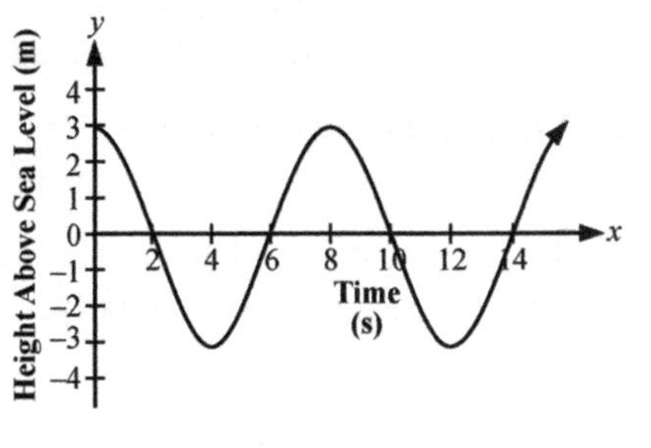

Numerical Response

40. To the nearest whole number, what is the approximate height of the boat, relative to sea level, at 17 s? __________

41. Which of the following statements about the function $f(x) = \cos x$ is **incorrect**?

A. The y-intercept is 1.

B. An x-intercept of the graph is $-450°$.

C. The equation of the horizontal midline axis is $y = 1$

D. The vertical distance between the minimum and maximum values is 2.

Use the following information to answer the next question.

The partial graphs of two sinusoidal functions are shown. The equation of Graph 1 is $y = a\sin(k(x - d)) + c$ for integers a, k, d, and c. Graph 2 is obtained by changing exactly two parameters in the equation of Graph 1.

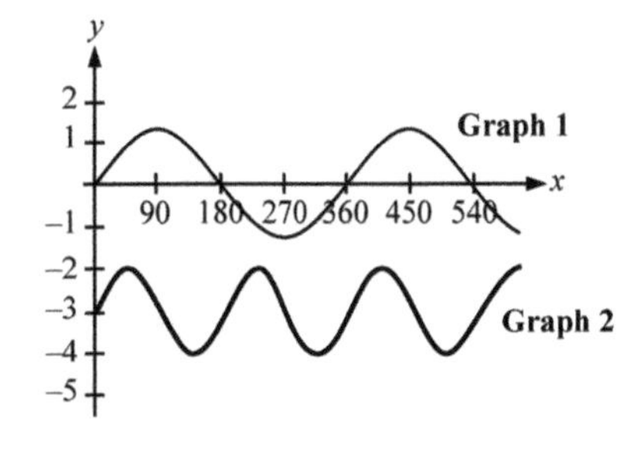

42. The two parameters that are changed are

A. a and c

B. a and d

C. k and c

D. k and d

Use the following information to answer the next question.

The water at the seaport of a city has a maximum depth of 17 m at 9 A.M. After this, the first minimum depth of 3 m occurs at 2.30 P.M.

43. If the relation between the depth, y, and the time, t, is a sinusoidal function, then the equation for the depth at any time is

A. $y = 11\cos(20°(t - 3)) + 17$

B. $y = 7\cos(32.7°(t - 9)) + 10$

C. $y = 11\cos(20°(t + 3)) - 17$

D. $y = 7\cos(32.7°(t + 11)) + 10$

44. Which of the following tables **best** represents a periodic function?

A.

Time	Distance
0	3
1	148
3	410
8	890
14	1 140
20	1 025
25	700

B.

Time	Distance
0	0
0.5	150
1	300
1.5	150
2	0
2.5	150
3	300

C.

Time	Distance
0	13
2	13
4	50
6	60
8	20
10	80
12	12

D.

Time	Distance
0	90
0.5	65
1	47
1.5	32
2	26
2.5	15
3	7

Use the following information to answer the next question.

The height of a chair on a ferris wheel follows the function $H(t) = 5.7\sin(0.31t) + 7.9$, where H is the height in metres and t is the time in seconds.

45. Which of the following statements describes the function if the ferris wheel had a diameter of 14 m?

A. The amplitude would change to 14, and the curve would stretch horizontally.

B. The period would change to 14, and the curve would stretch horizontally.

C. The amplitude would change to 7, and the curve would stretch vertically.

D. The period would change to 7, and the curve would stretch vertically.

Use the following information to answer the next multipart question.

46. A stone is stuck in the tread of the back tire of a bicycle. The given graph represents the height, h, in centimetres of the stone relative to the ground with respect to the angle, x, in degrees through which the tire is rotating.

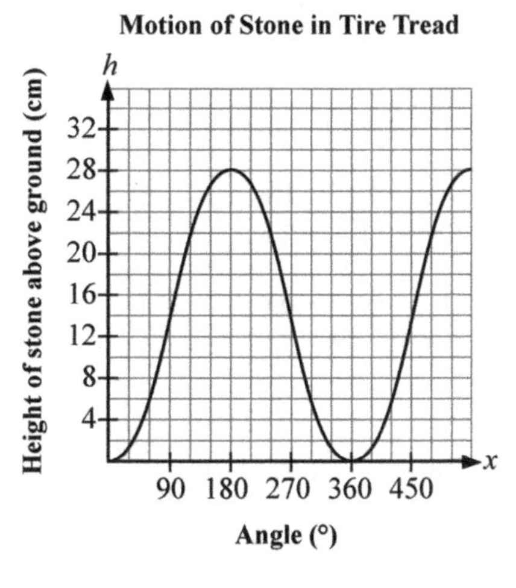

Numerical Response

a) The cosine function that corresponds to the graph of the height of the stone, h, in terms of the angle of rotation, x, is $h = -a\cos x + 14$. The value of a is __________.

b) The rock is dislodged from the tire tread after making $2\frac{2}{3}$ revolutions. Rounded to the nearest centimetre, what is the height, h, of the rock when it falls out of the tire? __________

Use the following information to answer the next question.

The following table gives the amount of daylight in a particular city in Ontario, at various dates of 2007, including those with most and least hours of daylight. The year 2007 was not a leap year.

Date	Amount of Daylight
February 21	10 h 34 min
April 21	14 h 00 min
June 21	16 h 07 min
August 21	14 h 02 min
October 21	10 h 32 min
December 21	8 h 18 min

47. Based on the information in the table, which of the following times would **most likely** be the number of hours of daylight on September 1, 2008?

A. 13 h 50 min

B. 13 h 25 min

C. 13 h 0 min

D. 12 h 45 min

PRACTICE TEST 2

1. The quadratic equation $4x^2 = 5x - 6$ has
   A. no real roots
   B. real and equal roots
   C. real and different roots
   D. one real root and one non-real root

2. The maximum value of the graph of the quadratic relation $f(x) = -2x^2 + 8x - 19$ is at the ordered pair
   A. $(-11, -2)$
   B. $(-2, -11)$
   C. $(2, -11)$
   D. $(11, -2)$

Use the following information to answer the next question.

> The owners of a stadium have determined that 8 000 people will attend a concert if the ticket price is \$40.00. However, for each \$2.00 increase in ticket price, it is estimated that 100 fewer people will attend the concert.

Open Response

3. How many people must attend the concert in order to make the maximum income, and what must the ticket price be in order to make the maximum income?

Open Response

4. Simplify the expression $x^3(2x - 7)^2 + 9x^4$.

5. Which of the following expressions is a simplified form of the expression $\frac{x^2 - 6x - 7}{x + 1} - \frac{2x + 12}{2x + 2} + \frac{x + 1}{x^2 - 1}$?
   A. $\frac{x^3 - 8x^2 - 14x + 5}{(x + 1)(x - 1)}$
   B. $\frac{x^3 - 8x^2 - 5x + 14}{(x + 1)(x - 1)}$
   C. $\frac{x^3 - 6x^2 + 14}{(x + 1)(x - 1)}$
   D. $\frac{x^3 - 6x^2 - 5x}{(x + 1)(x - 1)}$

6. The rational expression $\frac{6t^2 - 54}{3t^2 + 15t + 18}$ where $t \neq -2$ or -3 is equivalent to
   A. $\frac{2(t - 3)}{t + 2}$
   B. $\frac{2(t + 3)}{t + 2}$
   C. $\frac{t - 3}{t + 2}$
   D. $\frac{t + 3}{t + 2}$

Use the following information to answer the next multipart question.

7. Stephanie used her graphing calculator with a WINDOW setting of x:[−4.7, 4.7, 1] and y:[−3.1, 3.1, 1] to graph the exponential relation $y = \left(\frac{3}{2}\right)^x$.

a) Which of the following screens represents Stephanie's graph of $y = \left(\frac{3}{2}\right)^x$?

A. 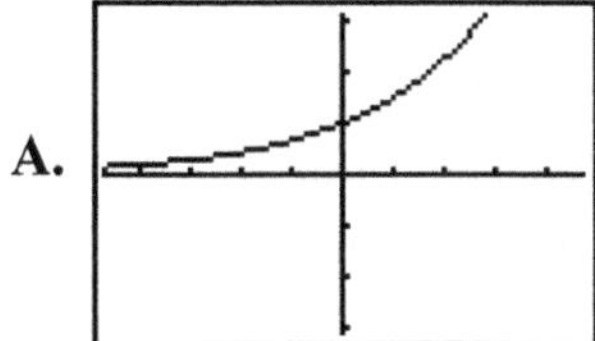

B. 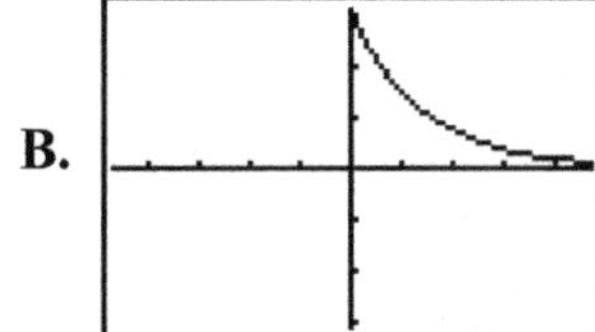

C. 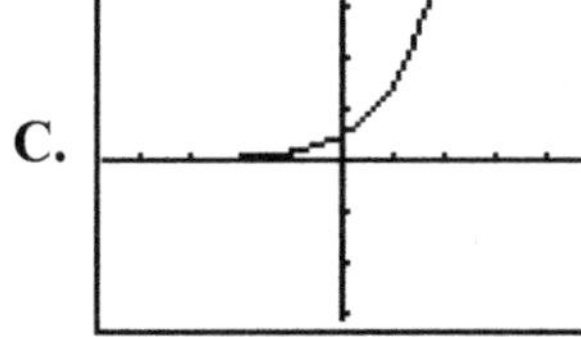

D. 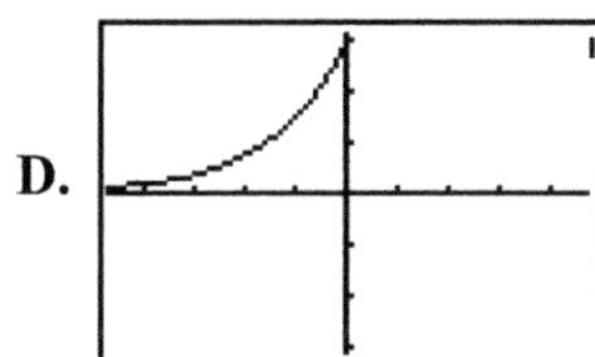

b) Stephanie concluded that $y = \left(\frac{3}{2}\right)^x$ could be defined as the function $f(x) = \left(\frac{3}{2}\right)^x$, since

A. for every x-coordinate on the graph, there was only one corresponding y-coordinate

B. every x-coordinate belonged to the set of real numbers

C. the graph never touched the x-axis

D. the graph was a smooth curve

Use the following information to answer the next question.

When simplified, $\dfrac{(9x^4y^3)^{\frac{1}{2}}}{x^3y^{\frac{1}{2}}}$ has the form cx^ay^b.

Numerical Response

8. The value of $a + b + c$ is _________.

9. Which of the following features does **not** describe the graph of $f(x) = 10^x$?

A. The range is $y > 0$.

B. The horizontal asymptote is $y = 0$.

C. The graph of $f(x) = 10^x$ is flatter on the left side of the y-axis than the graph of $f(x) = 8^x$.

D. The graph of $f(x) = 10^x$ is steeper on the right side of the y-axis than the graph of $f(x) = 12^x$.

Use the following information to answer the next multipart question.

10. Determine whether each of the following relations is exponential, linear, or quadratic. Show your proof in determining each relation.

Open Response

a) $y = 4x^2 - 1$

b) $y = 3^x$

c) $y = 2x + 2$

Open Response

11. Sketch the graph of $y = 5^{x-4} + 1$, and state the domain, range, and equation of the asymptote.

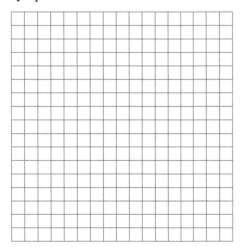

Numerical Response

12. If $f(x) = 243^x$ is written in an equivalent form as $f(x) = 81^{kx}$, the value of k to the nearest hundredth is __________.

13. The graph of the function $y = 7^x$ is horizontally translated 5 units to the right and 4 units down. The equation that represents the new graph is

A. $y = 7^{x+5} - 4$

B. $y = 7^{x+5} + 4$

C. $y = 7^{x-5} - 4$

D. $y = 7^{x-5} + 4$

Use the following information to answer the next question.

> A culture of bacteria triples every 5 min. At 4:27 P.M., the population is 50 000.
>
> The equation $P_t = P_0(3)^{\frac{t}{5}}$ can be used to determine the population P_t after t minutes when P_0 is the initial population.

Open Response

14. Determine the population 27 min earlier, at 4:00P.M.

Use the following information to answer the next question.

The point $\left(300°, -\frac{\sqrt{3}}{2}\right)$ is on the graph of $f(x) = \sin x$.

15. If an angle of 300° is drawn in standard position in the unit circle, then the corresponding point on the terminal arm is

A. $\left(\frac{\sqrt{2}}{2}, -\frac{\sqrt{3}}{2}\right)$

B. $\left(-\frac{\sqrt{2}}{2}, -\frac{\sqrt{3}}{2}\right)$

C. $\left(\frac{1}{2}, -\frac{\sqrt{3}}{2}\right)$

D. $\left(-\frac{1}{2}, -\frac{\sqrt{3}}{2}\right)$

Open Response

16. Rounded to the nearest tenth of a degree, what are the approximate values of θ in the trigonometric equation $5\tan\theta - 1 = 3$, where $0° \leq \theta < 360°$?

Open Response

17. Find the exact value of csc 45°.

Use the following information to answer the next question.

In attempting to prove an identity in which the left-hand side of the equation is $\frac{1 + \sin x}{1 - \sin x}$, a student performed the following steps:

Step 1

$$\frac{(1 + \sin x)(1 + \sin x)}{(1 - \sin x)(1 + \sin x)}$$

Step 2

$$\frac{1 + 2\sin x + \sin^2 x}{\cos^2 x}$$

Step 3

$$\frac{1}{\cos^2 x} + \frac{2\sin x}{\cos^2 x} + \frac{\sin^2 x}{\cos^2 x}$$

Step 4

$$\sec^2 x + 2\csc x \tan x + \tan^2 x$$

18. The student's first error was made in step

A. 1

B. 2

C. 3

D. 4

Use the following information to answer the next question.

Lexi is standing in her yard. She sees a cat sitting directly west of her position and a dog sitting directly east. Lexi's eye level is 1.48 m above the ground. For her to look directly at the cat, the angle of depression is 30°, and for her to look directly at the dog, the angle of depression is 25°.

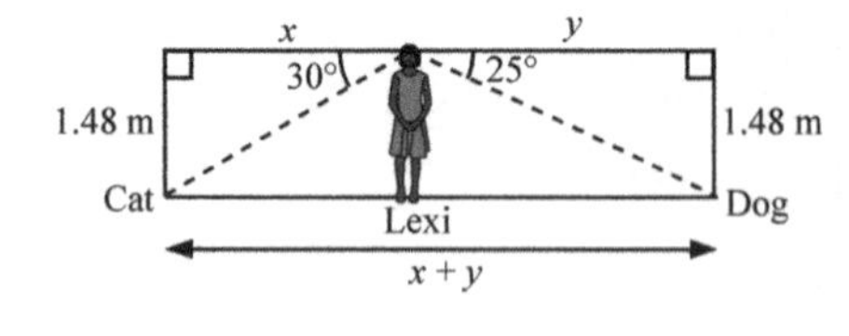

Open Response

19. Calculate the distance between the cat and the dog.

Use the following information to answer the next question.

Jeremy makes the following measurements as a surveyor so he can determine the distance, x, between the two caves.

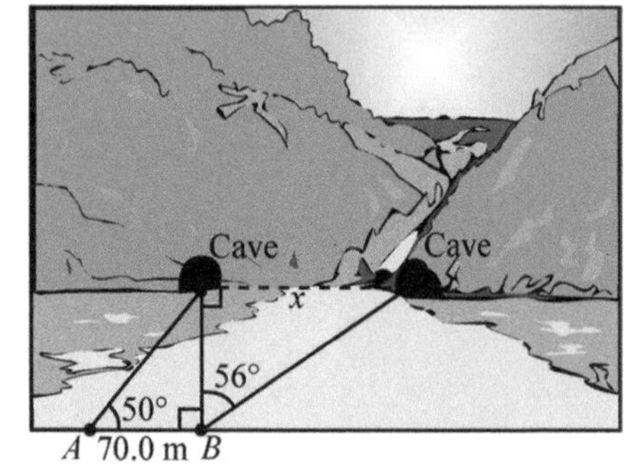

20. The distance, x, to the nearest tenth metre, between the two caves is

A. 56.3 m

B. 69.2 m

C. 100.6 m

D. 123.7 m

Use the following information to answer the next question.

The given table lists the amount of daylight for a city in Ontario, for various dates in 2007, including those with the most and least hours of daylight. The year 2007 was not a leap year.

Date	Amount of Daylight
February 21	10 h 42 min
April 21	13 h 49 min
June 21	15 h 41 min
August 21	13 h 50 min
October 21	10 h 41 min
December 21	8 h 43 min

Open Response

21. If the number of hours of daylight were a function of the days in a non-leap year, and if that function were periodic, then what would be the period of daylight time, to the nearest day? What would be the amplitude of the daylight time, to the nearest minute? Explain your answer.

Use the following information to answer the next question.

Four students examined the graph of $f(x) = \sin x$ and made the following observations.
Jeremy: The function increases between $-450°$ and $-270°$.
Emily: The minimum and maximum values occur every $180°$.
Derek: One of the minimum points of the graph occurs at an angle of $990°$.
Ralyn: An angle where the graph passes through its horizontal midline axis is at $-530°$

22. Which of the student's observations about the graph of $f(x) = \sin x$ is **incorrect**?

A. Jeremy

B. Emily

C. Derek

D. Ralyn

Open Response

23. Determine the transformations applied to the graph of $y = \sin x$ to obtain the graph of $y = -\frac{1}{2}\sin\frac{1}{3}(x + 48°) - 5$.

24. Hannah used several key points to draw the partial graph of $f(x) = \sin(x + 90°)$. Which of the following graphs **best** represents this function?

A. 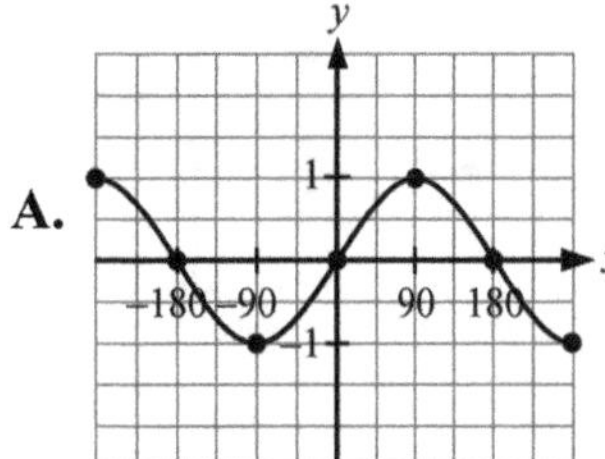

B. 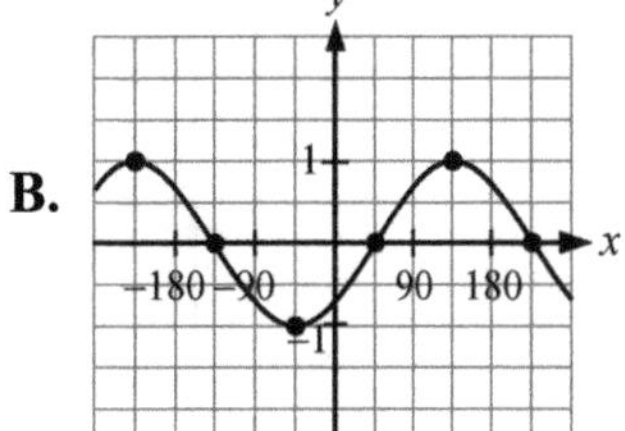

C. 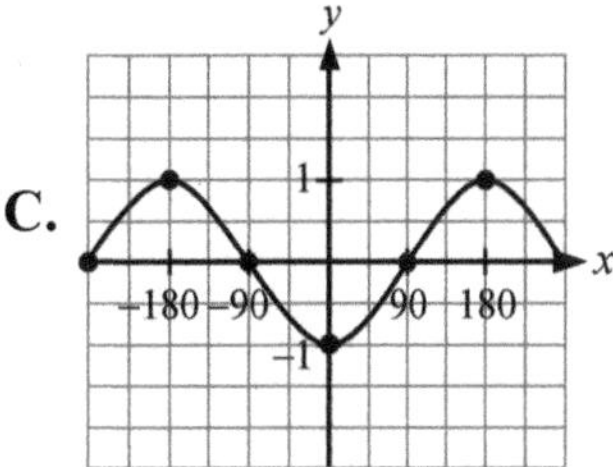

D. 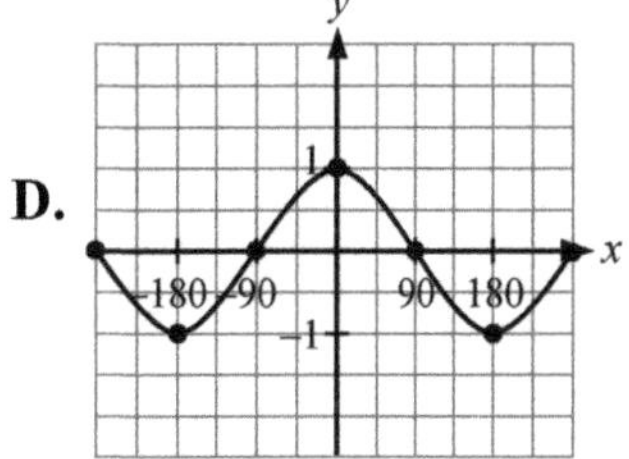

Use the following information to answer the next question.

Shama examines the given graphs.

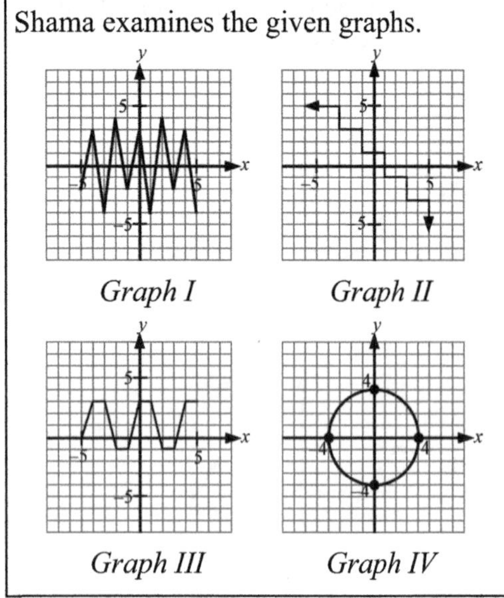

25. How many of the graphs represent a periodic function?

A. 1

B. 2

C. 3

D. 4

Use the following information to answer the next question.

At a home in Ontario, the water usage over a 12-month time period is shown in the given table.

Month	**Usage (m^3)**
Jan	12
Feb	11.5
Mar	10.5
Apr	10.2
May	11.2
Jun	12.4
Jul	13.2
Aug	13.0
Sep	12.4
Oct	11.2
Nov	9.8
Dec	11.4

Complete the following statements about the periodic function of the water usage over a 12-month time period:

Open Response

26. Explain how this data represents a periodic function, and state the range of the function.

Use the following information to answer the next question.

Logan went to the doctor and has his blood pressure measured. The graph of his blood pressure measurements is shown below.

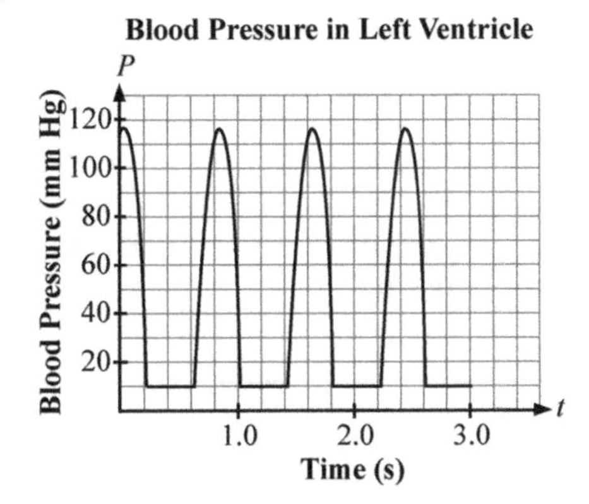

27. Logan revisited the doctor a week later and had his blood pressure measured and graphed. The only change to the graph was that the graph was stretched horizontally when compared to the graph above. This indicates that, compared to the first visit to the doctor,

A. Logan had an irregular heartbeat during the second visit.

B. Logan's blood pressure had increased.

C. Logan's heart was beating more quickly.

D. Logan's heart was beating more slowly.

Use the following information to answer the next question.

While breathing, the volume in your lungs is a periodic function of time. The graph below shows how the volume, V, in litres, changes over time, t, in seconds, for a particular person.

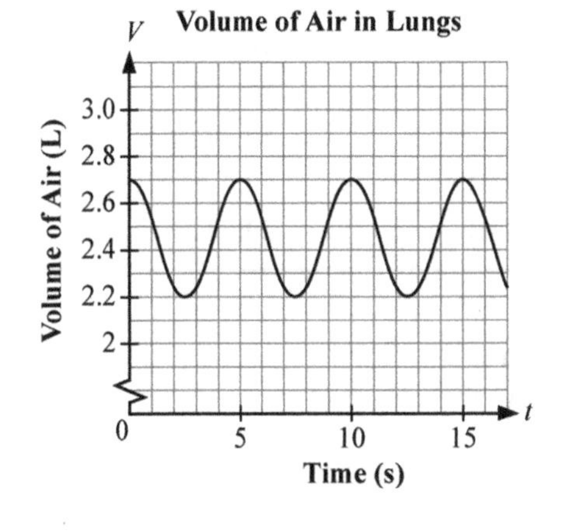

Numerical Response

28. If the length of time (period) for the person to inhale and exhale once is P seconds and the total volume exhaled each time a breath is taken is V litres, then the sum of the values $P + V$, to the nearest tenth, is __________.

ANSWERS AND SOLUTIONS — PRACTICE TEST 1

1. C	12. OR	21. OR	c) OR	40. 2
2. 12.0	13. A	22. a) 7.95	30. C	41. C
3. C	14. a) OR	b) A	31. C	42. C
4. B	b) OR	23. B	32. 5.2	43. B
5. B	c) OR	24. B	33. B	44. B
6. B	15. B	25. OR	34. 6	45. C
7. A	16. 4231	26. 165	35. A	46. a) 14
8. 8	17. A	27. B	36. D	b) 21
9. C	18. OR	28. OR	37. OR	47. B
10. OR	19. A	29. a) OR	38. B	
11. OR	20. C	b) OR	39. C	

1. C

Step 1
Solve the relations for y.

The relation $y^2 = 4x$ is the only relation in which y cannot be solved.

$y^2 = 4x$
$y = \pm\sqrt{4x}$
$y = \pm 2\sqrt{x}$

Step 2
Select a value for x to determine an ordered pair of each relation.
If a value of 9 is chosen for x, then substitute 9 into the equations.

For the relation $y = x^2 + 4x$,

$y = x^2 + 4$
$= (9)^2 + 4$
$= 81 + 4$
$= 85$

The ordered pair will be (9, 85).
For the relation $y = 4x - 5$,

$y = 4x - 5$
$= 4(9) - 5$
$= 36 - 5$
$= 31$

The ordered pair will be (9, 31).

For the relation $y^2 = 4x$,

$y = \pm 2\sqrt{x}$
$= \pm 2\sqrt{9}$
$= \pm 2(3)$
$= \pm 6$

The ordered pairs will be (9, 6) and (9, −6).
For the relation $y = 4$, every value of x has the y-value of 4.
Some of the ordered pairs will be, (9, 4), (10, 4), and (11, 4).

Step 3
Determine which relation is not a function.
In order for a relation to be a function, each x-value must have its own y-value.

The relation $y^2 = 4x$ is not a function. The x-value of 9 has two separate y-values. These values are 6 and −6.

2. 12.0

Substitute $-\frac{1}{2}$ for x and $f\left(-\frac{1}{2}\right)$ for $f(x)$ in the equation $f(x) = 8x^2 - 10x + 5$.

$f(x) = 8x^2 - 10x + 5$
$f\left(-\frac{1}{2}\right) = 8\left(-\frac{1}{2}\right)^2 - 10\left(-\frac{1}{2}\right) + 5$
$f\left(-\frac{1}{2}\right) = 8\left(\frac{1}{4}\right) + 5 + 5$
$f\left(-\frac{1}{2}\right) = 2 + 5 + 5$
$f\left(-\frac{1}{2}\right) = 12.0$

3. C

Step 1

Determine the domain of $f(x) = \frac{2}{x+3}$.

Since a replacement of −3 would make the denominator zero, the domain is $x \neq -3$.

Step 2

Determine the range of $f(x) = \frac{2}{x+3}$.

It is impossible to obtain a y-value of zero when dividing 2 by any real number other than zero. Therefore, the range is $y \neq 0$.

4. **B**

Step 1
Determine the domain of the inverse of the function. The range of the function is $y \geq 5$. Therefore, the domain of the inverse is $x \geq 5$.

Step 2
Determine the range of the inverse of the function. The domain of the function is $-2 \leq x \leq 6$. Therefore, the range of the inverse is $-2 \leq y \leq 6$.

5. **B**

Step 1
Replace $f(x)$ with y.

$$f(x) = \frac{1}{2}(x+6)^2 - 5$$
$$y = \frac{1}{2}(x+6)^2 - 5$$

Step 2
Interchange x and y.

$$y = \frac{1}{2}(x+6)^2 - 5$$
$$x = \frac{1}{2}(y+6)^2 - 5$$

Step 3
Solve for y.

$$\begin{aligned} x &= \frac{1}{2}(y+6)^2 - 5 \\ x+5 &= \frac{1}{2}(y+6)^2 \\ 2x+10 &= (y+6)^2 \\ \pm\sqrt{2x+10} &= y+6 \\ \pm\sqrt{2x+10} - 6 &= y \\ y &= \pm\sqrt{2x+10} - 6 \end{aligned}$$

Note that y cannot be replaced by $f^{-1}(x)$ since the inverse is not a function.

6. **B**

Consider the general equation
$y = af(k(x-d)) + c$.

Step 1

To vertically stretch the graph of $f(x) = \frac{1}{x}$ by a factor of 5, multiply the right side of the equation by $5(a = 5)$.

$$f(x) = \frac{1}{x}$$
$$f(x) = 5\left(\frac{1}{x}\right)$$
$$f(x) = \frac{5}{x}$$

Step 2
Substitute $x + 4$ for x in the equation $f(x) = \frac{5}{x}$ to translate the graph of $f(x) = \frac{5}{x}$ 4 units to the left $(d = -4)$.

$$f(x) = \frac{5}{x}$$
$$f(x) = \frac{5}{x+4}$$

7. **A**

When the function $g(x) = \sqrt{-x} + 2$ is compared to the function of the form $y = af(k(x-d)) + c$, it can be observed that $k = -1$ and $c = 2$. Therefore, there is a reflection about the y-axis and a vertical translation 2 units up. Graph A corresponds to these changes.

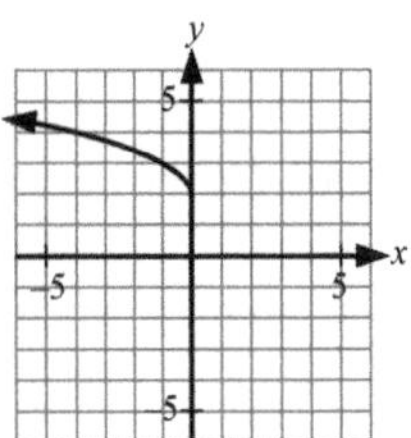

8. **8**

Express $f(x) = 3x^2 + 12x + 20$ in vertex form by completing the square.

$$\begin{aligned} f(x) &= 3x^2 + 12x + 20 \\ &= 3(x^2 + 4x) + 20 \\ &= 3(x^2 + 4x + 4 - 4) + 20 \\ &= 3(x^2 + 4x + 4) - 12 + 20 \\ &= 3(x+2)^2 + 8 \end{aligned}$$

From the function $f(x) = 3(x+2)^2 + 8$, the vertex is $(-2, 8)$. Therefore the minimum value is 8.

9. C

Step 1
Identify the length and width of the rectangle, and label the diagram.
Let x be the length (part of the barn wall) and y be the width (part of the existing fence) of the rectangular area.

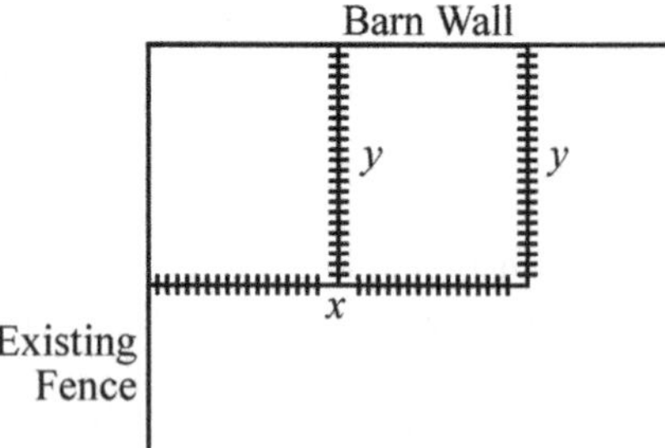

Step 2
Write an equation for the area, A, of the outer rectangle.
$A = xy$
Write an equation for the perimeter of fencing.
$P = x + 2y$.
The farmer has 200 m of fencing to complete the project.
Therefore, $x + 2y = 200$.
Solve for y.

$$\begin{aligned} y &= \frac{200-x}{2} \\ &= 100 - \frac{1}{2}x \end{aligned}$$

The enclosed area is $A = xy$.
Substitute $100 - \frac{1}{2}x$ for y in the area formula.

$$\begin{aligned} A &= x\left(100 - \frac{1}{2}x\right) \\ &= 100x - \frac{1}{2}x^2 \\ &= -\frac{1}{2}x^2 + 100x \end{aligned}$$

Step 3
Write $A = -\frac{1}{2}x^2 + 100x$ in completed square form.

$$\begin{aligned} A &= -\frac{1}{2}\left(x^2 - 200x\right) \\ &= -\frac{1}{2}\left(x^2 - 200x + 10\ 000 - 10\ 000\right) \\ &= -\frac{1}{2}\left(x^2 - 200x + 10\ 000\right) - 10\ 000\left(-\frac{1}{2}\right) \\ &= -\frac{1}{2}(x - 100)^2 + 5\ 000 \end{aligned}$$

Step 4
Determine the vertex of the parabola represented by the area function and identify the maximum area.
The vertex can be found in the completed square form of the equation.
From the equation $A = -\frac{1}{2}(x - 100)^2 + 5\ 000$, the vertex of the parabola is at $(100, 5\ 000)$.
Since the parabola opens down $(a < 0)$, the vertex corresponds to the highest point on the graph of the function.
The second coordinate of the vertex is the maximum value of the function.
The maximum area that can be enclosed is $5\ 000\ \text{m}^2$.

10. OR

Since the roots of the corresponding quadratic equation are the zeros of the function, the equation of the function must be
$f(x) = a(x - (2 + \sqrt{5}))(x - (2 - \sqrt{5}))$. Simplify.

$$\begin{aligned} f(x) &= a(x - 2 - \sqrt{5})(x - 2 + \sqrt{5}) \\ &= a(x^2 - 2x + \sqrt{5}x - 2x + 4 \\ &\quad - 2\sqrt{5} - \sqrt{5}x + 2\sqrt{5} - 5) \\ &= a\left(x^2 - 4x - 1\right) \end{aligned}$$

The point $(7, -40)$ must satisfy this equation.
Substitute this point into the equation.

$$\begin{aligned} -40 &= a\left((7)^2 - 4(7) - 1\right) \\ -40 &= a(49 - 28 - 1) \\ -40 &= a(20) \\ -2 &= a \end{aligned}$$

Find the equation of the function.

$$\begin{aligned} f(x) &= -2\left(x^2 - 4x - 1\right) \\ &= -2x^2 + 8x + 2 \end{aligned}$$

11. OR

Step 1
Determine the equations of the family of lines that have a slope of 2.
All lines with a slope of 2 have an equation of the form $y = 2x + k$, where k is the y-intercept.

Step 2
To determine the number of points of intersection, equate the two functions, and put the resulting equation in the form $ax^2 + bx + c = 0$.

$$\begin{aligned} 2x + k &= -x^2 + 8x \\ x^2 - 6x + k &= 0 \end{aligned}$$

Step 3

The value of the discriminant, $b^2 - 4ac$, dictates the number and nature of the solutions to an equation of the form $ax^2 + bx + c = 0$.

Substitute the known values into $b^2 - 4ac$.

$$\begin{aligned} b^2 - 4ac &= (-6)^2 - 4(1)k \\ &= 36 - 4k \end{aligned}$$

Step 4

Determine the value of k if there is one intersection.

If $b^2 - 4ac = 0$, there are two real, yet equal solutions to the equation, so there is one point of intersection.

$$\begin{aligned} 36 - 4k &= 0 \\ 36 &= 4k \\ 9 &= k \end{aligned}$$

The line $y = 2x + 9$ will intersect the parabola $f(x) = -x^2 + 8x$ at only one point.

Step 5

Determine the value of k if there are two intersections.

If $b^2 - 4ac > 0$, there are two real and different solutions to the equation and thus two points of intersection.

$$\begin{aligned} 36 - 4k &> 0 \\ 36 &> 4k \\ 9 &> k \end{aligned}$$

All lines with a slope of 2 and a y-intercept less than 9 will intersect the parabola $f(x) = -x^2 + 8x$ at two points.

Step 6

Determine the value of k if there is no intersection.

If $b^2 - 4ac < 0$, there are no real solutions to the equation and thus no points of intersection.

$$\begin{aligned} 36 - 4k &< 0 \\ 36 &< 4k \\ 9 &< k \end{aligned}$$

All lines with a slope of 2 and a y-intercept greater than 9 will not intersect the parabola $f(x) = -x^2 + 8x$ at any point.

12. OR

Determine the volume of a rectangular prism by multiplying the length, width, and height.

$$\begin{aligned} V &= lwh \\ &= (3x+1)(3x-1)(2x+3) \\ &= \left(9x^2 - 1\right)(2x+3) \\ &= 18x^3 + 27x^2 - 2x - 3 \end{aligned}$$

13. A

Step 1

Factor the denominators of the expression.

$$\begin{aligned} &\frac{x-3}{x^2-4} + \frac{x-2}{x^2-x-6} \\ &= \frac{x-3}{(x-2)(x+2)} + \frac{x-2}{(x-3)(x+2)} \end{aligned}$$

Step 2

Multiply the numerator and denominator of the first term by $x - 3$ and the numerator and denominator of the second term by $x - 2$.

$$\begin{aligned} &\frac{x-3}{(x-2)(x+2)} + \frac{x-2}{(x-3)(x+2)} \\ &= \frac{x-3}{(x-2)(x+2)} \times \frac{(x-3)}{(x-3)} + \frac{x-2}{(x-3)(x+2)} \times \frac{(x-2)}{(x-2)} \\ &= \frac{x^2-6x+9}{(x-2)(x+2)(x-3)} + \frac{x^2-4x+4}{(x-2)(x+2)(x-3)} \end{aligned}$$

Step 3

Add and collect the like terms.

$$\begin{aligned} &\frac{x^2-6x+9}{(x-2)(x+2)(x-3)} + \frac{x^2-4x+4}{(x-2)(x+2)(x-3)} \\ &= \frac{x^2-6x+9+x^2-4x+4}{(x-2)(x+2)(x-3)} \\ &= \frac{2x^2-10x+13}{(x-2)(x+2)(x-3)} \end{aligned}$$

14. a) OR

Use a table of values to determine the corresponding y-values for x-values of -3, -2, -1, 0, 1, 2, and 3 of the function $y = \left(\frac{1}{2}\right)^x$.

x	-3	-2	-1	0	1	2	3
y	$\left(\frac{1}{2}\right)^{-3} = 8$	$\left(\frac{1}{2}\right)^{-2} = 4$	$\left(\frac{1}{2}\right)^{-1} = 2$	$\left(\frac{1}{2}\right)^{0} = 1$	$\left(\frac{1}{2}\right)^{1} = \frac{1}{2}$	$\left(\frac{1}{2}\right)^{2} = \frac{1}{4}$	$\left(\frac{1}{2}\right)^{3} = \frac{1}{8}$

Then, plot these points, and join them with a smooth curve to get the graph shown.

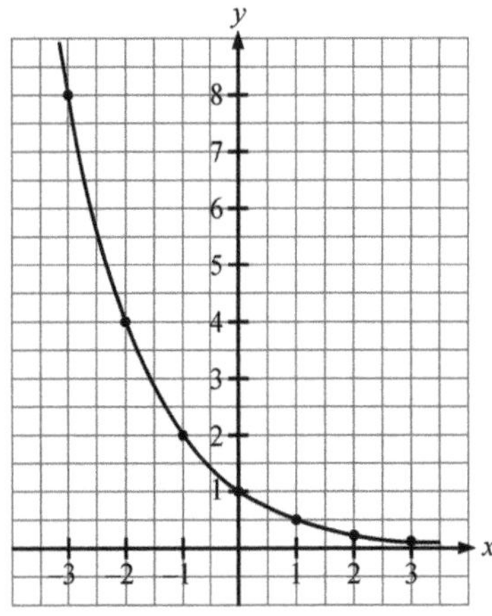

b) OR

The following features characterize the graph of $y = \left(\frac{1}{2}\right)^x$.

Domain: $x \in \mathbb{R}$ y-intercept: (0, 1)

Range: $y > 0$ x-intercept: None

Asymptote: $y = 0$

c) OR

Since the a value in $y = \left(\frac{1}{2}\right)^x$ is smaller and closer to the value of $a = 0$ than the a value in $y = \left(\frac{2}{3}\right)^x$, the graph of $y = \left(\frac{1}{2}\right)^x$ would be steeper on the left side of the y-axis and flatter on the right side of the y-axis.

15. B

Rewrite the expression $(-64)^{-\frac{2}{3}}$ with a positive exponent.

$$(-64)^{-\frac{2}{3}} = \frac{1}{(-64)^{\frac{2}{3}}}$$

Rewrite the denominator $(-64)^{\frac{2}{3}}$ as a radical, and simplify the expression.

$$\frac{1}{(-64)^{\frac{2}{3}}} = \frac{1}{(\sqrt[3]{-64})^2} = \frac{1}{(-4)^2} = \frac{1}{16}$$

16. 4231

Exponential decay functions (functions 2 and 4) are approaching the positive x-axis as x becomes increasingly large, so they will be the closest to the positive x-axis (of the four given functions). Of these two functions, the function with the smaller base (function 4) will be closer to the positive x-axis. For Exponential growth functions (functions 1 and 3), the larger the base, the quicker the function grows and the farther from the positive x-axis it will be. Since function 1 has the largest base, it is the farthest from the positive x-axis. Since the first, second, and fourth places have been determined, function 3 is third in the order. The final order is 4 231.

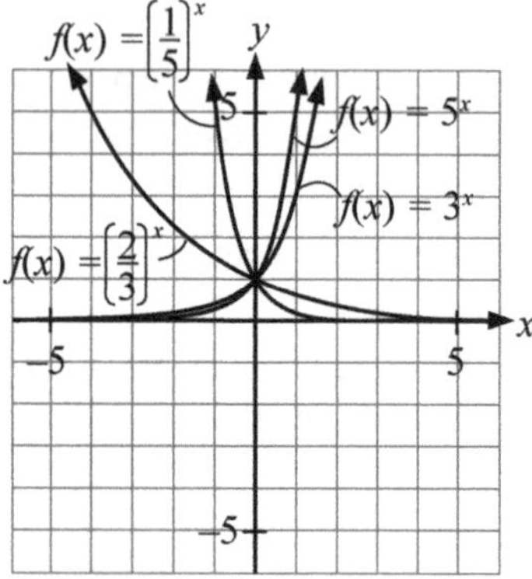

17. A

Calculate the first differences.

$8 - 6 = 2$
$10 - 8 = 2$
$12 - 10 = 2$
$14 - 12 = 2$

The first differences are all constant (2, 2, 2, 2), so this is a linear function.

18. OR

If $f(x) = 3^x$, then $g(x) = 4f(x+2) - 3$. Comparing $g(x) = 4f(x+2) - 3$ to a function of the form $y = af(x-d) + c$, where a corresponds to the vertical stretch factor, d corresponds to the horizontal translation, and c corresponds to the vertical translation, it can be seen that $a = 4$, $d = -2$, and $c = -3$.

To change the graph of the function $f(x)$ to the graph of $g(x)$, the graph of $f(x)$ would have to undergo the following transformations:

1. For $a = 4$, the graph of $f(x)$ would be stretched vertically about the x-axis by a factor of 4.
2. For $d = -2$ and $c = -3$, the graph of $f(x)$ would then be translated 2 units left and 3 units down.

19. A

The function needs to be written as $f(x)=3^{-(x-3)}$.
Obtain the graph of $f(x)=3^{-(x-3)}$ from the graph of $y=3^{x}$ by first reflecting in the y-axis and then translating horizontally 3 units to the right.
The original y-intercept of (0, 1) is now at (3, 1).
The new y-intercept is 27, and the horizontal asymptote is the line $y=0$.

20. C

Step 1

Express $f(x)=27^{x}$ with base 3.

$$\begin{aligned} f(x) &= 27^{x} \\ &= (3^{3})^{x} \\ &= 3^{3x} \end{aligned}$$

Step 2

Express each of the given alternatives with base 3, and compare to $f(x)=27^{x}=3^{3x}$.

Rewrite the function $g(x)=\left(\frac{1}{9}\right)^{-\frac{2}{3}x}$.

$$\begin{aligned} g(x) &= \left(\frac{1}{9}\right)^{-\frac{2}{3}x} \\ &= (3^{-2})^{-\frac{2}{3}x} \\ &= 3^{\frac{4}{3}x} \end{aligned}$$

The function $g(x)=\left(\frac{1}{9}\right)^{-\frac{2}{3}x}$ is not equivalent to the function $f(x)=27^{x}=3^{3x}$.

Rewrite the function $h(x)=81^{\frac{1}{2}x}$.

$$\begin{aligned} h(x) &= 81^{\frac{1}{2}x} \\ &= (3^{4})^{\frac{1}{2}x} \\ &= 3^{2x} \end{aligned}$$

The function $h(x)=81^{\frac{1}{2}x}$ is not equivalent to the function $f(x)=27^{x}=3^{3x}$.
The function $m(x)=3^{2x}$ is already written with base 3 and is not equivalent to the function $f(x)=27^{x}=3^{3x}$.

Rewrite the function $p(x)=9^{\frac{3}{2}x}$.

$$\begin{aligned} p(x) &= 9^{\frac{3}{2}x} \\ &= (3^{2})^{\frac{3}{2}x} \\ &= 3^{3x} \end{aligned}$$

The function $p(x)=9^{\frac{3}{2}x}$ is equivalent to the function $f(x)=27^{x}=3^{3x}$.

21. OR

The exponential function must have the form $f(x) = a(b)^x + c$.

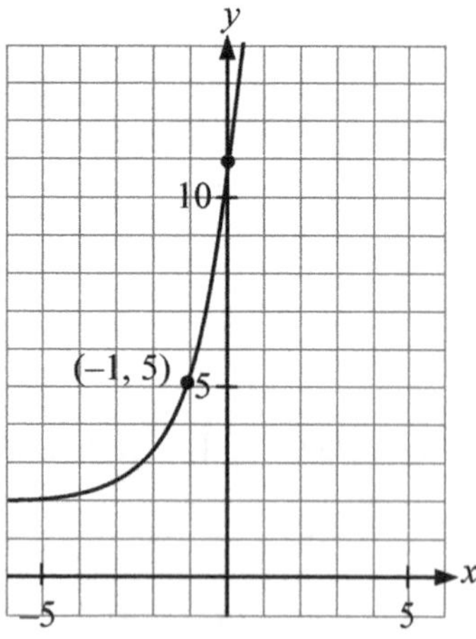

Step 1

Determine the value of parameter c.

The graph has a horizontal asymptote at $y = 2$, so the exponential function $f(x) = b^x$ has undergone a vertical translation of 2 units up. The value of parameter c is 2.

Step 2

Determine the value of parameter a.

The graph has a y-intercept of 11, which is 9 units above the horizontal asymptote. As such, the vertical stretch factor of the exponential function is 9; therefore, the value of parameter a is 9.

Step 3

Determine the value of parameter b.

Substitute the coordinates of the point $(-1, 5)$ and the values of a and c into the general equation $f(x) = a(b)^x + c$, and solve for b.

$$5 = 9(b)^{-1} + 2$$
$$3 = 9(b)^{-1}$$
$$3 = 9\left(\frac{1}{b}\right)$$
$$b = 3$$

Step 4

Express the exponential function in simplest terms. Substitute the values of a, b, and c into the equation of the form $f(x) = a(b)^x + c$.

$$f(x) = 9(3)^x + 2$$

The equation could be written in a different form since $9 = 3^2$.

$$\begin{aligned} f(x) &= 9(3)^x + 2 \\ &= 3^2(3)^x + 2 \\ &= 3^{x+2} + 2 \end{aligned}$$

From the simplified equation, the graph can be interpreted as the translation of the graph of $y = 3^x$ horizontally 2 units left and vertically 2 units up.

22. a) 7.95

Substitute the value of 100 m into d of the equation, and solve for the percentage, P.

$$\begin{aligned} P &= 100(0.975)^d \\ &= 100(0.975)^{100} \\ &= 7.951\ 728\ 986 \end{aligned}$$

Rounded to the nearest hundredth, this value is 7.95%.

b) A

An appropriate window setting, based on the result of $d = 100$ and $P = 7.95$, could be x:[0, 100, 10], y:[0, 100, 10]. Enter the function $P = 100(0.975)^d$ into [Y =] as Y_1 = 100(0.975)^X, and press GRAPH.

Then, use your VALUE feature by pressing 2nd TRACE 1 to enter x-values of 40 and 60, respectively, and get the corresponding y-values, as shown:

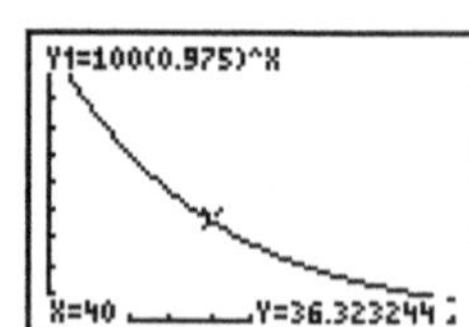

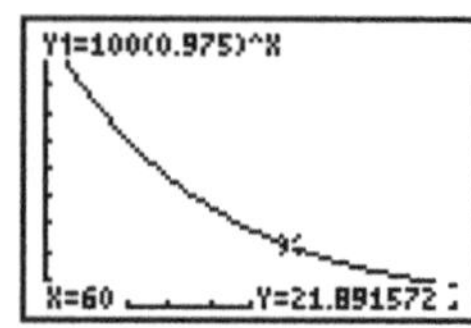

The difference between the two y-values (or P-values) is

36.323 244 – 21.891 572 = 14.431 672 or 14%.

23. B

Step 1
Test the function $f(x) = 2^x, x \in N, x \geq 2$.

$$\begin{aligned} f(2) &= 2^2 \\ &= 4 \\ f(3) &= 2^3 \\ &= 8 \\ f(4) &= 2^4 \\ &= 16 \end{aligned}$$

The sequence, 4, 8, 16, …, generated by this function is not consistent with the given sequence.

Step 2
Test the function $f(x) = 4(x+1), x \in W$.

$$\begin{aligned} f(0) &= 4(0+1) \\ &= 4 \\ f(1) &= 4(1+1) \\ &= 8 \\ f(2) &= 4(2+1) \\ &= 12 \end{aligned}$$

The sequence, 4, 8, 12, …, generated by this function is consistent with the given sequence.

Step 3
Test the function $f(x) = 4x + 8, x \in W$.

$$\begin{aligned} f(0) &= 4(0) + 8 \\ &= 8 \\ f(1) &= 4(1) + 8 \\ &= 12 \\ f(2) &= 4(2) + 8 \\ &= 16 \end{aligned}$$

The sequence, 8, 12, 16, …, generated by this function is not consistent with the given sequence.

Step 4
Test the function $f(x) = 2x^2, x \in N$.

$$\begin{aligned} f(1) &= 2(1)^2 \\ &= 2 \\ f(2) &= 2(2)^2 \\ &= 8 \\ f(3) &= 2(3)^2 \\ &= 18 \end{aligned}$$

The sequence, 2, 8, 18, …, generated by this function is not consistent with the given sequence.

Therefore, the function $f(x) = 4(x+1), x \in W$ would generate the sequence 4, 8, 12, 16, …

24. B

Step 1
Use the general term to calculate the first term.

$$\begin{aligned} t_1 &= 2(3)^{1-1} \\ &= 2(3)^0 \\ &= 2(1) \\ &= 2 \end{aligned}$$

Step 2
Calculate the second term.

$$\begin{aligned} t_2 &= 2(3)^{2-1} \\ &= 2(3)^1 \\ &= 2(3) \\ &= 6 \end{aligned}$$

Step 3
Calculate the third term.

$$\begin{aligned} t_3 &= 2(3)^{3-1} \\ &= 2(3)^2 \\ &= 2(9) \\ &= 18 \end{aligned}$$

The sequence 2, 6, 18,… is represented by the general term $t_n = 2(3)^{n-1}$.

25. OR

Step 1
Determine the first differences.

Subtracting the terms gives first differences.

$$\begin{aligned} 11 - 5 &= 6 \\ 21 - 11 &= 10 \\ 35 - 21 &= 14 \\ 53 - 35 &= 18 \end{aligned}$$

Step 2
Determine the second differences.

$$\begin{aligned} 10 - 6 &= 4 \\ 14 - 10 &= 4 \\ 18 - 14 &= 4 \end{aligned}$$

The second differences are constant at 4.

Step 3
Determine the recursive formula.

This sequence represents a discrete quadratic function and will therefore have a recursive formula of the form $t_1 = 5$, $t_n = t_{n-1} + an + b$, and $a = 4$.

$$\begin{aligned} t_2 &= t_1 + 4n + b \\ 11 &= 5 + 4(2) + b \\ 11 &= 13 + b \\ -2 &= b \end{aligned}$$

This gives a recursive formula of $t_1 = 5$,
$t_n = t_{n-1} + 4n - 2, n > 1$.

Step 4
Verify the recursive formula.

$$\begin{aligned} t_3 &= t_2 + 4(3) - 2 \\ &= 11 + 12 - 2 \\ &= 21 \\ t_4 &= t_3 + 4(4) - 2 \\ &= 21 + 16 - 2 \\ &= 35 \end{aligned}$$

Therefore, the recursive formula is $t_1 = 5$,
$t_n = t_{n-1} + 4n - 2, n > 1$.

26. 165

Step 1
Add together the first and second terms to form the third term, and add the second and third terms to form the fourth term, and so on.

$t_n = t_{n-1} + t_{n-2}$
$t_3 = 3 + 3$
$= 6$
$t_4 = 6 + 3$
$= 9$
$t_5 = 9 + 6$
$= 15$

Step 2
Continue this process until the 10th term.

$t_6 = 15 + 9$
$= 24$
$t_7 = 24 + 15$
$= 39$
$t_8 = 39 + 24$
$= 63$
$t_9 = 63 + 39$
$= 102$
$t_{10} = 102 + 63$
$= 165$

Therefore, the 10th term in this sequence is 165.

27. B

Step 1
Use the general term $t_n = 4n$ to generate the sequence, and determine the common ratio.
The terms are 4, 8, 12, 16, …, and the ratio between consecutive terms is 2, $\frac{3}{2}$, $\frac{4}{3}$.

Since the ratio is not constant, this is not a geometric sequence.

Step 2
Use the general term $t_n = 4n^2$ to generate the sequence, and determine the common ratio.
The terms are 4, 16, 36, 64, …, and the ratio between consecutive terms is 4, $\frac{18}{8}$, $\frac{16}{9}$.

The ratio is not constant, so this is not a geometric sequence.

Step 3
Use the general term $t_1 = 4$, $t_n = 4t_{n-1} + 4$, $n > 1$ to generate the sequence, and determine the common ratio.
The terms are 4, 20, 84, 340, …, and the ratio between consecutive terms is 5, $\frac{21}{5}$, $\frac{85}{21}$.

The ratio is not constant, so this is not a geometric sequence.

Step 4
Use the general term $t_n = 4^n$ to generate the sequence, and determine the common ratio.
The terms are 4, 16, 64, 256, …
There is a constant ratio of 4 between consecutive terms, so the sequence is geometric.

28. OR

Step 1
Determine the general term of the sequence.
The sequence is geometric. The first term (a) is $\frac{1}{64}$, and the common ratio (r) is 2. Substitute the values into the formula for the general term $t_n = ar^{n-1}$, and solve.

$t_n = \frac{1}{64}(2)^{n-1}$
$= (2^{-6})(2)^{n-1}$
$= 2^{-6+n-1}$
$= 2^{n-7}$

Therefore, the general term of the sequence is $t_n = 2^{n-7}$.

Step 2
Find the 12th term.

$t_{12} = 2^{12-7}$
$= 2^5$
$= 32$

Therefore, the 12th term is 32.

29. a) OR

Step 1

Since there are two pieces of information given, use the sum formula $S_n = \frac{n}{2}(2a+(n-1)d)$ to write two equations with the unknowns a and d.

Write the equation for the sum of the first eight terms (equation 1).

$$S_n = \frac{n}{2}(2a+(n-1)d)$$
$$212 = \frac{8}{2}(2a+(8-1)d)$$
$$212 = 4(2a+7d)$$
$$① \ 53 = 2a+7d$$

Write the equation for the sum of the first twelve terms (equation 2).

$$S_n = \frac{n}{2}(2a+(n-1)d)$$
$$438 = \frac{12}{2}(2a+(12-1)d)$$
$$438 = 6(2a+11d)$$
$$② \ 73 = 2a+11d$$

Step 2

Subtract equation 1 from equation 2 to solve for d.

$$\begin{aligned} ② \quad 2a+11d &= 73 \\ ① \quad \underline{2a+7d} &\underline{= 53} \\ 4d &= 20 \\ d &= 5 \end{aligned}$$

Step 3

Substitute the value of $d = 5$ into $53 = 2a+7d$.

$53 = 2a+7d$
$53 = 2a+7(5)$
$53 = 2a+35$
$18 = 2a$
$9 = a$

Step 4

Determine the first four terms in the series.

$t_1 = 9$

$t_2 = 9+((2)-1)5$
$= 14$

$t_3 = 9+((3)-1)5$
$= 19$

$t_4 = 9+((4)-1)5$
$= 24$

Therefore, the first four terms in the series are 9, 14, 19, and 24.

b) OR

Step 1

Since there are two pieces of information given, use the sum formula $S_n = \frac{n}{2}(2a+(n-1)d)$ to write two equations with the unknowns a and d.

Write the equation for the sum of the first eight terms (equation 1).

$$S_n = \frac{n}{2}(2a+(n-1)d)$$
$$212 = \frac{8}{2}(2a+(8-1)d)$$
$$212 = 4(2a+7d)$$
$$① \ 53 = 2a+7d$$

Write the equation for the sum of the first twelve terms (equation 2).

$$S_n = \frac{n}{2}(2a+(n-1)d)$$
$$438 = \frac{12}{2}(2a+(12-1)d)$$
$$438 = 6(2a+11d)$$
$$② \ 73 = 2a+11d$$

Step 2

Subtract equation 1 from equation 2 to solve for d.

$$\begin{aligned} ② \quad 2a+11d &= 73 \\ ① \quad \underline{2a+7d} &\underline{= 53} \\ 4d &= 20 \\ d &= 5 \end{aligned}$$

Step 3

Substitute the value of $d = 5$ into $53 = 2a+7d$.

$53 = 2a+7d$
$53 = 2a+7(5)$
$53 = 2a+35$
$18 = 2a$
$9 = a$

Step 4

Determine the 20th term in the series using the general term formula for an arithmetic sequence $t_n = a+(n-1)d$.

Substitute $a = 9$ and $d = 5$.

$t_{20} = 9+(20-1)(5)$
$= 9+(19)(5)$
$= 9+95$
$= 104$

The 20th term in the series is 104.

c) OR

Step 1

The sum of the first n terms in an arithmetic series can be found using the formula

$S_n = \frac{n}{2}(2a + (n - 1)d)$.

Determine an equation for the sum of the first 8 terms in the arithmetic series. This equation will be equation 1.

$$S_n = \frac{n}{2}(2a + (n - 1)d)$$
$$212 = \frac{8}{2}(2a + (8 - 1)d)$$
$$212 = 4(2a + 7d)$$
$$① \; 53 = 2a + 7d$$

Step 2

Determine an equation for the sum of the first 12 terms in the same arithmetic series. This equation will be equation 2.

$$S_n = \frac{n}{2}(2a + (n - 1)d)$$
$$438 = \frac{12}{2}(2a + (12 - 1)d)$$
$$438 = 6(2a + 11d)$$
$$② \; 73 = 2a + 11d$$

Step 3

Solve for d by solving the system of linear equations given by 1 and 2.

Subtract equation 1 from equation 2.

$$② \; 73 = 2a + 11d$$
$$① \; \underline{53 = 2a + 7d}$$
$$20 = 4d$$
$$5 = d$$

Step 4

Solve for a by substituting $d = 5$ into either equation 1 or 2.

Using equation 1, a can be determined as follows:

$$53 = 2a + 7d$$
$$53 = 2a + 7(5)$$
$$53 - 35 = 2a$$
$$18 = 2a$$
$$9 = a$$

Step 5

Determine the sum of the first 20 terms using the formula $S_n = \frac{n}{2}(2a + (n - 1)d)$ and the values $a = 9$, $d = 5$.

$$S_n = \left(\frac{n}{2}\right)(2a + (n - 1)d)$$
$$S_{20} = \frac{20}{2}(2(9) + (20 - 1)(5))$$
$$S_{20} = 10(18 + 19(5))$$
$$S_{20} = 10(113)$$
$$S_{20} = 1\ 130$$

The sum of the first 20 terms in the given arithmetic series is 1 130.

30. C

The 30 distances Betty runs form an arithmetic series with a first term of $a = 4\ 000$ m and a common difference of $d = 500$ m. The total distance that Betty runs is the sum of the 30 terms. Substitute the given variables into the formula

$S_n = \frac{n}{2}(2a + (n - 1)d)$.

$$S_n = \frac{n}{2}(2a + (n - 1)d)$$
$$S_{30} = \frac{30}{2}(2(4\ 000) + (30 - 1)(500))$$
$$= 15(8\ 000 + 14\ 500)$$
$$= 337\ 500 \text{ m}$$

31. C

Step 1

Determine the common difference between consecutive terms in the sequence.

$$848.72 - 824 = 24.72$$
$$874.18 - 848.72 = 25.46$$
$$900.41 - 874.18 = 26.23$$

There is no common difference since the differences are not constant (24.72, 25.46, and 26.23).

Step 2

Determine the common ratio between consecutive terms.

$$\frac{848.72}{824} = 1.03$$
$$\frac{874.18}{848.72} = 1.03$$
$$\frac{900.41}{80\ 074.18} = 1.03$$

The common ratio is 1.03.

Step 3
Determine the interest rate.

Because the given sequence is geometric, the function that represents the sequence must represent compound interest.

The function $f(x) = 800(1.03)^x$ will generate the terms of the sequence.
Comparing the function to the compound interest formula $A = P(1+i)^n$, this function describes a principal amount of \$800 invested at 3%/*a* compounded annually.

32. 5.2

Substitute $FV = \$738$, $PV = \$600$, and $n = 4 \times 12 = 48$ into the compound interest formula $FV = PV(1+i)^n$, where i represents the monthly interest rate.

$$\begin{aligned} 738 &= 600(1+i)^{48} \\ 1.23 &= (1+i)^{48} \\ (1.23)^{\frac{1}{48}} &= \left((1+i)^{48}\right)^{\frac{1}{48}} \\ 1.004\,3221 &\approx 1+i \\ 0.004\,3221 &\approx i \end{aligned}$$

The monthly interest rate is approximately 0.004 3221. Therefore, the yearly rate is approximately $0.004\,3221 \times 12 = 0.051\,865$.
To the nearest tenth of a percentage, the yearly interest rate is 5.2%.

33. B

Step 1
Use a TI-83 or similar graphing calculator to calculate the future value of each option.

For option 1, input the given data into the TVM Solver by pressing APPS 1:Finance 1:TVM Solver.

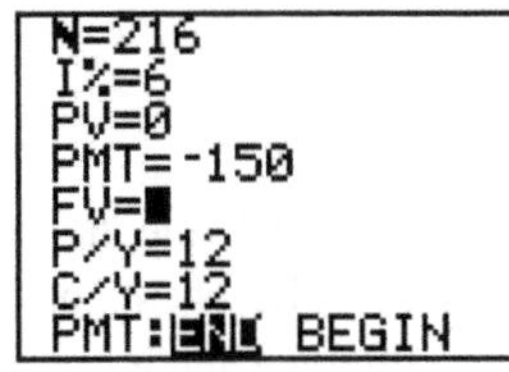

Highlighting FV and pressing SOLVE, or ALPHA ENTER, gives a value of 58 102.98.

For option 2, input the given data into the TVM Solver.

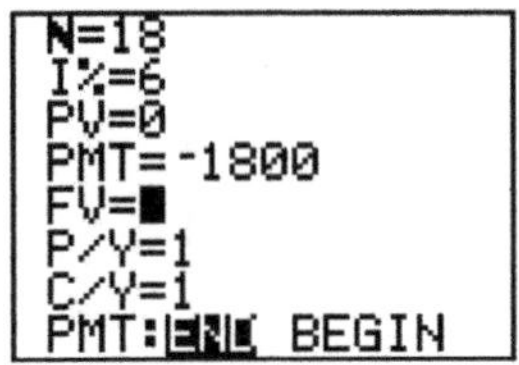

Highlighting FV and pressing SOLVE, or ALPHA ENTER, gives a value of 55 630.17.

Step 2
Subtract the two future values.
58 102.99 – 55 630.17 = 2 472.81

To the nearest whole number, the difference between the two options is \$2 473.

34. 6

Step 1
Determine the values of *a* and *b*.

To find the exact value of cos 30°, use the 30-60-90 triangle and the definition of the trigonometric ratios.

$$\begin{aligned} \cos 30^\circ &= \frac{\text{adjacent}}{\text{hypotenuse}} \\ &= \frac{\sqrt{3}}{2} \end{aligned}$$

Therefore, $a = 3$, $b = 2$.

Step 2
Determine the value of *c*.

A calculator will show that $\sin 90^\circ = 1$.

Therefore, $c = 1$.

Step 3
Add the three values.

$$\begin{aligned} a+b+c &= (3)+(2)+(1) \\ &= 6 \end{aligned}$$

35. A

Step 1

In degree mode, enter $\cos^{-1}(-0.266)$ into a scientific calculator to determine the first solution to the nearest tenth.

$\theta_1 \approx 105.4°$

Step 2

Determine the second solution.

Find the reference angle.

$180° - 105.4° = 74.6°$

Referring to the CAST rule, the second solution is found in quadrant III, where cosine is negative.

$$\begin{aligned}\theta_2 &= 180° + \text{reference angle}\\ &\approx 180° + 74.6°\\ &\approx 254.6°\end{aligned}$$

To the nearest tenth, $\theta = 105.4°$ and $254.6°$.

36. D

Step 1

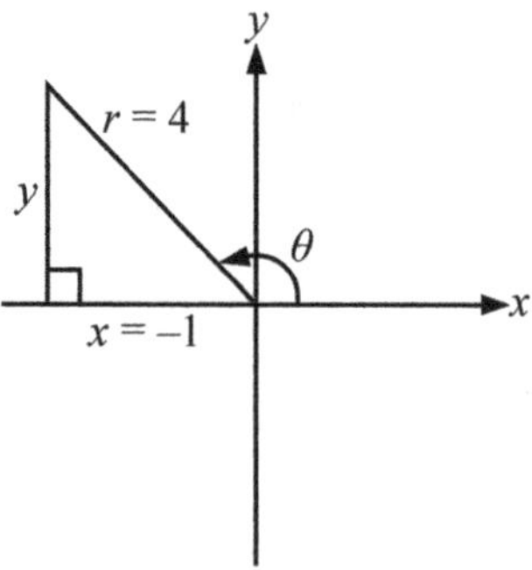

Sketch a diagram representing angle θ.

$$\begin{aligned}\cos\theta &= \frac{x}{r}\\ &= -\frac{1}{4}\end{aligned}$$

The possible values are $x = -1$ and $r = 4$.

Step 2

Determine the value of y.

Apply the Pythagorean theorem.

$$\begin{aligned}x^2 + y^2 &= r^2\\ (-1)^2 + y^2 &= 4^2\\ 1 + y^2 &= 16\\ y^2 &= 15\\ y &= \pm\sqrt{15}\end{aligned}$$

Since θ is in quadrant II, y must be positive. Therefore, $y = \sqrt{15}$.

Step 3

Determine the exact values of $\csc\theta$ and $\cot\theta$.

$$\begin{aligned}\csc\theta &= \frac{\text{hypotenuse}}{\text{opposite}}\\ &= \frac{r}{y}\\ &= \frac{4}{\sqrt{15}}\\ &= \frac{4\sqrt{15}}{15}\end{aligned}$$

$$\begin{aligned}\cot\theta &= \frac{\text{adjacent}}{\text{opposite}}\\ &= \frac{x}{y}\\ &= \frac{-1}{\sqrt{15}}\\ &= -\frac{\sqrt{15}}{15}\end{aligned}$$

37. OR

Use a chart to prove the given identity.

	LHS	RHS
	$\sqrt{\frac{1-\sin\theta}{1+\sin\theta}}$	$\sec\theta - \tan\theta$
Multiply by $\sqrt{\frac{1-\sin\theta}{1-\sin\theta}}$.	$=\sqrt{\frac{1-\sin\theta}{1+\sin\theta}\times\frac{1-\sin\theta}{1-\sin\theta}}$	
	$=\sqrt{\frac{(1-\sin\theta)^2}{1-\sin^2\theta}}$	
Apply the Pythagorean identity.	$=\sqrt{\frac{(1-\sin\theta)^2}{\cos^2\theta}}$	
	$=\sqrt{\left(\frac{1-\sin\theta}{\cos\theta}\right)^2}$	
	$=\frac{1-\sin\theta}{\cos\theta}$	
Separate the numerator.	$=\frac{1}{\cos\theta}-\frac{\sin\theta}{\cos\theta}$	
Apply trigonometric identities.	$=\sec\theta-\tan\theta$	
	= RHS	

You may also use this alternate solution.

	LHS	RHS
	$\sqrt{\frac{1-\sin\theta}{1+\sin\theta}}$	$\sec\theta - \tan\theta$
Multiply by $\sqrt{\frac{1-\sin\theta}{1-\sin\theta}}$.	$=\sqrt{\frac{1-\sin\theta}{1+\sin\theta}\times\frac{1-\sin\theta}{1-\sin\theta}}$	$=\frac{1}{\cos\theta}-\frac{\sin\theta}{\cos\theta}$
	$=\sqrt{\frac{(1-\sin\theta)^2}{1-\sin^2\theta}}$	$=\frac{1-\sin\theta}{\cos\theta}$

	LHS	RHS
Apply the Pythagorean identity.	$=\sqrt{\dfrac{(1-\sin\theta)^2}{\cos^2\theta}}$ $=\sqrt{\left(\dfrac{1-\sin\theta}{\cos\theta}\right)^2}$ $=\dfrac{1-\sin\theta}{\cos\theta}$	= LHS

Since the left-hand side of the equation is equal to the right-hand side of the equation for both solutions, the identity is proven using either method.

38. B

Step 1
Complete the diagram provided.
From the scenario described, it is reasonable to think that there are two points along the walking path that are 90 m away from the park light.

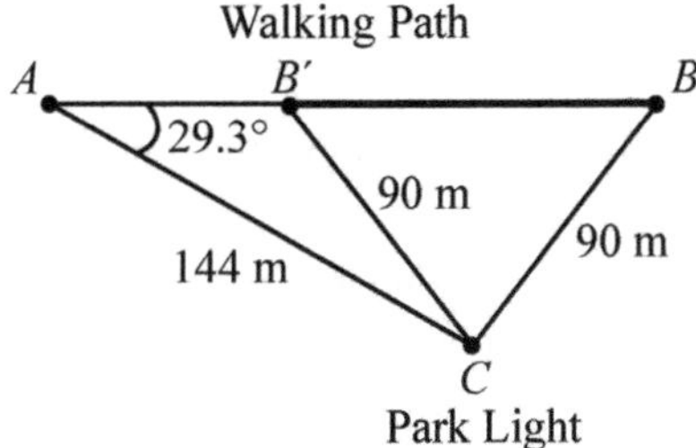

If the diagram is correct, the ambiguous case of the sine law must apply. This must be verified.
If $a > b\sin A$, there are two triangles possible: ΔABC and $\Delta AB'C$, provided $a < b$. From the diagram, it can be seen that
$A = 29.3°$, $a = 90$ m, $b = 144$ m, and $a < b$.
$90 > 144\sin 29.3°$
$90 > 70.471\ 073\ldots$
The ambiguous case of the sine law applies.

Step 2
There are two triangles to consider: ΔACB and $\Delta ACB'$. Determine the measure of angle B using the sine law.

$$\frac{\sin B}{b} = \frac{\sin A}{a}$$
$$\frac{\sin B}{144} = \frac{\sin 29.3°}{90}$$
$$\sin B = \frac{144\sin 29.3°}{90}$$
$$\sin B \approx 0.783$$
$$\angle B \approx 51.5°$$

Step 3
Determine the measure of angle B'.
Because $\Delta B'CB$ is an isosceles triangle, $\angle CB'B = \angle CBB' \approx 51.5°$.
As such, the measure of $\angle AB'C \approx 180° - 51.5° \approx 128.5°$(angle measure of a straight line).

Step 4
Determine the length of AB.
Case 1: $(B \approx 51.5°)$

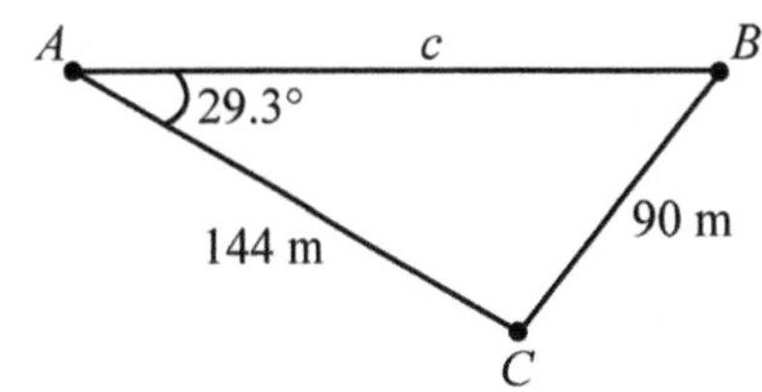

$$C \approx 180° - (29.3° + 51.5°)$$
$$C \approx 180° - 80.8°$$
$$C \approx 99.2°$$
Use the sine law to find c.
$$\frac{c}{\sin C} = \frac{a}{\sin A}$$
$$\frac{c}{\sin 99.2°} \approx \frac{90}{\sin 29.3°}$$
$$c \approx \frac{90\sin 99.2°}{\sin 29.3°}$$
$$c \approx 181.5 \text{ m}$$

Step 5
Determine the length of AB'.
Case 2: $(B' \approx 128.5°)$

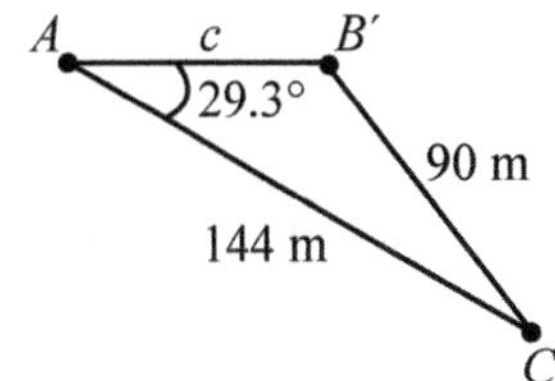

$$C \approx 180° - (29.3° + 128.5°)$$
$$C \approx 180° - 157.8°$$
$$C \approx 22.2°$$
Use the sine law to find c.
$$\frac{c}{\sin C} = \frac{a}{\sin A}$$
$$\frac{c}{\sin 22.2°} \approx \frac{90}{\sin 29.3°}$$
$$c \approx \frac{90\sin 22.2°}{\sin 29.3°}$$
$$c \approx 69.5 \text{ m}$$

Step 6
Determine how much of the walking path is illuminated.

The portion of the walking path illuminated by the light is the difference between the c-values of the two triangles.

$181.5 - 69.5 = 112.0$ m

Therefore, 112.0 m of the walking path is illuminated by the park light.

39. C

Step 1
Calculate the distance across the river.

In ΔRBS, use the tangent ratio to find the length of line segment RB.

$$\tan 73° = \frac{\text{opposite}}{\text{adjacent}}$$
$$\tan 73° = \frac{RB}{25}$$
$$25\tan 73° = RB$$
$$81.77 \text{ m} \approx RB$$

Step 2
Calculate the height of the cliff.

In ΔRBT, use the tangent ratio to determine the length of line segment TB.

$$\tan 39° = \frac{\text{opposite}}{\text{adjacent}}$$
$$\tan 39° \approx \frac{TB}{81.77}$$
$$81.77\tan 39° \approx TB$$
$$66.22 \text{ m} \approx TB$$

The height of the cliff is about 66 m.

40. 2

Extrapolate the curve to 18 s, and draw a vertical line at 17 s to determine the approximate height.

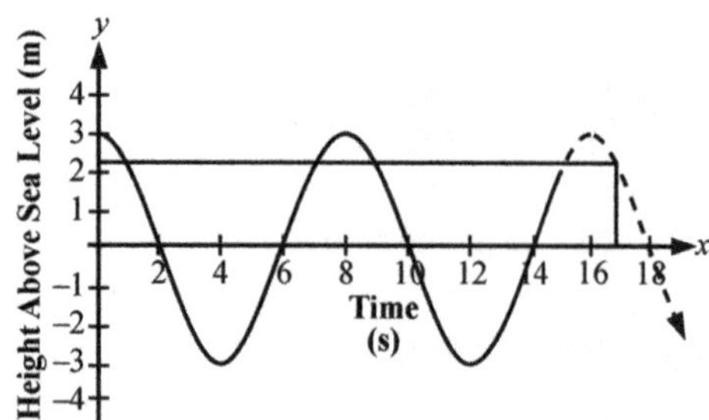

The graph shows that at 17 s, the height of the boat is just over 2 m above sea level.

To the nearest whole number, the height of the boat is 2 m.

41. C

The equation of the horizontal midline axis is not $y = 1$; it is $y = 0$.

$$y = \frac{\text{max} + \text{min}}{2}$$
$$= \frac{1 + (-1)}{2}$$
$$= 0$$

Therefore, the statement "The equation of the horizontal midline axis is $y = 1$" is incorrect.

Since,
$$f(0) = \cos(0°)$$
$$= 1$$

Therefore, the y-intercept is 1.

Any x-intercept of $f(x) = \cos x$ is $x = 90° + 180°n,\ n \in I$.

When $n = -3$
$$x = -3(180°) + 90°$$
$$= -450°$$

Therefore, $-450°$ is an x-intercept of the graph of $f(x) = \cos x$.

The maximum value is 1, and the minimum value is -1 for the graph of $f(x) = \cos x$.

Therefore, the vertical distance between these values is $1 - (-1) = 2$.

42. C

Step 1
Identify Graph 1.

Graph 1 is the graph of $y = \sin x$ with an amplitude of $a = 1$, a period of 360 ($k = 1$), a phase shift of $d = 0$, and a vertical displacement of $c = 0$.

Step 2

Compare Graph 2 with Graph 1 to determine which values have to be changed in Graph 1 to get Graph 2.

Consider the following characteristics of both graphs:

- Amplitude—there is no difference in amplitude between the two graphs; therefore, $a = 1$ for both graphs.
- Period—the period of Graph 1 is 360, and the period of Graph 2 is 180. Therefore, there is a horizontal stretch by a factor of $\frac{1}{2}$ and k is changed from 1 to 2.
- Phase shift—there is no horizontal translation for either graph, so $d = 0$ for both graphs.
- Vertical displacement—Graph 2 is shifted 3 units downward from Graph 1; therefore, c is changed from $c = 0$ in Graph 1 to $c = -3$ in Graph 2.

Therefore, Graph 2 is obtained from Graph 1 by changing the parameters k and c.

43. B

The depth of water can be represented by this graph.

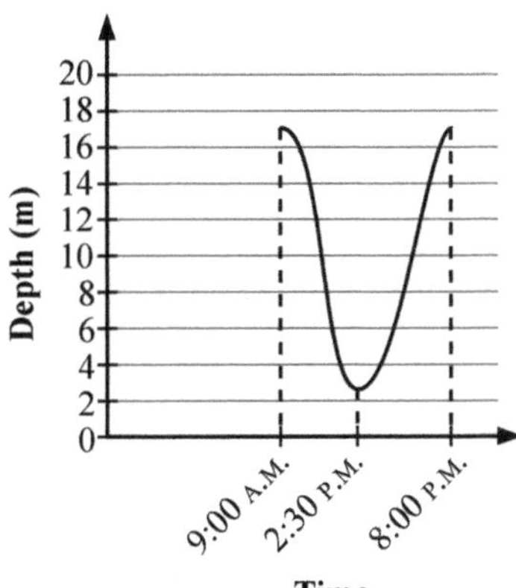

The equation of depth, y, at any time, t, is given in the form $y = a\cos[k(t-d)] + c$.

Step 1

Determine the value of a.

$$a = \frac{\text{max} - \text{min}}{2} = \frac{17-3}{2} = \frac{14}{2} = 7 \text{ m}$$

Step 2

Determine the value of k.

The period of the function is used to solve for k.

The maximum depth is attained at 9 A.M. The next consecutive maximum depth is attained at 8 P.M.

The duration from 9 A.M. to 8 P.M. is 11 h; therefore, the period of the function is 11 h.

$$\frac{360^\circ}{|k|} = 11$$
$$k = \frac{360^\circ}{11}$$
$$k \approx 32.7^\circ$$

Step 3

Determine the values of d and c.

Since the first maximum occurs after 9 h when compared to the graph of $y = \cos t$, the phase shift of the function is 9 units to the right, or $d = 9$.

The vertical translation of the curve is determined by the horizontal axis.

$$c = \frac{\text{max} + \text{min}}{2} = \frac{20}{2} = 10$$

The required equation for the depth y at any time t is $y = 7\cos(32.7^\circ(t-9)) + 10$.

44. B

A sinusoidal function has a regular, repeating pattern over a constant interval.

Table A contains data that increases until a maximum distance is obtained and then starts to decrease. However, there is no evidence that this pattern will repeat.

In table B, the data begins to repeat, and there is a constant interval present.

Table C contains data that seems irregular (in that it reaches a maximum point and a sudden minimum). However, this does not occur over a constant interval, and the data may or may not repeat.

In table D, the data decreases at a steady rate. This is consistent with a linear relationship.

Therefore, table B is the best representation of a periodic function.

45. C

The value of a would change to 7, and the curve would stretch farther away from the horizontal axis because amplitude, in this case, is determined by the radius (or diameter divided by two) of the ferris wheel. The radius is a measure of the distance from the middle to the top or from the bottom to the middle of the wheel. The function would be $H(t) = 7\sin(0.31t) + 7.9$.

46. a) 14

In the function $h = -a\cos x + 14$, the value a represents the amplitude.

Amplitude is $a = \frac{\text{max} - \text{min}}{2} = \frac{28 - 0}{2} = 14$.

Therefore, the value of a in the equation $h = -a\cos x + 14$ is 14.

b) 21

Step 1
Determine the period of the graph.
The period of the graph is 360°.

Step 2
Determine the height of the rock after two revolutions.
After two complete revolutions, the rock has passed through $2 \times 360° = 720°$. At that point, the rock would be at a height of $h = 0$ cm.

$$\begin{aligned} &h(0°) \\ &= h(2 \times 360°) \\ &= h(720°) \\ &= 0 \text{ cm} \end{aligned}$$

Step 3
Calculate the angle that the tire passes through in $\frac{2}{3}$ of a cycle.

$$\frac{2}{3} \times 360° = 240°$$

Step 4
Determine the height of the rock after a 240° rotation.
According to the graph, after a 240° rotation, the height of the rock is approximately 21 cm.

$$\begin{aligned} h &= 0 + 21 \\ &= 21 \text{ cm} \end{aligned}$$

Since this pattern is the same through each revolution, the height of the rock after $2\frac{2}{3}$ revolutions (which is 240° more than 720°) is approximately 21 cm.

47. B

Since the amount of daylight reduces by 3 hours and 30 minutes from August 21 to October 21, it would be expected that the daylight would reduce by a portion of this amount by September 1.
The difference between August 21 to October 31 is 61 days, and the difference between August 21 to September 1 is 11 days. Thus, the portion of daylight lost is likely to be about $\frac{11}{61}$ or $\frac{1}{6}$. One sixth of 3 hours and 30 minutes is 35 minutes. Subtracting 35 minutes from the August 21 daylight amount of 14 h 02 minutes gives 13 h 27 minutes. The closest value to this is 13 h 25 min.

ANSWERS AND SOLUTIONS — PRACTICE TEST 2

1. A	**b) A**	**12. 1.25**	**19. OR**	**26. OR**
2. C	**8. 3**	**13. C**	**20. D**	**27. D**
3. OR	**9. D**	**14. OR**	**21. OR**	**28. 5.5**
4. OR	**10. a) OR**	**15. C**	**22. D**	
5. B	**b) OR**	**16. OR**	**23. OR**	
6. A	**c) OR**	**17. OR**	**24. D**	
7. a) A	**11. OR**	**18. D**	**25. B**	

1. A

Step 1
Rewrite the equation in $ax^2 + bx + c = 0$ form.

$$4x^2 = 5x - 6$$
$$4x^2 - 5x + 6 = 0$$

Step 2
Identify the values of a, b, and c.
$a = 4$
$b = -5$
$c = 6$

Step 3
Determine the value of the discriminant.

$$\begin{aligned} b^2 - 4ac &= (-5)^2 - 4(4)(6) \\ &= 25 - 96 \\ &= -71 < 0 \end{aligned}$$

Step 4
Predict the nature of the roots of the equation.

Since the value of the discriminant is less than 0, the equation has no real roots.

2. C

Step 1
Change the form of the function by completing the square.

$$\begin{aligned} f(x) &= -2x^2 + 8x - 19 \\ &= -2(x^2 - 4x) - 19 \\ &= -2\left(x^2 - 4x + \left(\frac{-4}{2}\right)^2 - \left(\frac{-4}{2}\right)^2\right) - 19 \\ &= -2(x^2 - 4x + 4 - 4) - 19 \\ &= -2(x^2 - 4x + 4) + 8 - 19 \\ &= -2(x - 2)^2 - 11 \end{aligned}$$

This function is in the form $f(x) = a(x - h)^2 + k$, where $a = -2$, $h = 2$, and $k = -11$.

Step 2
Determine the maximum value of the function.

The vertex of the parabola is at $(2, -11)$, and the parabola opens downward because $a < 0$. Therefore, the maximum value of the graph of the given quadratic function is located at its vertex.

The maximum value is at the ordered pair $(2, -11)$.

3. OR

Step 1
Assign variables to represent the independent and dependent variables.

Let I represent income.

Only one income can exist for the given number of people in attendance. Therefore, income is a function of the number of people in attendance.

Only one income can exist for a given value of n, so the income is a function of n. Only one income can exist for a given ticket price, so the income is also a function of the ticket price.

Therefore, the value of n represents either the number of \$2.00 increases in the ticket price or the number of 100-person decreases in people attending the concert.

Step 2
Write an equation relating the variables.

Relate income (I) as a function of n.

Based on a ticket price increase of n \$2.00 amounts, the ticket price increases to $\$(40 + 2n)$, and the number of people attending decreases to $(8\ 000 - 100n)$.
Income = (price per ticket)(number of people)
$I = (40 + 2n)(8\ 000 - 100n)$

Step 3
Expand and collect like terms.

$I = 320\ 000 - 4\ 000n + 16\ 000n - 200n^2$

$I = -200n^2 + 12\ 000n + 320\ 000$

The equation of this function represents a parabola that opens downward and has an I-intercept of 320 000.

Complete the square as follows:

$I = -200n^2 + 12\ 000n + 320\ 000$

$I = -200(n^2 - 60n + \underline{\qquad\qquad}) + 320\ 000$

$I = -200(n^2 - 60n + 900 - 900) + 320\ 000$

$I = -200(n^2 - 60n + 900) - 900(-200) + 320\ 000$

$I = -200(n^2 - 60n + 900) + 180\ 000 + 320\ 000$

$I = -200(n - 30)^2 + 500\ 000$

Step 4
Determine the vertex.

From the equation $I = -200(n - 30)^2 + 500\ 000$, the vertex of the parabola is at (30, 500 000).
The second coordinate of the vertex is the value of the maximum of the function.

Step 5
Solve the problem.
The maximum income is \$500 000, and it occurs when $n = 30$.
Determine the number of people attending.

- The number of people attending is represented by $(8\ 000 - 100n)$.
- When $n = 30$, the number of people attending is $(8\ 000 - 100[30]) = 5\ 000$.

Determine the ticket price.

- The ticket price is represented by $\$(40 + 2n)$.
- When $n = 30$, the ticket price is $\$(40 + 2[30]) = \$100$.

The product of the ticket price and the number of people attending should be the value of the maximum income represented by the second coordinate of the vertex of the parabola.

$$\begin{aligned} I &= (\text{price per ticket})(\text{number of people}) \\ &= (\$100)(5\ 000) \\ &= \$500\ 000 \end{aligned}$$

4. OR

Step 1
Use the FOIL method to simplify the expression.

$$\begin{aligned} &x^3(2x - 7)^2 + 9x^4 \\ &= x^3(2x - 7)(2x - 7) + 9x^4 \\ &= x^3(4x^2 - 14x - 14x + 49) + 9x^4 \\ &= x^3(4x^2 - 28x + 49) + 9x^4 \end{aligned}$$

Step 2
Use the distributive property.

$$\begin{aligned} &x^3(4x^2 - 28x + 49) + 9x^4 \\ &= 4x^5 - 28x^4 + 49x^3 + 9x^4 \end{aligned}$$

Step 3
Collect and simplify all like terms.

$$\begin{aligned} &4x^5 - 28x^4 + 49x^3 + 9x^4 \\ &= 4x^5 - 19x^4 + 49x^3 \end{aligned}$$

5. B

Step 1
Factor, where possible, each numerator and denominator.

$$\begin{aligned} &\frac{x^2 - 6x - 7}{x + 1} - \frac{2x + 12}{2x + 2} + \frac{x + 1}{x^2 - 1} \\ &= \frac{(x + 1)(x - 7)}{x + 1} - \frac{2(x + 6)}{2(x + 1)} + \frac{(x + 1)}{(x + 1)(x - 1)} \end{aligned}$$

Step 2
Simplify by dividing out (cancelling) the common factors from the numerator and denominator of each separate rational expression.

$$\begin{aligned} &= \frac{(x + 1)(x - 7)}{x + 1} - \frac{2(x + 6)}{2(x + 1)} + \frac{(x + 1)}{(x + 1)(x - 1)} \\ &= \frac{(x - 7)}{1} - \frac{(x + 6)}{(x + 1)} + \frac{1}{(x - 1)} \end{aligned}$$

Step 3
Determine the lowest common denominator.
The lowest common denominator is the product of the terms in the denominator.
The lowest common denominator is $(x + 1)(x - 1)$.

Step 4
Rewrite each of the rational expressions as equivalent expressions using the lowest common denominator.

$$\begin{aligned} &= \frac{(x - 7)(x + 1)(x - 1)}{(x + 1)(x - 1)} - \frac{(x + 6)(x - 1)}{(x + 1)(x - 1)} \\ &+ \frac{(x + 1)}{(x - 1)(x + 1)} \\ &= \frac{(x^2 - 6x - 7)(x - 1)}{(x + 1)(x - 1)} - \frac{x^2 + 5x - 6}{(x + 1)(x - 1)} \\ &+ \frac{x + 1}{(x + 1)(x - 1)} \\ &= \frac{x^3 - 7x^2 - x + 7}{(x + 1)(x - 1)} - \frac{x^2 + 5x - 6}{(x + 1)(x - 1)} \\ &+ \frac{x + 1}{(x + 1)(x - 1)} \end{aligned}$$

Step 5
Simplify and then collect like terms in the numerators and keep the denominators the same.

$$\begin{aligned} &\frac{(x^3 - 7x^2 - x + 7)}{(x + 1)(x - 1)} - \frac{(x^2 + 5x - 6)}{(x + 1)(x - 1)} \\ &+ \frac{(x + 1)}{(x + 1)(x - 1)} \\ &= \frac{x^3 - 7x^2 - x + 7 - x^2 - 5x + 6 + x + 1}{(x + 1)(x - 1)} \\ &= \frac{x^3 - 8x^2 - 5x + 14}{(x + 1)(x - 1)} \end{aligned}$$

6. **A**

Step 1
Factor the numerator and the denominator.

$$\frac{6t^2-54}{3t^2+15t+18}=\frac{6(t^2-9)}{3(t^2+5t+6)}=\frac{6(t-3)(t+3)}{3(t+2)(t+3)}$$

Step 2
Divide out (cancel) out the common factors from the numerator and denominator.
The common factors are 3 and $(t+3)$.

$$\frac{6(t-3)(t+3)}{3(t+2)(t+3)}=\frac{3(2)(t-3)(t+3)}{3(t+2)(t+3)}=\frac{2(t-3)}{t+2}$$

Therefore, the equivalent expression is $\frac{2(t-3)}{t+2}$.

7. **a) A**

In order to graph the exponential relation $y=\left(\frac{3}{2}\right)^x$ in your graphing calculator, it needs to be entered into the $[Y_1=]$ feature with brackets around the base as follows.

$Y_1=\left(\frac{3}{2}\right)$^$X$

Then, set your WINDOW to the given settings of x:[−4.7, 4.7, 1] and y:[−3.1, 3.1, 1], and press GRAPH.

The graph that should appear on your screen is the one shown in choice A. Since $y=\left(\frac{3}{2}\right)^0=1$, the graph has a y-intercept of 1.

b) A

In order for $y=\left(\frac{3}{2}\right)^x$ to be a function, every x-value or x-coordinate on the graph can only have one corresponding y-value or y-coordinate.

8. **3**

Step 1

Simplify the expression $\frac{(9x^4y^3)^{\frac{1}{2}}}{x^3y^{\frac{1}{2}}}$.

$$\frac{(9x^4y^3)^{\frac{1}{2}}}{x^3y^{\frac{1}{2}}}=\frac{3x^2y^{\frac{3}{2}}}{x^3y^{\frac{1}{2}}}=3x^{2-3}y^{\frac{3}{2}-\frac{1}{2}}=3x^{-1}y^1$$

Step 2
Determine the value of $a+b+c$.

Since $\frac{(9x^4y^3)^{\frac{1}{2}}}{x^3y^{\frac{1}{2}}}$ has the form cx^ay^b when simplified, $a=-1$, $b=1$, and $c=3$.

$$a+b+c=-1+1+3=3$$

9. **D**

Since the value of $b=12$ in $f(x)=12^x$ is greater than $b=10$ in the original function $f(x)=10^x$, the graph of $f(x)=12^x$ is steeper on the right side of the y-axis than the graph of $f(x)=10^x$.

In general, the graphs of $y=b^x$ ($b>0$, where $b\neq 1$) have a range of $y>0$ and a horizontal asymptote at $y=0$.

As the value of the base, b, increases, the graph of an exponential function becomes flatter on the left side of the y-axis and steeper on the right side of the y-axis. Since the value of $b=10$ in the function $f(x)=10^x$ is greater than the value of $b=8$ in the function $f(x)=8^x$, the graph of $f(x)=10^x$ would be flatter on the left side of the y-axis than the graph of $f(x)=8^x$.

10. **a) OR**

One method of determining whether the relation is linear, quadratic, or exponential is to compare the first and second differences and the rates of change. Make a table of values for each relation and compare the results.

$y = 4x^2 - 1$

x	y	1st diff	2nd diff	Rate of change
–3	35			
		} –20		} 3/7
–2	15		} 8	
		} –12		} 1/5
–1	3		} 8	
		} –4		} 1/3
0	–1		} 8	
		} 4		} –3
1	3		} 8	
		} 12		} 5
2	15		} 8	
		} 20		} 7/3
3	35			

The first differences and the rate of change are not constant, however the second differences are, so this is a quadratic relation.

b) OR

$y = 3^x$

x	y	1st diff	2nd diff	Rate of change
–3	1/27			
		} 2/27		} 3
–2	1/9		} 4/27	
		} 2/9		} 3
–1	1/3		} 4/9	
		} 2/3		} 3
0	1		} 4/3	
		} 2		} 3
1	3		} 4	
		} 6		} 3
2	9		} 12	
		} 18		} 3
3	27			

The first and second differences are not constant, however the rate of change is, so this is an exponential relation.

c) OR

$y = 2x + 2$

x	y	1st diff	Rate of change
–3	–4		
		} 2	} 1/2
–2	–2		
		} 2	} 0
–1	0		
		} 2	} undefined
0	2		
		} 2	} 2
1	4		
		} 2	} 3/2
2	6		
		} 2	} 4/3
3	8		

Since the first differences are constant, this is a linear relation. The rate of change in a linear relation is not constant.

11. OR

Step 1

Sketch the graph of $y = 5^x$.

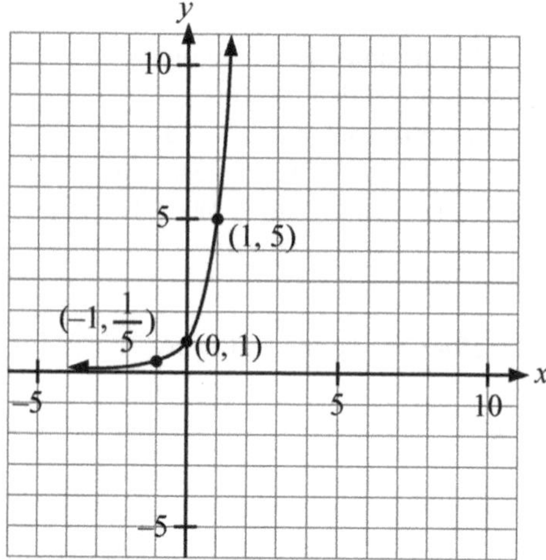

Step 2

Determine the transformations required to produce the graph of $y = 5^{x-4} + 1$.

The equation $y = 5^{x-4} + 1$ can be written as $y - 1 = 5^{x-4}$. To arrive at the equation $y - 1 = 5^{x-4}$, it is necessary to substitute $y - 1$ for y and $x - 4$ for x in the equation $y = 5^x$.

The graph of $y = 5^{x-4} + 1$ is produced by translating the graph of $y = 5^x$ 1 unit up and 4 units to the right.

Step 3

Sketch the graph of $y = 5^{x-4} + 1$.

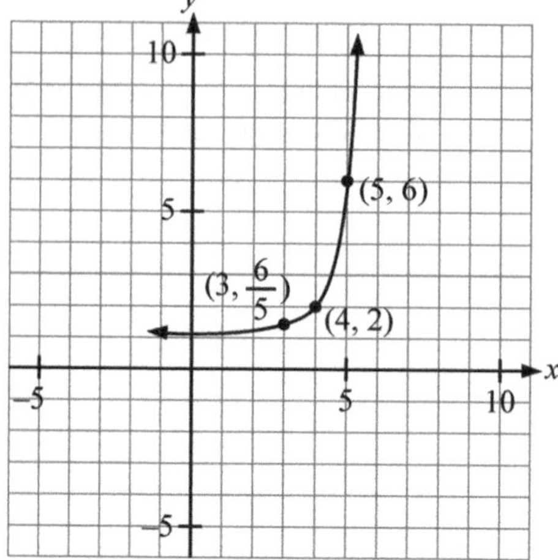

Step 4

From the graph of $y = 5^{x-4} + 1$, state the domain, range, and equation of the asymptote.

The domain is $x \in R$.

The range is $y > 1$. The range of the function $y = 5^x$ is $y > 0$. The graph of the function $y = 5^{x-4} + 1$ is $y > (0 + 1)$ or $y > 1$ since the graph of $y = 5^x$ is translated 1 unit up.

The equation of the horizontal asymptote is $y = 1$. The equation of the horizontal asymptote of the graph of the function $y = 5^x$ is $y = 0$. The equation of the horizontal asymptote of the graph of the function $y = 5^{x-4} + 1$ is $y = (0 + 1)$ or $y = 1$ since the graph of $y = 5^x$ is translated 1 unit up.

12. 1.25

The value of k is the solution to the equation $243 = 81^k$.

Step 1

Express both sides as powers of 3.

$$243 = 81^k$$
$$(3^5) = (3^4)^k$$
$$3^5 = 3^{4k}$$

Step 2

Equate the exponents, and solve for k.

$$5 = 4k$$
$$\frac{5}{4} = k$$
$$1.25 = k$$

13. C

The equation of the transformed function can be obtained by substituting $x - 5$ for x, since the graph is horizontally translated 5 units to the right, and substituting $y + 4$ for y, since the graph is vertically translated 4 units down.

$$y + 4 = 7^{x-5}$$

$y + 4 = 7^{x-5}$ can also be written as $y = 7^{x-5} - 4$.

14. OR

Method 1

Substitute 50 000 for P_t and 27 for t. Solve for P_0.

$$P_t = P_0(3)^{\frac{t}{5}}$$
$$50\ 000 = P_0(3)^{\frac{27}{5}}$$
$$50\ 000 \approx P_0(377.0985)$$
$$\frac{50\ 000}{377.0985} \approx P_0$$
$$P_0 \approx 132.59$$
$$P_0 \approx 132$$

Notice that 132.59 is rounded down because there cannot be a fraction of a bacterium.

Method 2

Substitute 50 000 for P_O and -27 for t (since it is 27 min earlier). Solve for P_t.

$$P_t = P_o(3)^{\frac{t}{5}}$$
$$= 50\ 000(3)^{-\frac{27}{5}}$$
$$\approx 50\ 000(0.002\ 651\ 8272)$$
$$\approx 132.59$$
$$\approx 132$$

The population at 4:00 P.M was approximately 132.

15. C

Since the point is on the unit circle, then $x^2 + y^2 = 1$ for any ordered pair (x, y). Since the y-value on the graph is the same as the y-value on the unit circle, then $y = -\frac{\sqrt{3}}{2}$.

Thus,

$$x^2 + \left(-\frac{\sqrt{3}}{2}\right)^2 = 1$$
$$x^2 + \frac{3}{4} = 1$$
$$x^2 = \frac{1}{4}$$
$$x = \pm\frac{1}{2}$$

Because an angle of 300° in standard position has its terminal arm in quadrant IV, the x-value is positive and therefore, equal to $+\frac{1}{2}$.

Thus, the point on the terminal arm is $\left(\frac{1}{2}, -\frac{\sqrt{3}}{2}\right)$.

16. OR

Step 1
Rewrite the trigonometric equation in terms of $\tan\theta$.

$$5\tan\theta - 1 = 3$$
$$5\tan\theta = 4$$
$$\tan\theta = \frac{4}{5}$$

Step 2
Calculate the reference angle, θ_{ref}, using a calculator.

Use a calculator to determine the approximate value.

$$\theta_{ref} = \tan^{-1}\left(\frac{4}{5}\right)$$
$$\theta_{ref} \approx 38.7°$$

Step 3

Determine the solutions for $\tan\theta = \frac{4}{5}$ with the domain $0° \leq \theta < 360°$.

According to the CAST rule, tangent is positive in quadrants I and III. Therefore, the reference angle $\theta_{ref} \approx 38.7°$ is a solution.

Determine the measure of the angle with a terminal arm in quadrant III by adding the reference angle to 180°.

$$\theta \approx 180° + 38.7°$$
$$\theta \approx 218.7°$$

The approximate values of θ in the trigonometric equation $5\tan\theta - 1 = 3$, where $0° \leq \theta < 360°$, are 38.7° and 218.7°.

17. OR

$$\csc 45° = \frac{1}{\sin 45°}$$

(use the exact value for sin 45°)

$$\csc 45° = \frac{1}{\frac{1}{\sqrt{2}}}$$
$$\csc 45° = \sqrt{2}$$

18. D

In step 1, the student multiplied the numerator and the denominator by $1 + \sin x$.

$$\frac{(1+\sin x)(1+\sin x)}{(1-\sin x)(1+\sin x)}$$

The student did not make any errors in step 1.

In step 2, the student simplified the resulting expression.

$$\frac{1 + 2\sin x + \sin^2 x}{1 - \sin^2 x}$$

Then, the student applied the Pythagorean identity to the denominator.

$$\frac{1 + 2\sin x + \sin^2 x}{\cos^2 x}$$

The student did not make any errors in step 2.

In step 3, the student rewrote the expression as follows:

$$\frac{1}{\cos^2 x} + \frac{2\sin x}{\cos^2 x} + \frac{\sin^2 x}{\cos^2 x}$$

The student did not make any errors in step 3.

In step 4 the student applied the reciprocal and quotient identities.

$$\frac{1}{\cos^2 x} + 2 \times \frac{1}{\cos x} \times \frac{\sin x}{\cos x} + \frac{\sin^2 x}{\cos^2 x}$$
$$\sec^2 x + 2\sec x\tan x + \tan^2 x$$

The student's first error occurs in step 4. The student incorrectly replaced $\frac{1}{\cos x}$ with $\csc x$ instead of $\sec x$.

19. OR

The distance between the cat and the dog can be represented by $x + y$, where x represents the distance between Lexi and the cat and y represents the distance between Lexi and the dog.
Note that $x + y$ at eye level will be the same as $x + y$ on the ground.

Step 1
Determine the distance, x, between Lexi and the cat.

$$\tan 30° = \frac{1.48}{x}$$
$$x\tan 30° = 1.48$$
$$x = \frac{1.48}{\tan 30°}$$
$$x = 2.563\ 435\ldots$$

Step 2
Determine the distance, y, between Lexi and the dog.

$$\tan 25° = \frac{1.48}{y}$$
$$y\tan 25° = 1.48$$
$$y = \frac{1.48}{\tan 25°}$$
$$y = 3.173\ 870\ldots$$

Step 3
Determine the distance, $x + y$, between the cat and the dog.
$x + y = 2.563\ 435\ldots + 3.173\ 870\ldots$
$x + y \approx 5.74$
The cat and the dog are approximately 5.74 m apart.

20. D

Draw and label a diagram that represents this situation. Let C_1 and C_2 be the points that represent the cave.

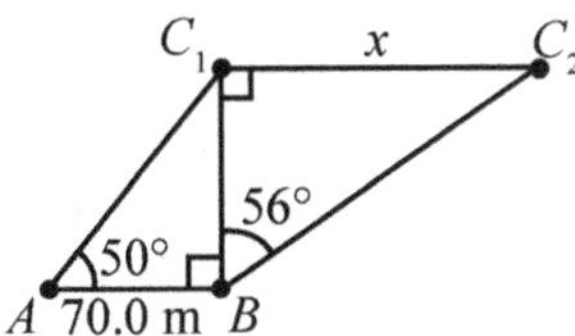

First, find the distance of BC_1.

$$\tan 50° = \frac{BC_1}{70.0}$$
$$70.0(\tan 50°) = BC_1$$
$$BC_1 = 83.422\ 751\ 48$$

Next, find the distance between the caves, x.

$$\tan 56° = \frac{x}{83.422\ 751\ 48}$$
$$83.422\ 751\ 48(\tan 56°) = x$$
$$x \approx 123.7$$

The distance between the caves, to the nearest tenth metre, is 123.7 m.

21. OR

Since Earth travels around the sun once (1 cycle) every 365 days, the period would be equal to this repeated cycle. Therefore, the period would be 365 days.

To find the amplitude, a, you need to know the minimum and maximum amounts of daylight time in the year. The minimum amount of daylight is 8 h and 43 min, which occurs on December 21. The maximum amount of daylight is 15 h and 41 min, which occurs on June 21.

Determine the amplitude, a, as follows:

$$a = \frac{\text{maximum} - \text{minimum}}{2}$$
$$= \frac{15\text{ h }41\text{ min} - 8\text{ h }43\text{ min}}{2}$$
$$= \frac{6\text{ h }58\text{ min}}{2}$$
$$= 3\text{ h }29\text{ min}$$

The amplitude of the function is 3 h 29 min of daylight time.

22. D

Ralyn's observation is incorrect. The angles occurring on the horizontal midline axis, $y = d = 0$, are the x-intercepts. The x-intercepts occur when $x = 180n°, n \in I$. Thus, solve for "n" when $x = -530°$.

$$-530° = 180n°$$
$$\frac{-530°}{180°} = n$$
$$n = -2.9444\ldots$$

Since n does not equal an integer, $-530°$ does not lie on the horizontal midline axis of the graph of $f(x) = \sin x$.

Jeremy's observation is correct. The sine function increases for intervals $(-90 + 360n)° < x < (90 + 360n)°, n \in I$, and when $n = -1$, you get $(-90 - 360)° < x < (90 - 360)°$, or $-450° < x < -270$.

Emily's observation is correct. The period is 360° for $f(x) = \sin x$, which indicates the interval between successive maximum values or successive minimum values. Thus, the interval between minimum and maximum values would be $\frac{360°}{2} = 180°$.

Derek's observation is correct. Minimum points occur at angles of $-90°, 270°, 630°, \ldots$ or $(-90 + n360)°, n \in I$.
When $n = 3, \theta = -90 + 3(360)° = 990°$. Thus, there is a minimum point at 990°.

23. OR

Step 1
Rewrite the trigonometric function in the form of $y = a\sin[b(\theta - c)] + d$.
Rewrite the value of c as $(\theta - c)$.

$$y = -\frac{1}{2}\sin\frac{1}{3}(x + 48°) - 5$$
$$y = -\frac{1}{2}\sin\frac{1}{3}(x - (-48°)) - 5$$

Step 2
Identify the value of a and its effect on the graph.

$$a = -\frac{1}{2}$$

The graph is stretched vertically about the x-axis by a factor of $\frac{1}{2}$ and then reflected in the x-axis.

The amplitude of the sine function is $\left|-\frac{1}{2}\right| = \frac{1}{2}$.

Step 3
Identify the value of b and its effect on the graph.
Since the value of $b = \frac{1}{3}$, the graph is stretched horizontally about the y-axis by a factor of 3.
The new period of the transformed graph is calculated by substituting the value of b into the expression $\frac{360°}{|b|}$.

$$\frac{360°}{|b|} = \frac{360°}{\left|\frac{1}{3}\right|} = 360° \times 3 = 1\ 080°$$

Step 4
Identify the value of c and its effect on the graph.
$c = -48°$
Since the value of c is negative, the graph shifts 48° to the left.

Step 5
Identify the value of d and its effect on the graph.
$d = -5$
Since the value of d is negative, the graph moves 5 units down.

24. D

Since $f(x) = \sin(x + 90°)$ is in the form $f(x) = \sin(x - d)$, Hannah should have used angle values of $x = d + 90°n$, $n \in I$ to sketch her graph. These values could be generated using the recursive formula $x = -90° + 90°n$, $n \in I$. Then if Hannah substituted $n = -2, 1, 0, 1, 2, 3, 4$, she would generate angle values of $-270°$, $-180°$, $-90°$, $0°$, $90°$, $180°$, and $270°$. The given table of values shows the angles, x, and their corresponding $f(x)$ values.

x	$f(x) = \sin(x + 90°)$
$-270°$	$f(-270°) = \sin(-270° + 90°) = 0$
$-180°$	$f(-180°) = \sin(-180° + 90°) = 1$
$-90°$	$f(-90°) = \sin(-90° + 90°) = 0$
$0°$	$f(0°) = \sin(0° + 90°) = 1$
$90°$	$f(90°) = \sin(90° + 90°) = 0$
$180°$	$f(180°) = \sin(180° + 90°) = -1$
$270°$	$f(270°) = \sin(270° + 90°) = 0$

Therefore, graph D best represents $f(x) = \sin(x + 90°)$ because it passes through all the points represented in the table above.

25. B

The maximum and minimum values of Graph I repeat at regular intervals throughout the domain. Therefore, Graph I represents a periodic function.

The vertical and horizontal changes are not consistent throughout the domain of Graph II. Therefore, Graph II does not represent a periodic function.

The maximum and minimum values of Graph III repeat at regular intervals throughout the domain. Therefore, Graph III represents a periodic function.

The vertical and horizontal changes are not consistent throughout the domain of the Graph IV. Therefore, Graph IV does not represent a periodic function.

Two of the four given graphs represent a periodic function.

26. OR

This is a periodic function since the y-values go through a repeated cycle throughout the given x-intervals. This is evident because the y-value starts high (12) in January, drops to a low y-value (10.2) in April, and then goes back up to a high y-value (13.2) in July. This pattern then repeats itself from July to December. Therefore, the data cycles through its y-values about every 6 to 7 months. The range of the function is defined as minimum $\le y \le$ maximum. The minimum is 9.8 m^3 and the maximum is 13.2 m^3. Thus, the range is $9.8\ m^3 \le y \le 13.2\ m^3$.

27. D

A horizontal stretch of the graph indicates that the period of the graph would be longer. This means that Logan's heart was beating more slowly, to accommodate this increase in period (time).

28. 5.5

Upon examination of the graph, the length of time between the first two successive maximum values is 5 seconds. This is the time required for the person to inhale and exhale once. Therefore, the value of $P = 5$. To find the total volume exhaled each time you need to find the maximum and minimum volumes of air in the lungs during a breath. According to the graph, the maximum volume is 2.7 litres and the minimum volume is 2.2 litres. Therefore, the total volume exhaled in a breath is $2.7 - 2.2 = 0.5$ litres. Therefore, the sum of the values $P + V$ is $5 + 0.5 = 5.5$.

Appendices

Math 11 – Functions and Applications – Formula sheet

Functions and Equations

Linear Relations

Linear Function: $f(x) = mx + b$

Quadratic Relations

Quadratic Function:

Standard form: $f(x) = ax^2 + bx + c, \quad a \neq 0$

Vertex form: $f(x) = a(x-h)^2 + k, \ a \neq 0$

Factored form: $f(x) = a(x-r)(x-s), \ a \neq 0$

Quadratic Equation: $0 = ax^2 + bx + c, \ a \neq 0$

Quadratic Formula: $x = \dfrac{-b \pm \sqrt{b^2 - 4ac}}{2a}$

Discriminant: $D = b^2 - 4ac$

Exponential Relations

Exponential Function: $f(x) = a^x$, $a > 0$ and $a \neq 1$

Exponential Growth / Decay: $y = ab^x$, where b is the growth/decay factor

Sine Relations

Sine Function: $f(x) = \sin x$

Transformed forms: $f(x) = a\sin x$

$f(x) = \sin(x-d)$

$f(x) = \sin x + c$

Exponent Rules

Multiplication: $x^m \times x^n = x^{m+n}$

Division: $\dfrac{x^m}{x^n} = x^{m-n}$

Power: $(x^m)^n = x^{mn}$

Definitions: $x^0 = 1, \ x \neq 0$

$x^{-m} = \dfrac{1}{x^m}$

$x^{\frac{m}{n}} = \sqrt[n]{(x)^m}$

$x^{-\frac{m}{n}} = \dfrac{1}{\sqrt[n]{(x)^m}}$

Finance

Simple Interest: $I = Prt$

Compound Interest: $A = P(1+i)^n$ or $FV = PV(1+i)^n$

Total Interest: $I_T = A - P$ or $I_T = FV - PV$

Trigonometry

Right Triangles

Pythagorean Theorem: $a^2 + b^2 = c^2$

Primary trigonometric ratios:

Sine ratio: $\sin A = \frac{\text{opposite}}{\text{hypotenuse}}$

Cosine ratio: $\cos A = \frac{\text{adjacent}}{\text{hypotenuse}}$

Tangent ratio: $\tan A = \frac{\text{opposite}}{\text{adjacent}}$

Acute Triangles

Sine Law: $\frac{a}{\sin A} = \frac{b}{\sin B} = \frac{c}{\sin C}$

Cosine Law:

$$a^2 = b^2 + c^2 - 2bc(\cos A)$$

$$\cos A = \frac{b^2 + c^2 - a^2}{2bc}$$

GLOSSARY

annuity
An amount payable at regular intervals (as yearly or quarterly) for a certain or uncertain period.

Arithmetic Sequence
A sequence, such as 1, 5, 9, 13, 17 or 12, 7, 2, –3, –8, –13, –18, that has a constant difference between terms. The first term is a1, the common difference is d, and the number of terms is n.

Arithmetic Series
A series such as 3+7+11+15+...+99 or 10+20+30+...+1 000 which has a constant difference between terms. The first term is a1, the common difference is d, and the number of terms is n. The sum of an arithmetic series is found by multiplying the number of terms times the average of the first and last terms.

compound interest
The method for calculating the interest where new interest is determined from the total of initial investment and previously earned interest.

cosine ratio
The cosine for the acute angle A in a right triangle is the ratio of the length of the side adjacent to the acute angle to the length of the hypotenuse: $\cos A = \frac{\text{adjacent}}{\text{hypotenuse}}$

domain
The set of all input elements, x, for which a particular relation is defined.

exponential expression
A mathematical statement made up of a base and an exponent, also called a power.

function
A special relation (x, y) in which there is exactly one corresponding y-value for every x-value.

function notation
Notation that describes the output or range value, $f(x)$, as a result of an input or domain value of x in a function, f. Function notation can also describe the relationship between one variable as a function of another variable; for example, $h(t) = 2t - 1$ describes the relationship between the height, $h(t)$, as a function of time, t.

Geometric Sequence
A sequence such as 2, 6, 18, 54, 162 or 3, 1, 13, 19, 127, 181 which has a constant ratio between terms. The first term is a1, the common ratio is r, and the number of terms is n.

Geometric Series
A series such as 2+6+18+54+162 or 3+1+13+19+127+181 which has a constant ratio between terms. The first term is a1, the common ratio is r, and the number of terms is n.

inverse functions
The inverse of a function is formed by interchanging the x and y coordinates in the ordered pairs of the function, or by interchaning the variables x and y in the equation defining the function.

linear relation
A relation in which the first differences are equal, the rate of change is constant, and the graph is a straight line. The equation of a linear relation has a degree of 0 or 1; for example, $y = 2$ has a degree of 0 and $y = 2x + 3$ has a degree of 1.

maximum
when a parabola opens downward, the maximun is the y-coordinate of the highest point.

minimum
when a parabola opens upward, the minimum is the y-coordinate of the lowest point.

polynomial
An algebraic expression consisting of one or more terms connected with addition or subtraction signs; for example, 5, $4xy^2$, and $x^3 - 2x + 5$.

power
An expression with a base and an exponent such as a^n, in which a is the base and n is the exponent.

Pythagorean theorem
For any right triangle, the area of the square built upon the hypotenuse of a right triangle is equal to the sum of the areas of the squares upon the remaining sides. If c is the length of the hypotenuse and a and b are the lengths of the legs, then $a^2 + b^2 = c^2$.

quadratic function
A quadratic function is a function of the form $y = ax^2 + bx + c$, where $a \neq 0$.

radical
An expression consisting of the radical sign (√).

range
The set of all output elements, y, for which a particular relation is defined.

relation
Any set of ordered pairs $(x,\ y)$ in which x is the input element and y is the corresponding output element.

right triangle
A triangle that has one right angle of 90°.

simple interest
Interest that is caulcated only on the principal amount.

sine ratio
The sine ratio for the acute angle A in a right triangle is the ratio of the length of the opposite side to the length of the hypotenuse:

$$\sin A = \frac{\text{opposite}}{\text{hypotenuse}}$$

sinusoidal
A succession of waves or curves.

tangent ratio
The tangent ratio for the acute angle A in a right triangle is the ratio of the length of the opposite side to the length of the adjacent side:

$$\tan A = \frac{\text{opposite}}{\text{adjacent}}$$

transformation
A transformation is a movement that alters the position or size of a geometric figure. It can be a translation, reflection, rotation or a dilation.

translation
A translation is a transformation that moves a point or image from one position to another along a vertical, horizontal, or diagonal line.

vertical asymptotes
vertical lines that a graph of will approach, but never cross or touch.

x-intercept
The value of x for a point that has a y-value of zero, or the point where a line crosses the x-axis.

NOTES